HARVEY †

Henry Harvey, blac

William, blacksmitl
1698

John, blacksmitl
1730—18

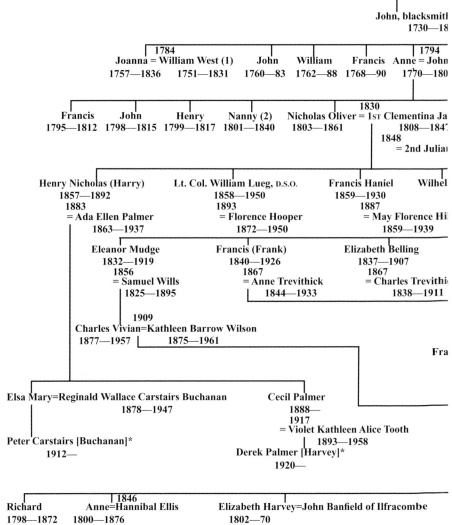

		1784					1794
Joanna	= William West (1)	John	William	Francis	Anne	= John
1757—1836	1751—1831	1760—83	1762—88	1768—90	1770—180	

Francis	John	Henry	Nanny (2)	Nicholas Oliver	1830 = 1st Clementina Ja
1795—1812	1798—1815	1799—1817	1801—1840	1803—1861	1808—184'
					1848 = 2nd Juliaı

Henry Nicholas (Harry)	Lt. Col. William Lueg, D.S.O.	Francis Haniel	Wilhel
1857—1892	1858—1950	1859—1930	
1883	1893	1887	
= Ada Ellen Palmer	= Florence Hooper	= May Florence Hi	
1863—1937	1872—1950	1859—1939	

Eleanor Mudge	Francis (Frank)	Elizabeth Belling
1832—1919	1840—1926	1837—1907
1856	1867	1867
= Samuel Wills	= Anne Trevithick	= Charles Trevithi(
1825—1895	1844—1933	1838—1911

1909
Charles Vivian=Kathleen Barrow Wilson
1877—1957   1875—1961

Fra

Elsa Mary=Reginald Wallace Carstairs Buchanan	Cecil Palmer
1878—1947	1888—
	1917
	= Violet Kathleen Alice Tooth
	1893—1958

Peter Carstairs [Buchanan]*
1912—

Derek Palmer [Harvey]*
1920—

	1846		
Richard	Anne=Hannibal Ellis	Elizabeth Harvey=John Banfield of Ilfracombe	
1798—1872	1800—1876	1802—70	

		1867		1865
Jane	Charles	John Harvey=Jane Cole	Richard	Jane Stewart=Edwar
1838—1840	1838—1911	Merchant	1842—1930	1842—1921
		1840—99		
	1867		1865	
	=Elizabeth Belling Harvey		=Fanny Bruges Hillard	

† A table of the descendants of William

The tables were compiled by the author from various

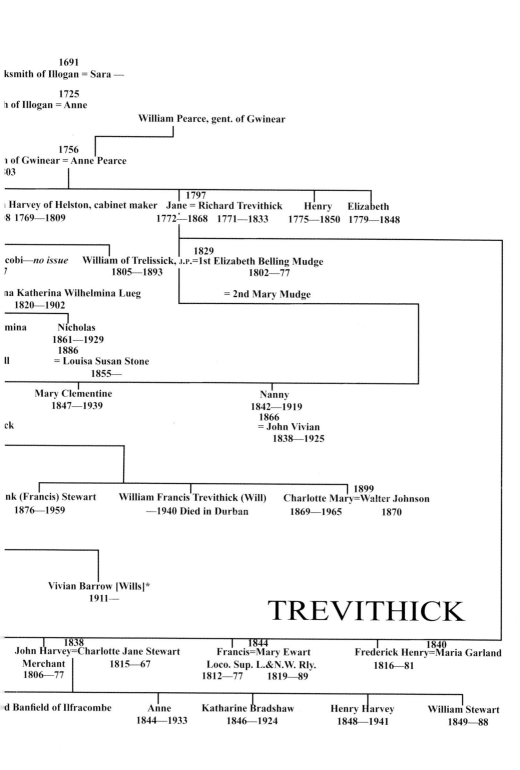

1691
ksmith of Illogan = Sara —

1725
h of Illogan = Anne

William Pearce, gent. of Gwinear

1756
a of Gwinear = Anne Pearce
03

Harvey of Helston, cabinet maker   **1797**
8 1769—1809   Jane = Richard Trevithick   Henry   Elizabeth
   1772—1868   1771—1833   1775—1850   1779—1848

1829
cobi—*no issue*   William of Trelissick, J.P.=1st Elizabeth Belling Mudge
7   1805—1893   1802—77

na Katherina Wilhelmina Lueg   = 2nd Mary Mudge
   1820—1902

mina   Nicholas
   1861—1929
   1886
ll   = Louisa Susan Stone
   1855—

Mary Clementine   Nanny
1847—1939   1842—1919
   1866
ck   = John Vivian
   1838—1925

nk (Francis) Stewart   William Francis Trevithick (Will)   **1899**
1876—1959   —1940 Died in Durban   Charlotte Mary=Walter Johnson
   1869—1965   1870

Vivian Barrow [Wills]*
1911—

TREVITHICK

1838   **1844**   **1840**
John Harvey=Charlotte Jane Stewart   Francis=Mary Ewart   Frederick Henry=Maria Garland
Merchant   1815—67   Loco. Sup. L.&N.W. Rly.   1816—81
1806—77   1812—77   1819—89

d Banfield of Ilfracombe   Anne   Katharine Bradshaw   Henry Harvey   William Stewart
   1844—1933   1846—1924   1848—1941   1849—88

West and Joanna Harvey is given in the other end papers.

sources in 1966, in which year those marked * were on the Board of Directors.

TIMBER, COAL & BUILDERS' MERCHANTS, HARBOUR PROPRIETORS & WHARFINGERS

HARVEY & CO LTD

Hayle Cornwall

LLOYDS AGENTS
PENZANCE · FALMOUTH
HELSTON · CAMBORNE
TRURO · PORTHLEVEN
& FOX, STANTON & CO.
PENRYN & GRAMPOUND RD.

TELEPHONE - HAYLE 2203-3 LINES   TELEGRAMS - 'HARVEY, HAYLE'

ALL COMMUNICATIONS TO BE ADDRESSED TO THE COMPANY

AUTHORISED DISTRIBUTORS

PRODUCTS

YOUR REF: OUR REF:

JH/JB

25th April, 1960.

Edmund Vale Esq.,
Tyn-y-Maes,
Bethesda,
BANGOR. Caernarvonshire.

Dear Sir,

      A few years ago we engaged a local Historian
to gather material from our almost complete records to
form the basis for the History of this Company, which
played such an important part in the field of engineering
in the last Century.

      The result of this research has been written
up in draft form, and consists of about 300 pages of
typescript covering the History of the Company from its
foundation in 1779 to the present day.

      It is considered that although it may have
only limited appeal, the History should be published by
this Company. We understand that you compiled a History
of English China Clays, Ltd., and shall be glad to know
if you would undertake to write up our History from the
material which has been gathered, and if so your fee for
so doing. We should, of course, be pleased to send you
our manuscript for perusal.

           Yours faithfully,
         HARVEY & COMPANY LIMITED.
         per

               J.HIGGANS   Secretary

Frontispiece: Letter from John Higgans, Company Secretary for Harvey and
Co, to Edmund Vale regarding the potential for a history of the company.

THE HARVEYS OF HAYLE

Thank you, Mr and Mrs Horwell
for putting me on to the
local bush telegraph.
Bob Vale, publication day,
20.X.09

THE
HARVEYS OF HAYLE
ENGINE BUILDERS, SHIPWRIGHTS, AND MERCHANTS OF CORNWALL

EDMUND VALE

Original Maps by Ruth Vale

The Trevithick Society

First published 1966 by
D. BRADFORD BARTON LTD TRURO
for HARVEY & CO LTD HAYLE

© EDMUND VALE 1966

© THE TREVITHICK SOCIETY 2009

ISBN 978 0 904040 78 4 (Hardback)
ISBN 978 0 904040 79 1 (Softback)

Printed by:
Short Run Press Ltd.
Bittern Road, Sowton Industrial Estate, Exeter EX2 7LW

Typesetting and layout by:
Peninsula Projects, 29 Tolver Road, Penzance TR18 2AQ

CONTENTS

LIST OF ILLUSTRATIONS

engine supplied to the Great Western Railway in 1879 for works at the Severn Tunnel. She started in 1880 and ran continuously until 1961. The numerous contrivances all operated by the beam are well seen. Left to right; cylinder, valve-gear, boiler-pump, air-pump for condenser, plunger-pump. The cataracts (not reproduced) would be situated below the valve-gear on the ground-floor. The engine-house is on four floors as is clearly indicated.

MAPS AND DIAGRAMS

NOTE TO THE REVISED EDITION

Nearly fifty years ago my father started his study of the Harveys and, in that historically brief time, nearly all our industry and a very great deal else has passed out of British ownership. There remains one thing, however, that cannot be bought, sold or taken over and that is the remarkable achievement of the Cornish nation, which in those days of early industrial development produced pioneer inventors and engineers whose daring and expertise were in demand in every continent. This is a part of their story and tells how much of their success was made possible by the foresight, and the equipment and quality, of Cornwall's first foundry owners, the Harveys in Hayle It is still the only published account to date and to the Trevithick Society I am grateful for, and honoured with, their intention to keep it in print.

To the names of those who so generously helped my father should now be added those who responded so enthusiastically to the idea of a new edition. Mr Charles Thurlow, author and publisher of St Austell, who swiftly passed me on to the Trevithick Society whose Chairman Mr Philip M Hosken has milling and baking ancestors as well-known in Hayle in their day as the Harveys. Mr Kingsley Rickard vice-Chairman and my mentor in all things Cornish who like Mr Hosken is a Bard of the Cornish Gorseth. Mr Pete Joseph, Society Curator for his patience, advice and crucial help and Mr Graham Thorne, Society Publications Officer and my link from some 400 miles away, with the onus of editing and bringing this new edition to press.

In Hayle, a chance meeting in The Farm shop with Mr Glen Horwell, who had inherited tools thought to have been made by Harveys, led to his wife contacting Mrs Vida Ellis of Trannack Farm, St Erth Praze. She insisted on my coming to tea later to meet a Mrs Ruth Taylor, descendant of Henry Harvey, who in turn gave the Society much help and information. Then Mr Brian Sullivan, Hayle's historian and author of a scholarly Hayle Trail which tells of no less than eighty-six things of interest to the visitor and who suggested that I visit the newly formed Hayle Community Archive in the care of Ms Georgina Schofield. Finally to Mr John Higgans, retired Director, for many years Harvey's Company Secretary and also an author and historian of Hayle affairs, who for seven years was the constant support and link between my father and the company.

To them, One and All, I owe my deepest gratitude.

Robert Vale

The Trevithick Society would also like to thank the following for their help in preparing this new edition. L. J. Bullen, Camborne; Rory Cook, The Science Museum, London; Alison Hodge, Penzance; Brian Jones, Abingdon; Dr. Noel Meeke, Hereford Waterworks Museum Trust; Phil Moncton, Penzance; John Pollard and Laura Christon, Harvey's Foundry Trust; Mr & Mrs Priddle, Wayside Museum, Zennor and Michael Tonking, South Africa.

Edmund Vale 1888-1969

THE AUTHOR

Edmund Vale, M.A. [Cantab] was born in 1888 at Greenfield Hall, Flintshire, his father being the Vicar of Helsby. On a second visit to Cornwall in 1913, after conducting a boys' camp there, he decided to return to Gloucester on foot. With his collie dog, Pharaoh, and a tent he left Penzance and, on the way through Fowey, he called on Sir Arthur Quiller-Couch, who was the new Professor of English Literature at Cambridge. He had shown an interest in the young student's published poetry and now encouraged him to write about everything. With this advice and spur he was to devote the rest of his life to literature, except for service as an army officer in both wars.

History, topography, travel, two novels, a film scenario, thirty broadcast talks and contributions to over thirty publications kept his pen busy, beside having five board games made and marketed. He did work for the Canadian Pacific and LMS railways and before going to St. John's College, had visited the Canaries, Belgium, Iceland, the Mediterranean and Japan.

Of the books, perhaps the best remembered are *See for Yourself, The Mail-Coach Men of the Late 18th Century, How to Look at Old Buildings* and, for the younger generation, Batsford's Heritage Series on *Abbeys, Churches and Cathedrals*. A request by Fine Spinners and Doublers, Ltd. for a popular account of the Cotton industry produced *The World of Cotton*. For Robert Hale's County Series he wrote the volume on *Shropshire* and edited Methuen's Little Guides Series, contributing a new edition of *Cambridge and its Colleges*. Two books on a maritime theme were *Shipshape* [Dent, 1931 and 1934] and *The Way of Ships* [Country Life, 1938]. An autobiography, *Straw into Gold*, appeared in 1939 and *An Outline of English Architecture* in 1966.

In all this he was constantly aided by his artist wife Ruth [1888-1978], who illustrated several works and for this book, drew the maps. Edmund Vale died in 1969.

Robert Vale
11th April 2009

INTRODUCTION

It is a sad fact that those who create our history seldom receive the credit due to them. The world is slowly becoming aware that it was the steam engines of Richard Trevithick's design that drove most of early industry and transport; but history is not as simple as that.

It was the skill and resources of John Harvey and his son Henry, Trevithick's in-laws, which turned the output of his fervid mind into reality. James Watt and several others had ideas about high-pressure steam engines but it was the ability of the Harveys to build Trevithick's successful boiler that eventually made everything possible. During the nineteenth century, in a small Cornish village without iron or coal, Harvey & Co built the finest steam pumping engines for mines and municipalities throughout the world.

The true story of this important contribution to the progress of Mankind would probably not have been told without the research by Edmund Vale contained in this book. Here we have a gripping story that needs to be told time and time again. To achieve this we are grateful for the thoughtfulness and generosity of Robert Vale, Edmund's son, who has granted the Trevithick Society the continuing rights to republish this remarkable story of Cornish engineering and endeavour.

Philip M Hosken
Chairman
The Trevithick Society
2009

PREFACE

THE STORY OF THE HARVEYS OF HAYLE SHOULD HAVE been written long ago by Samuel Smiles, for its characters have all those qualities of initiative and resolution which the author of *Self Help* so much admired. Moreover, this is a success story, and Smiles liked his heroes to justify his doctrine of rewarded endeavour by succeeding. It is odd that he should have missed such a golden opportunity.

The tale begins in 1779 when a village blacksmith, John Harvey, moved his forge to the coast, at the Hayle estuary, and there also built a small iron foundry — the very first to be set up in Cornwall. It at once met an urgent need on the part of the neighbouring tin mines which were still using wooden pipes for draining their shafts. John bought coal for his furnace from a local company of copper-smelters who imported it in their own vessels from South Wales, across the water. They sold coal to the mines for their steam engines, also timber and any other commodity which the adventurers needed. Bad roads cut them off from all communications with those markets except by sea.

John started his enterprise without any capital except for savings and current earnings but his new business was brisk and, as soon as he could afford it, he bought a ship of his own, and became an independent importer of his necessities in coal and pig-iron. To keep his vessel constantly in service and well filled he began to import also for the mines. This infuriated the copper company who had hitherto enjoyed a monopoly as mine-merchants. They were rich and powerful and singularly vindictive, and they tried by every means to dislodge him from his precarious foothold on ground whose boundaries were debatable, to cut off his access to the sea, or to destroy his business in some other way, resorting to physical violence when all else failed.

John had four sons. In the early years, he placed great reliance on these boys as future helpers in the struggle for survival, but he lost the two eldest through sickness and, in 1780, the third, then aged twenty-two, was killed

PREFACE

by an accident in his father's works. The remaining boy, Henry, was just turned fifteen. He was but a small lad yet he had two sterling qualities, a quick intelligence and a capacity for sound judgment. At sixteen, he was acting as clerk to his father and, in his absence, managing the business.

There were four daughters, three of whom married. The eldest, Joanna, took for her husband William West, a skilful mechanic who owned a smithy at Helston but specialised in clock-making. The next, Anne, married John Harvey, a cabinet-maker of Helston — her father's namesake, but not known to be a relative. The third, Jane, married Richard Trevithick, then a young mines engineer, but latterly to become world famous as a pioneer in the development of the steam engine.

John died in 1803, having the year before, made Henry his partner by deed, assigning to him half his business assets. The young man was then twenty-five years old, lacking capital, continually harassed by the powerful competitor, and getting no support for his rights of tenancy from wealthy but indifferent landlords. William West, the clever mechanic and stout partisan of the family, had been employed at the foundry for some time. And now, he in the works and Henry in the office, strove to keep the two-fold venture going on the slender means available. But Henry's mind was fixed on expansion and, to gain the necessary funds, he allowed himself to be drawn into a co-partnership, but soon found himself without any effective voice in the conduct of affairs. Moreover, the business was deteriorating and running into danger. Yet, by the agreement, the partnership was bound to run for twenty-one years before any change could be made. Henry entered a plea in chancery for an immediate dissolution. In this he was successful, but was then faced with the problem of buying out his capitalist yokefellows.

The firm at once reverted to the family name of Harvey & Co., standing for himself, his well-tried brother-in-law, William West, and his unmarried sister, Elizabeth. But, from that time forth, it was he, alone, who guided the destinies of the Company. From the original plant, the iron foundry, this main stem, grew rapidly in girth and ramified into many branches, while the detail of their foliage was entirely mastered by Henry who kept full control of all. Williams's *Commercial Directory for Cornwall*, issued in 1847, gives this under Hayle—

Harvey & Co., Millers, Engineers, Iron Founders, Iron and Coal Merchants, Shipbuilders, Ship-owners, Ironmongers, Wholesale Grocers, Tea-dealers, and General Merchants and Ropemakers.

PREFACE

In that year they had just completed the construction of the largest steam engine in the world for the Dutch Government, and had achieved a place among the foremost engineering firms in Great Britain. In the following year, Henry, who had remained a bachelor, handed everything over for the benefit of his numerous nephews and nieces, vesting all the properties and finances of the business in three trustees, in whose hands were also placed full control and management, though left free to take whatever course they should choose in prevailing circumstances, in the best interests of all concerned.

The nineteenth century was England's Golden Age in wealth and power, towards the consummation of which her engineers, manufacturers, merchants, and shipbuilders had played so large a part. And it was exactly at the end of the first and most adventurous half of the century that Henry died — in May 1850. He had become the equal of its chief industrial magnates but, unlike many of them, he had never sought public notoriety. He is still talked of in the place which he created as "The little Cap'n".

Harvey & Co. is still very much in being on the same site where John Harvey came in 1779 to set about his enterprise, and four of the present directors are descended from the founder. But, with changing conditions, they have retained only one of the many trades they formerly carried on, that one which John Harvey adopted as his second choice. They are merchants, but not mines-merchants, for they have long outlived the mining industry in Cornwall which has shrunk almost to vanishing-point. In its place, the dominant demand comes from the building trades and they are builders' merchants.

For a firm which has been established close on two centuries, the records are wonderfully complete, with business correspondence going back to 1791. The only considerable gap in the series of letter-books is between 1796 and 1809. After that they are continuous, except for the middle volume of 1847, down to 1903, the last year before the engineering works and shipyard were closed. Down to 1839 all letters had been entered by handwriting on stout hand-made paper (from which fair copies would be sent out). The clerks wrote in a clear copperplate hand, and the ink they used has remained static. But then there came what must have been regarded as a great advance in office equipment — a copying-press. The impressions left by this machine have not stood the test of time. Many letters have faded so far as to make them difficult to read, others have faded entirely out, leaving a blank page. But one can generally pick up the

23

thread from the "in" letters.

There is also a fair collection of the necessary office books (though with much larger gaps in their sequence) — cash-books, ledgers, stem-books, recording hours of labour and overtime, minute-books, and others. All these archives, down to 1903, have now been deposited for posterity at the County Record Office in Truro, where they may be inspected by arrangement with the County Archivist. But one source of information that would have been of great value to the student of mechanical evolution is missing; the old machine drawings, of which hardly any have survived.

Anyone wishing to scan the "in" letters must be struck, if not daunted, by the formidable mass that will confront him. Stacked in fat bundles of several thousands to one year (or only a part of it) they cover, like their fellows in the bound books, all departments of the multiple industry down to 1852, when it was decided to divide the business, the families of Harvey and West keeping the main stem — the foundry, wharves, shipyard, ropewalk, and lime-kilns, with the merchanting of iron, timber, and coal; the Trevithicks taking the remaining trades and premises and forming a separate company under their own name. Thenceforward, the correspondence and books follow only the fortunes of the Harvey and West families, still trading as Harvey & Co.

The "in" letters, though so vast in bulk, are by no means so complete as the "outs". Many are missing at odd junctures — sometimes spoiling the course of a good story. I have heard it said that when these documents were stored in the old office, and probably regarded as so much lumber, a clerk would save a match to light his pipe by picking one out and using it as a spill. But now, how fascinating these old letters are to read! They reflect standards of life and trends of thought and outlook from the middle years of George III to the early days of King Edward VII. They have special interest as a commentary on the work-a-day and not the well-to-do world, and they are fascinating by reason of the wide range of contacts with so many different trades embraced by these almost universal suppliers from the producers of pig-iron to the makers of clay pipes.

In perusing these old letters of the long-departed, so earnestly and urgently expressed, one picks out personalities who grow in the imagination to almost lifelike stature and become engaging acquaintances by proxy. Regularly, in bundle after bundle, appear the genial and picturesquely worded epistles of the Norwegian shippers of timber, constantly verging on breaking off their long connection with the hard-bargaining master of

Hayle Foundry but, in the end, submitting. It is, in fact, a great charm of the collection that the salty air from the open sea is constantly blowing away the smoke of the furnaces and interrupting an arid interchange of business palaver, in a letter from one of those bluff, daring, and eminently loyal men, the seamen of Harvey's fleet of sailing ships, couched in simple language, unmasked by the conventional forms of commerce, who notify the office every time they make port.

Interleaving the letters, there occur at fairly regular intervals, printed circulars and price-lists from home and foreign merchants. The most intriguing of the series is the one issued by J & J Colman (brothers whose names appeared on mustard tins). They were then extensive dealers in East Anglian grain, with offices in Norwich and London and Harvey was a long-standing customer. The circulars they issued gave not only current prices of grain but a sprightly worded weather-commentary (typical of the racy Norfolk manner), showing how prevailing conditions were affecting crops and the market.

The story of the Harveys of Hayle is not only a very long one but one lacking a denouement, for it is still being told. But the chief wonder of it is how it ever came about, and it is on that phase that I have concentrated, dwelling in considerable detail on the early period of the enterprise down to its consolidation, the climax of which was reached in the year 1852. To bring its remaining history, from then on up-to-date, similarly expanded, would have required more than one volume. The second phase was from 1852 to 1904, when the works and shipyards were closed, and I have only touched on that part in a single chapter summarising the main events, giving a table in the appendix (p. 365) showing the several changes in the constitution of the Company and its board.

Mr. T. R. Harris, who is so well known in the West of England as an authority on Cornish mining and engineering, had access to the Harvey archives some years ago, when they were still stored in the old office premises of the Company, and produced a most admirable set of notes on the whole of all three phases. Even in this abridged form, his summary ran to 318 foolscap pages. It contains a great deal of detail not found in my account which had to be expressed in narrative form. It has now been deposited with the other documents at the Record Office at Truro.

I have based my story entirely on my own researches and all inferences which I have drawn are mine. But I had the privilege of inspecting Mr. Harris's notes before they were made available to the public at Truro, and such support as they gave me in guidance I gratefully acknowledge.

During the summer of 1962, my attention was drawn to some fresh material which had come to light in the shape of a special edition of Francis Trevithick's Life of his father, produced solely for the author in four folio volumes. The text was interleaved with blank pages, on which were mounted about two hundred original business and family letters. Some of them had been reproduced in the Life, but most had never been printed or, apparently, seen by other biographers of the engineer. The books belonged to a private collector (who wished to remain anonymous) who had placed them on temporary loan at the City Museum, Leicester. The letters nearly all related to the affairs of Richard Trevithick during his lifetime and at his death. There were some from Henry Harvey which had not been printed or copied into the letter-books at Hayle. I spent two days at Leicester looking through them and have based one or two statements on what I found.

In preparing the following History, my thanks are due to the Chairman and Directors of Messrs. Harvey & Company Limited for their courtesy and co-operation, in particular to Mr. V. B. Wills for access to a number of private letters and documents not forming part of the main collection of the Harvey papers and to Mr. J. T. W. Higgans, a perpetual source of help and encouragement from beginning to end; to Mr. H. L. Douch, Keeper of that unique repository of Cornish treasure, the Royal Institution of Cornwall, one so human as well as learned that his office is an ever-open entertaining room; Mr. P. L. Hull, County Archivist, whose patience I had to tax incessantly at a time when an acute shortage of storage space created difficulties for himself and his clients; furthermore, I would return thanks to Mr. A. Stowers of the Science Museum at South Kensington; Mr. G. C. Berry of the Metropolitan Water Board; Mr. T. C. Stephens of the Severn Tunnel Pumping Station; Mr. J. H. Trounson; Col. C. J. H. Mead; the Vicars of St. Erth, Gwinear, and Stithians, for giving me free access to their parish records and other kindnesses; Mr. G. A. Chinnery, Keeper of Archives to the City Museum, Leicester; Mr. R. Jarvis, Archivist and Librarian, H. M. Customs and Excise, and Mr. A. G. Coping of the same service at St. Ives — many happy hours have I spent in his little office, quaintest and most romantic-looking of all our customhouses, poring over ancient shipping registers while, lying handy on the table, was a large brass telescope, leather-jacketed and wreathed with a sailorly Turk's head, issued for smuggler-spotting in far off days when the offing was crowded with sail, and duly signed for with all other effects by each incoming preventive officer.

In Holland, I found the memory of the Harveys of Hayle green and honoured in the neighbourhood of that great undertaking, the draining of the Haarlem Meer, and my thanks are due for help and guidance there to Prof. Dr.-Ing. L. Vahl, Ir. L. Hupkes and Ir. I. A. A. Schepers, members of the Cruquius Foundation which preserves the engine of that name, and to Ir. Badon Ghijben who spared me so much time.

The chief repository of the fund of Carnsew and Copperhouse tradition, on which I have been privileged to draw during many perambulations of local landmarks, is Mr. Gartrell Harvey, master-craftsman, and member of a family that has served the Company for three generations, though unrelated so far as is known to his namesakes of Gwinear and Helston. Out of this living source has come a lubricant for the dry cogs of the documentary record and my very particular thanks go to him.

Map 1. Hayle and Environs: locations of various places named in the text.

I

THE YOUTH OF STEAM

IF CORNWALL IS MENTIONED THESE DAYS — ESPECIALLY the western end of the peninsula — it raises visions of a splendid holiday playground, a region of towering granite cliffs thrust out into the Atlantic, of high moors fragrant with the smell of gorse and ling and gemmed with the little blue scabious, whose colour seems to have been pre-ordained to match the wide expanses of sea and sky: an area where human habitation is hardly represented except by the tombs, temples, and hut-circle dwellings of prehistoric peoples. Other relics indeed there are of a much more recent date, but time has dealt with them so effectively that they seem as picturesque as ruined Norman peel-towers. They add to, rather than detract from, that sense of detachment from the workaday world for which this countryside is now so famous.

It is hard to realise that so recently as the first half of the nineteenth century this part of the delectable Duchy could have been well described as an industrial area — the high moors dotted with smoking chimneys and their neighbourhood defaced with spoilbanks and other features offensive to our ideas of "amenity". Yet so it was! Mines were then at work, producing tin, copper, and other minerals, each with its steam pumping-engine, sending out the black fumes of Welsh coal continually by day and night. Nearly all signs of that intense activity have been swept away. Under the genial Cornish climate a remarkable reclamation by nature and agriculture has taken place. Of those very numerous granite-built engine-houses, only very few remain. They were nearly square in plan, stood three storeys high, and had a turret-like chimney at one corner, so that in their decay they look more feudal than industrial. Thus, in this romantic background they sort well with the cromlechs and the stone circles and the Celtic forts. But, taking them for what they really are — monuments to the First Age of Power — they must surely touch the imagination even more vitally than

29

all the other bygones.

Mining for tin has gone on since prehistoric times, but down to near the end of the seventeenth century it was almost all of an alluvial character, the valley bottoms being worked for pebbles and grains washed down from metallic lodes in the higher ground, through the natural weathering of the rocks. This process was called streaming. In that same century there was an increased demand for tin, probably due to a higher standard of living after the Restoration of the monarchy, in which the use of pewter became much more general all over England. The yeoman class, which had been content to use wooden platters and drinking vessels, now replaced these with services of pewter ware. By the end of Queen Anne's reign, the veins, themselves, were being exploited by deep mining and the adventurers were then faced with the all-important problem of how to keep the workings drained and dry. The same advances in technique, followed by the same problem, were also taking place elsewhere in the United Kingdom, in the mines of coal and lead.

As the Cornish mines were nearly all on high ground, some relief from flooding could be given by the time-honoured method of driving an adit tunnel from the shaft to a point in the open air nearer sea-level, having a slight fall towards the latter. Some of these rock-hewn passages were very long and made to serve several mines, such as the Great Adit which, with its branches, had an extent of more than thirty miles. There were manual pumps of the chain-and-rag type, but to keep them going constantly by relays of hands was such a severe task that, according to William Pryce[1], many men were actually worked to death. Pumps driven by water-wheel could only be used where a stream happened to be near a mine, which was seldom. The horse-whim had been introduced early in the eighteenth century. It was operated by horses yoked beneath the lower rim of a circular drum — the *cage* — which revolved and, by a spur-gear, moved a winch which lowered and hoisted large buckets — *kibbles* — as in a well. It was a process of intermittent bailing, but the weight of rope, added to that of the water to be drawn, limited the depth from which two, or even four horses could work it.

The answer to the problem lay in the development of steam-power. The pioneer in this field was Thomas Savery, a Devonian, born in the first year of the Commonwealth régime. He took out several patents, though not the

---

[1] *Mineralogia Cornubiensis,* London 1778.

one for raising water until 1698, when William III was nearing the end of his reign. Only a year after gaining his rights he applied for an extension of time, and Parliament obligingly granted him a generous one, making his patent valid until 1733.

Savery's device was beautifully simple. It consisted of a small boiler, an empty vessel called the *receiver*, two non-return valves, and two stopcocks. From the vessel a pipe descended to the water which was to be raised; another pipe rose above it to the point of discharge. An attendant stood by to manipulate the two stopcocks at the proper moments. The first action filled the receiver with steam from the boiler, which was then cut off; the next allowed cold water to pour over the vessel, which condensed the steam in it. This formed a vacuum and caused the water in the lower pipe to rise, due to atmospheric pressure. It filled the receiver and was held there by one of the non-return valves. When the boiler stopcock was again opened steam pressure forced the water up the delivery pipe, displacing its contents while the remainder of the column was held there by another non-return valve until the next thrust.

Savery issued a pamphlet called *The Miner's Friend* to publicise his machine but as the limit of its lifting-power was only about sixty feet it did not recommend itself to the adventurers and only appears to have been put to practical use in a few large private houses. The inventor died in 1715, nineteen years short of the date his patent was due to expire, leaving the rights in the hands of his executors. Meanwhile, another Devonian, Thomas Newcomen, had invented an engine which used the same powers of steam and vacuum but on quite a different principle and much more effectively. The history of his machine (as of Newcomen's whole career) is obscure, but it was produced and put into service in Savery's lifetime and, as his patent covered the manufacture of any engine worked by steam, it is inferred that the two men must have come to some financial arrangement about the making and selling of it.

Newcomen used a cylinder as receiver, standing vertically above the boiler. The whole thing being so much larger than its predecessor, it required a specially built engine-house to work in. Within the cylinder (which had an open top) was a piston attached to one end of a large wooden beam that was pivoted on the wall of the engine-house. The rest of the beam protruded into the open air, its far end being immediately above the opening of the mine-shaft. To this end was hitched the succession of long rods that went down to the pump in the bottom of the mine. As the piston

31

rose to the top of the cylinder steam was admitted below it and suddenly condensed by a spray of cold water injected into the cylinder. A vacuum was thus created which caused the piston to descend by the pressure of the atmosphere. This tilted the beam and worked the pump at the bottom of the shaft. At the end of the stroke the weight of the pump-rods was sufficient to tilt the beam the other way and draw the piston up again, when the cycle of events was repeated. Flexibility of movement between the vertical and horizontal units was allowed for by giving the beam arched heads and attaching them to piston and pump-rods by chains. All these machines are now classed as "atmospheric" but, at the time, the fundamental source of their energy was observed to be heat and they were called fire-engines — a name which stuck to them for a long while.

The first successful Newcomen engine was got to work at a coal mine near Dudley Castle in Staffordshire in 1712, after which many were installed at collieries in the Midlands and North of England. Cornwall was not long in taking advantage of the new fire-engine and it is believed that one was installed in the Duchy as early as 1716.

We who live at the other end of the great Steam Age are so much accustomed to the idea of a piston working up-and-down in a cylinder that it takes an effort of the imagination to realise the cleverness and originality of Newcomen's invention. Compared with his engine, Savery's was an academic toy. At a single stride this Dartmouth ironmonger hit on the one thing — cylinder and piston — which, with all later modifications, remained the fundamental instrument of steam power until the invention of the turbine. The Newcomen engine suffered from many drawbacks, due to its elementary design and the very restricted state of mechanical arts of its time, but it remained unrivalled for half-a-century.

The next step was taken by James Watt. His name has been more loudly proclaimed, but he might never have had anything to do with steam engines if it had not happened that he was employed by the College of Glasgow to clean and adjust their scientific instruments. Among these was the model of a Newcomen engine which was out of order. He succeeded in getting it to go but was puzzled by the difficulty he had in keeping it running. In setting himself to find the answer to this riddle he managed to put his finger on the weakest spot in Newcomen's design, which was loss of heat at every stroke due to the spray of cold water injected into the cylinder to condense the steam, which it did but, at the same time, chilled both cylinder and piston. It was another nine years (1765) before

32

he thought of the sovereign remedy, namely not to condense the steam in the cylinder but in a separate vessel. Then the necessary vacuum under the piston would still be created but cylinder and piston would remain hot and energy would be conserved. He took out his patent in 1769. His patron and partner in the patent at that time, who enabled him to meet the expenses of his venture, was Dr. John Roebuck, the founder and proprietor of the great Carron Iron Works in Scotland. To him he was tied financially, although another rich and enterprising manufacturer in the Midlands was keenly interested in the invention and would have liked to join forces. But his ideas of commercialising it on a large scale did not fit in with the more limited ones of Roebuck and he kept out. This was Matthew Boulton of the Soho Manufactory in Birmingham, which had already earned for itself an almost world-wide fame for the excellence of its productions in copper, bronze, silver plate, and ormolu. These were all works of art, and the success which Boulton had met with in their creation must have been partly due to his good judgement as a connoisseur. To meddle with machinery might have been thought to be something quite alien to his nature. But, like his contemporary, Josiah Wedgwood, Boulton was even more powerfully endowed with a flair for business. When it happened unexpectedly in 1773 that the great ironmaster of the north went bankrupt, Boulton claimed from the receivers, as payment for a debt, John Roebuck's two-thirds share in Watt's patent. The next year, Mr. and Mrs. James Watt left Scotland for Birmingham and, backed by Boulton's money and the facilities of the Soho works, the inventor concentrated all his energies on improving his engine. Boulton had a large circle of influential friends and, through their combined efforts they persuaded Parliament, against strong opposition, to grant an extension to the patent of twenty-five years. It was now to remain in force down to the year 1800.

Fortune, which had struck down poor Roebuck, to Watt's great advantage (as it certainly turned out to be), now favoured him with a second random stroke. Another drawback to the Newcomen engine, though not due to a fault in its design, was the difficulty in making its cylinder so true that the piston would fit closely throughout its stroke. Various materials were tried, including wood[1]. The most workable in early days was found to be brass, but the cost was prohibitive. The engine built in 1725 at Edmonstone, near Edinburgh, had a twenty-nine inch diameter brass cylinder, but the price

[1] James Brindley's engine with wooden cylinder is described by Samuel Smiles in his *Lives of Engineers*, John Murray, London, 1862,

for making this single member of the machine was £250. About that time Abraham Darby of Coalbrookdale had discovered how to smelt iron by pit-coal instead of charcoal, after which, cylinders in cast iron were cheap to make, and Darby was turning out many for Newcomen engines. But it was impossible to machine their interiors with sufficient accuracy to make the piston steam-tight. No boring-mill could cope with a cylinder of fire-engine size that was true in two dimensions throughout its length, until John Wilkinson of Bersham perfected a machine which did so. Wilkinson's new boring-mill was actually set up in 1774, the year in which Watt joined Boulton in Birmingham. But it was Matthew Boulton who was the first to take advantage of the new invention and to send urgently to Bersham for a cylinder cast and bored in the new manner. If the Newcomen engine had been able to have a true-bored cylinder it would have made it a much more efficient machine. And so the timely appearance of Wilkinson's precision tool made all the difference in the world to the success of the Boulton and Watt engine, affecting its efficiency, its greater economy in fuel, and its price in production. Provided with this new facility as well as the extension of the patent the great commercial invasion of pits and mines of every kind began. It reached Cornwall in 1777.

II

JOHN HARVEY OF GWINEAR

IN 1775 — TWO YEARS BEFORE THE FIRST BOULTON AND
Watt engine was erected in Cornwall — Richard Trevithick moved
what was left of the venerable Newcomen machine from Carloose to
Dolcoath mine on the northern slope of Carn Brea Hill. It had been in
service for at least forty years and, with the exception of its boiler, forty-
five inch cylinder, and great wooden beam, it was practically worn out.
Trevithick made improvements in the boiler and the valve-gear in keeping
with more advanced ideas. They were probably in line with those made by
John Smeaton in that same year in the engine he erected at Chacewater.
Smeaton must have made some acquaintance with Cornish affairs when
he erected the Eddystone lighthouse and been in still closer touch with
them when, in 1766, he undertook the building of St. Ives harbour.
Though primarily a civil engineer, the mechanics of prime movers had
always intrigued him. He had applied his scientific training to the design
of water-wheels and windmills and was now bent on doing the same for
the atmospheric engine.

Smeaton's achievement at Chacewater was hailed as the last word in
the Newcomen principle and it certainly acquitted itself well in the thing
which was of the utmost importance to the Cornish miner —a saving of
fuel. This mattered much less where the majority of these engines had
been set to work, namely in the coal mines. But Cornwall had no coal; it
was only imported at great expense.

The old Newcomen boiler was a very elementary affair, a bowl-shaped
vessel identical with the ordinary washhouse "copper", heated like that
vessel by a fire in a simple grate underneath. An account of the Carloose
transfer is given by Richard's son, Francis. He says "The greatest
improvement . . . was Trevithick's new semi-circular boiler-top which . . .
took the place of the original flat top weighted down by slabs of granite."

JOHN HARVEY OF GWINEAR

This Richard was the father of his more celebrated namesake who made the first motor road-carriage and the first railway locomotive. He was mineral agent for the great estate of the Bassetts of Tehidy in the parish of Illogan, where some of the most important mines in Cornwall were situated. He was also acknowledged as the principal engineer in all the western mines. The detailed costs of this removal and re-erection stand recorded in one of his notebooks[1]. Among them is an entry of £33 1s. 9d. paid to John Harvey "and partners" for putting in the boiler (that is, encasing it in brickwork) and building the engine-house.

John Harvey was a blacksmith, and came of a family skilled in that trade. His grandfather, Henry Harvey, had worked the forge at Illogan, north of Redruth, in the seventeenth century. John had moved out of the parish into the neighbouring one of Gwinear, where he had the smithy on Carnhell Green, south of Camborne. It is rather surprising to find him at the Dolcoath site not engaged in smith work but bricklaying and masonry, but it shows that his competence extended to more than one trade.

Among the new fittings that Trevithick provided, two sets of pumps are noted which he had ordered from "the Dale Company" (that is, the foundry of Abraham Darby, at Coalbrookdale) and John Jones & Co. of Bristol, costing £131 9s. 4d., and £118 6s. 10d., respectively. This included carriage by land and water, but they seem large sums until it is realised that the word "pumps" was then used to mean pipes as well. The latter were also of cast-iron (a great improvement on the old wooden ones) made in lengths of about ten feet with flanged ends which could be bolted together. The actual pumps (for lifting water), were of the bucket variety (as in the village pump) with clack valves. It was another handicap from which these mines suffered that there was no foundry in Cornwall. Pump barrels were still made of wood and the long range of pipes, up which the water was drawn from the bottom of the mine to the surface, or to adit-level, was composed of a series of tree-trunks bored by hand-auger and fitted into each other end-to-end. All these wooden appliances gave constant trouble. The Coalbrookdale Company had been making substitutes in cast-iron for some time, but the cost of their transport from Shropshire to a Cornish port and then overland on bad roads to the mine made the Adventurers slow to adopt them. While these difficulties must have been plain to everyone, and rich landowners and merchants were ready to speculate freely in the

[1] *Life of Richard Trevithick* by Francis Trevithick. See Appendix I.

36

fortunes of the mines, it was a humble member of the community, a man of small capital but broad vision, who took the initiative in finding a solution, John Harvey, the blacksmith of Gwinear.

It cannot be said when or for how long John Harvey had thought of starting a local foundry where pipes and pumps and engine parts could be cast and supplied to neighbouring mines, eliminating the several drawbacks of long transport. It was probably a long thought of slow but certain growth, as the steps he took to achieve, and then to consolidate his project, were sure steps and those of a far-sighted man. The technique of iron-founding is very different from that of the blacksmith's forge — how did he learn? There is a local legend about that, but it is one that has been circulated in like cases so often from classical times onwards, that one cannot take it seriously. It is said that he took a cargo of scrap-iron across the Bristol Channel to the ironworks at Neath and then disguised himself as a half-witted beggar, and so was given some lowly employment in the works where he learned the secret of the art of casting pipes.

That he actually made the voyage in question is a historical fact as a letter which he wrote to his wife on that occasion has fortunately been preserved. It is worth quoting, not for establishing the legend, but because it gives the only flash of insight into his personality which survives. That he had unusual ability and firmness of character we gather from future events, but the letter shows that, in addition, he was a kindly and good-hearted man. It is dated the year following that in which he did the work at Dolcoath.

Mrs Joanna Harvey
at Gwinear
Near Helston   Neeth
Cornwall   July 16th 1776
Dr and loving wife

This with due respects I hope corns hoping it will find you in Good Health as it Leaves me, Thanks be to God for it. When I left hayle I was troubled to see you Greaveing. I saw you walking up and Down the beach but culd not Speake to me. About ten o'clock I had a little Quame (qualm) which hould till two, at which time we almost lost Sight of Land with a fresh Gale & a very great Sea. I for amusement imployd my Self in catching of Mackrill. The Next Day we made the land, and at Night ankerd at Neath. On Friday Sold the iron but cannot way it until Monday and shall proseed as fast as possible that I may be home in the time Propos*d*. I lodges with Mr Will*m* Morgan who behave exceeding Sivile. Give my best love to my Dear Children & hopes Dear wife you will not Truble. I likes my Journey & believes it will not be amiss. I am sorry this cannot

37

come as soon as I could wish by Reason it must go to bristole. I desiar you will send an inclosd lettar for me to Mr James Harvey at bristole that I may know how you are & your affars. Give my love and sarviss to all Enquiring friends Desiring Mr. David Marten & Co Richard Pearce will manage your Husbandry afars. And so Rest Dear wife from your Ever Loving Husband and Faithful Frend   John Harvey

The cargo of scrap iron which John Harvey had brought to Wales would be sold for the purpose of converting it into wrought or malleable iron, and it would seem likely that he would not have had to resort to any disguise in order to be shown over the works through the courtesy of his customer or the good offices of the civil Mr. Morgan. And, as he was visiting Bristol before returning home, he would, no doubt be welcomed there by the ironfounders, as his friend, Richard Trevithick, was dealing with them for pump and pipe castings. But there would be other means of getting at least hearsay information from other friends among the engineers of the mines, notably the Hornblower family (of whom more hereafter), members of which are known to have paid frequent visits to the Coalbrookdale works.

The next scrap of news is wrapped up in another legend. It tells how the squire of Clowance, Sir John St. Aubyn, was out beagling on a Sunday morning and lost a silver buckle off one of his shoes. He turned into John Harvey's smithy saying "How can I go to church with one buckle?" to which the smith replied "Give me one of your old silver spoons and lend me that buckle, and I'll soon set you up again". Sir John, who was certainly born with the requisite article in his mouth, can hardly have carried it about with him. However, a silver spoon was produced (Clowance being only a little more than two miles away) and the new buckle ready in time for service. St. Aubyn, thus gratified, was moved to ask John Harvey what he would do if he had some of his money; "Why" says Harvey "go down to Hayle and make cast-iron pumps in place of wooden ones."

The incident has the ring of truth about it. How the versatile blacksmith could respond to an emergency was likely to be remembered as characteristic of the man. And perhaps the reported talk in the smithy had some significance. At any rate, a few years later, John Harvey gained the desired footing at Hayle as a sub-tenant of St. Aubyn, though by then it was another Sir John who reigned at Clowance[1].

[1] The 5th baronet, more distinguished in public life than his predecessor. An M.P. for three successive Cornish constituencies, a Fellow of the Royal Society, the Society of Antiquaries, and the Linnean Society, a collector, especially of Cornish minerals. His portrait painted by Reynolds and Opie.

CARNSEW[1]

The River Hayle — meaning "The Salty One" — evidently takes its name not from its source but its mouth, where it forms a large land-locked lagoon of two lobes before passing out through a narrow gap into the bay of St. Ives.[1] The river enters this estuary at the western end of the greater lobe, where its channel washes the shore and forms the boundary of the parish of Lelant, whose fine old church, standing alone on a green eminence overlooks the broad tidal lake. On the south side of the lagoon, and at a point which is nearly mid-way, a small stream called the Penpol River falls into it and meets another coming from the east which (at the present time) is called the Copperhouse River. They join each other below a narrow passage which almost closes the lesser lobe of the lagoon that, stretching out another mile to the eastward, forms the second tidal lake.

St. Ives Bay has one of the finest strands in all Britain. From where the River Hayle enters it to Godrevy Point, at the tip of its eastern crescent, lie four miles of hard sandy beach. It is the perfect playground for the family holiday-maker but, in old days, it was the source of endless trouble. The antiquary, John Leland, who visited St. Ives in 1538 found people bitterly complaining about blown sand drifting up their gardens and choking their small harbour. Immediately behind the beach just mentioned is the promontory separating it from the eastern lobe of the Hayle estuary. Here the blown sand has built up a prodigious range of dunes whose crests reach two hundred feet above the sea, called the Towans of Hayle. On the landward side, the parishioners of Phillack, settled round their church, have, in the past, been robbed of many fields and dwellings, foundered in the sand beyond redemption.

The lagoon, itself, had suffered doubly from sand, both airborne and sea-borne, so that when the tide was out it was seen as a huge expanse threaded by shallow channels. When John Harvey came to Hayle in 1779 these channels were only kept open by the main river and the two lesser streams. The part where he had gained his lease was called Carnsew on the south side of the estuary, forming, with its long sandy foreshore, the upper wedge-tip of the parish of St. Erth, separated on the left hand from that of Lelant by the Hayle River and from that of Phillack by the little meandering Penpol brook.

But for that troublesome legacy of sand in St. Ives Bay, the Hayle delta offered perfect facilities for shipping, being completely sheltered in all weathers from the wild Atlantic. But in spite of its drawbacks it does seem to have been frequented by ships, off and on, from earliest times. At

[1] It is now considered that Hayle, Hel or Hele in Cornish, means estuary or saltings.

Carnsew[1], itself, there is a prehistoric fort which must have been made to guard a tribal fleet and repel sea-rovers. There are indications that shipping came here in the Middle Ages and more certain proof of it in the sixteenth and seventeenth centuries. On the Lelant shore, where the main channel of the Hayle River runs, there are stone quays that must be quite, or nearly, two centuries old, and a student of archaeology might pick out the ruins of much earlier ones. But the modern commercial history of the Hayle estuary began on the further side where the two lobes meet at a narrow passage and the Penpol River emerges and must have formed a pool at the confluence of the waters where ships of shallow draft could lie.

It should be mentioned here that we are fortunate in possessing a contemporary account of most of the persons connected with this new development which was destined to produce both the town and harbour of Hayle. The *Parochial History of Cornwall* by Davies Gilbert appeared in 1838 when the author was seventy-one years old. He lived not far from Hayle, at Tredrea, in the parish of St. Erth, and he was able to make brief comment, from actual acquaintance or reliable hearsay, on the personalities of those pioneers, from John Curnow to John and Henry Harvey. Gilbert did not assume this name (which was that of his wife) until 1817. His own was Giddy, and in that name he has left a voluminous correspondence (now mainly preserved in the Royal Institution of Cornwall at Truro), but I shall generally refer to him by the one he adopted. As a man of science, he was far ahead of his time and, among his many attainments was that of the presidency of the Royal Society.

In, or near, the year 1740 a trading company was formed, of which the managing partner was that John Curnow, just mentioned, the others being William Lemon, Samuel Stephens, and Thomas Daniell. They were men of substance and also of such outstanding parts as to gain particular notices in Gilbert's work. Curnow, a native of Ludgvan, was an able merchant, Stephens came of a St. Ives family which had become considerable land-

---

[1] The name Carnsew may recall an Elizabethan episode in the Hayle estuary. When the Mines Royal Company established themselves at Neath in 1584 their adviser about Cornish copper was William Carnsew of Bokelly, St. Kew, mentioned in Carew's Survey as "a Gentleman of good qualitie, discretion, and learning, and well experienced in these mynerall causes". They procured ore from mines in the far western area and had it shipped across to Wales. A letter to their agent in Cornwall in 1585 mentions "Your owre [ore] of St dives [St Ives] is very harte to melt it, hopinge we will over com it, what St. Ust [St. Just] owrs will do we longe to see". If they shipped from Hayle, Carnsew's name might have become attached to the locality.

owners through success in the same occupation. William Lemon was one of those exceptional persons for whose production the climate of the eighteenth century seems to have been particularly favourable — especially in Cornwall. He came from Germoe, the parish which lies between St. Erth and Mount's Bay, and first made his mark by opening a mine at a farm in Ludgvan with two co-adventurers (of whom more hereafter). They quickly made a very lucky strike and the mine was aptly named Wheal Fortune[1]. Here they placed a Newcomen engine—one of the first to be installed in Cornwall. "Mr. Lemon" says Gilbert "is said to have gained from Wheal Fortune ten thousand pounds; and, thus enabled to execute more extensive plans, he removed to Truro, and commenced working the great Gwennap mines on a scale never witnessed before, and perhaps never contemplated, in Cornwall". He "soon became the principal merchant and tin-smelter in Cornwall. But the energies of his mind were not limited to these undertakings, great as they were; he cultivated a taste for literature, and, what is extremely unusual, acquired, amidst business, and at a middle age, the power of reading the Classic authors in their original language". So he became known as "the great Mr. Lemon" and, out of respect for his "commanding genius", the people of Truro are said to have withdrawn from their doors or windows as he passed through the street".

Thomas Daniell was another go-ahead fellow, though enriched by the simpler process of matrimony. He had been chief clerk to William Lemon, on whose death in 1760, "Mr. Daniell was enabled by the bounty of his wife's uncle, to take all the large mercantile concern on himself" (that is, from W. L's executors). This uncle was none other than Ralph Allen of Prior Park, Bath, the first great reformer of the British Post Office, who added to his gifts several shiploads of Bath stone with which Daniell built himself the most magnificent house in Truro

This powerful quartet formed the trading company already mentioned and built stone quays on either side of the narrows between the two lobes of the Hayle estuary. The particular business in which this company was embarked was that of mine-merchant, a trade which, at that time, was growing rapidly in importance and profit-making. The mine-merchant supplied the mine-adventurers with necessities that they were constantly in need of in large quantities and were unobtainable except by sea and, thereafter, by the shortest possible land route, for the roads were still

[1] Wheal, the old Cornish *whel*, a mine.

in the state described by Carew in Elizabethan days as "farre, foul, and cumbersome wayes". The principal items were coal and timber. The tinners, who had always smelted their ore locally, using charcoal as the fuel, were now, since the introduction of the reverbatory furnace, using coal. So were the Newcomen engines which were steadily increasing in number and were inordinately coal-greedy and wasteful in consumption. They were assembled on the spot from large castings and other parts, which had all to be imported in the same way. The demand was also for endless quantities of rope, ironmongery, bricks, and lime.

In spite of its drawbacks, due to that old bugbear, the sand, the Hayle estuary had advantages for the mine-merchant over every other anchorage in Cornwall. It was nearer to the principal tin and copper mines than the havens on the south coast and, in voyages to South Wales and Bristol (where the trade was mainly conducted), it avoided the dangerous passage round the Land's End. Its disadvantages were due to the bar at the mouth of the estuary and the shallow channels inside. The new Company's wharves could only be reached at the height of spring tides (once a fortnight), and not on all spring tides. Once there, a vessel had generally to wait the return of the next spring tide before going to sea again. At other times, ships must lie much further away from the quays and discharge into lighters or on the sandbanks for pack-mules or carts to carry the cargoes inshore. St. Ives and Lelant were convenient only for mines in the far west of the peninsula. To reach those of the south and east there was no way over the Hayle River except by the bridge at St. Erth churchtown or at a low tide ford in Lelant and then by a long trek over the sands which could not well bear more weight than that of a horseman with passenger riding pillion.

In spite of these difficulties, the venture was profitable. The Company was able to fill its vessels in outward as well as inward voyages for those which brought supplies for the mines could return to Wales or Bristol with copper ore. Copper needed a melting temperature five times higher than tin, and attempts to smelt it at home in the county, either with charcoal or coal, had always met with failure. The process remained in the hands of those old-established specialists, the smelters of South Wales and Bristol who had fuel in abundance close at hand.

The Company had been settled about thirteen years when a new prospector came to try his fortune as mine-merchant in the Hayle estuary. This was Thomas Pascoe. He was a member of an old local family and does not appear to have meddled in trade before. The best site having been occupied, he elected to try his luck at Carnsew, whose situation has already been described. Carnsew was an estate, part of the ancient manor of Trewinnard, now in the hands of three different landlords. The whole consisted only of about ninety acres of dry land with foreshore rights over the contiguous sands as far as low water-mark, spring tides. The three several parts were owned respectively by Sir John St. Aubyn, Humphrey Mackworth Praed, and three co-heirs of John Hearle. It was Sir John's third which Pascoe took on a ninety-nine year lease dependent on "three lives", for the modest rent of three pounds per annum.

The ninety-nine year lease for three lives was a common tenancy in Cornwall. It meant that three people who were alive at the time of the transaction would be named and the lease could extend for the time stated if any one of the trio survived for so long. On those terms, the only chance of getting the full benefit of the deed would be if one of the chosen lives were a baby of one year old and lived to be a centenarian. On the other hand, one of the recurrent epidemics might carry off all three of the young parties within a year or two, when the lease would likewise expire. Pascoe's nominees for his ninety-nine years tenancy were his children Thomas, James, and Hannah. What his plans were for developing his projected business at Carnsew does not appear. He took the place in 1753 and in three years time he went bankrupt. But, as up to that date he had not started any works whatever on his land, his money must have been dropped in mine speculation, a thing that could happen as suddenly as the making of a fortune.

One of the assignees in Pascoe's bankruptcy was George Blewett, a rich and successful magnate, who would have noted the happy issue of the enterprise of Messrs. Curnow, Lemon and partners and had his eye on the possibilities of the Hayle estuary. He now wished to take up the lease which Pascoe forfeited but, being an assignee of the bankrupt, he was barred from doing so in his own name. He got a business friend to stand in temporarily for him, one Thomas Dewen. Now, it will be remembered that William Lemon made his money by a lucky strike at Wheal Fortune. He worked the mine with two partners, George Blewett and Thomas Dewen who benefited in like manner. Since then, Blewett, like Lemon, had gone from strength to strength. Davies Gilbert gives us some interesting particulars. "At the foot of the Mount (St. Michael's Mount, Marazion) a small pier existed from a time probably anterior to the monastery itself, but in the early part of the last century a lease on lives was granted to Mr. George Blewett, the early associate, and in some degree rival, of the great Mr. Lemon. This gentleman rebuilt the pier on a very enlarged scale, and concentrated here almost the whole commerce of Penwith Hundred, which has since his time gone to Penzance and Hayle". Elsewhere we are told that "Mr. George Blewett, rising from the lowest origin, is said to have accumulated a hundred thousand pounds. On the death of his only son (John) the property went to a nephew, and the whole has been dissipated".

The bounds of the Carnsew thirds were rather vague. The whole tripartite estate was only partly enclosed. It contained crofts, commons, and some waste ground edging the foreshore. The latter and the whole foreshore were classed together as the *wastrel*. The wastrel was shared by all three holders of the estate and no boundaries were acknowledged on it except those which delimited the parish of St. Erth by the natural courses of the Hayle and Penpol Rivers, as visible only when the tide was at its lowest ebb. The only building of any kind on the premises was a cottage occupied by someone of the name of Honeychurch.

Blewett, having gained the St. Aubyn third, would wish to start his new venture of mine-merchant at a point nearest the sea and possibly he also wished to secure the whole of the foreshore rights for himself to eliminate the chance of yet another competitor in his line setting up in the estuary. At any rate, before proceeding further, he managed to gain leases on the other two thirds of Carnsew within the next two years. The lease for the third belonging to Humphrey Mackworth Praed (99 years for three lives at £3 p.a.) was signed in 1756, the lives being those of Bulkley Mackworth Praed, John Blewett (G. B's son), and Hugh Edwards. That which had belonged to John Hearle, owner of the famous Poldice mine, was lately come into the hands of his three daughters and co-heiresses and, in 1758, a lease from them was granted at the same rental as the other two, also for ninety-nine years and for the same three lives mentioned in the Praed agreement.

George Blewett was now in sole possession of Carnsew and he set about forming a company to exploit his bargain. The deed of co-partnership was signed and sealed just five months after the acquisition of the final third, and the names of the parties reveal how skilfully George had arranged matters in advance. They were Humphrey Mackworth Praed (lessor of the Praed third and father of one of the lives nominated in two of the leases), James Edwards (father of another life nominated in two of the leases), the accommodating Thomas Dewen (who, by now, had re-let the Pascoe lease to Blewett), and Abel Angove, a large landowner of Illogan.

THE CARNSEW CHANNEL

The Company set to work with energy on the preparation of their business premises, but these, strange to say, were not sited on any of the land which Blewett had so patiently acquired but on that trifling purtenance thereof, the wastrel. The most northerly point of the Carnsew foreshore was nearest to tidal water which was still separated from it by a large sandbank. They had the choice of making use of the hollow in the sand kept open by the feeble stream of the Penpol River, which gave a depth of a few feet on the higher tides, or cutting a new and more direct channel through the great sandbank. As the Penpol River emptied itself into the pool by Curnow & Co's. quays it might have caused some friction between two competitors in the same trade if that way from Carnsew had been attempted and, as Blewett and Lemon had worked so closely together in the past, it was no doubt felt that a clash should, if possible, be avoided. At any rate Blewett built his stone quay a little to the west of the rivulet and cut a channel in the sand down to the tideway[1]. It is possible that a natural gulley or runnel already existed which formed the basis of this artificial cut but, under the re-sanding conditions prevailing in the estuary it must have required constant maintenance.

Within five months of the formation of the company, Blewett sub-let the southern part of Carnsew (comprising 26 acres) for ninety-seven years (the limit of the Pascoe lease) to Francis Paynter of Trelissick. Paynter was a country gentleman whose land abutted on Carnsew and he seems to have wished to take in a little extra ground for agricultural purposes. He was related to the Hearle family and steward of the Hearle estate and not likely to become a competitor in trade.

The works going forward on the wastrel were, in addition to the stone quay, a counting-house, storage sheds, and a timber-pound. Between this establishment and the northern part of Carnsew, which was still retained, the road from Camborne and Redruth, joined by another going south, passed down on to the beach making for Penzance across the sands and the ford of the Hayle River at Lelant. This gave communication to the mining areas both east and south. Celia Fiennes, who wrote an account of her ride to Land's End in 1698, would have used this road but found the sands covered by a spring-tide when she got to Hayle.

[1] Several old men who remembered these events, when questioned in 1829, said the Carnsew Channel was not cut until later, but their evidence here and on other points was conflicting and unreliable. As the quay, so placed, would obviously be useless without some such access I have ventured to take the above for granted.

The new venture seems to have met with reasonable success and, if there was rivalry between the two traders, tolerance prevailed. It continued in being for twelve years when only one of the partners remained in the business. That was Humphrey Mackworth Praed, and in 1770 he assigned his rights in the northern part of Carnsew, including the quay and buildings to another trader, William Cornish, for a rental of £3 and, in addition, a premium of £450. What success this newcomer had in carrying on the trade is not recorded, but he does not seem to have been very active. He did, however, add a dwelling-house to the property which was located near the quay and then, in 1777, he assigned the northern part of Carnsew to the widow, Margaret Berriman, for a consideration of £300 in addition to an annual payment of £3 a year. But there was an important exception, for Cornish retained that small part north of the road containing his business premises — the quay, the timber-pound, and associated buildings including the new house. The latter he appears to have let separately to John Ellis and it is shown on estate maps as late as 1810 as "Mr. Ellis's House".

No explanation is forthcoming as to why this lady should pay such a large sum for a seemingly unprofitable part of the Carnsew estate, but the fact that she did so affected the future course of this story profoundly.

Shortly after this last parcel deal Cornish died and, in 1779, his widow re-let the excepted portion where the trade was carried on to John Dunkin and Thomas Ellis (a son or near relative of the said John?) for a premium of £350, and the following year they formed a partnership which included William Harris, Pascoe Grenfell and William Richards. The deed was signed on the 14th of October, 1780 and, it will be remembered that that was the year after John Harvey had arrived at Carnsew to set up his iron foundry. But before it can be told how and where he managed to get a footing among these various sub-tenants, and what happened to him, the reader must be taken back some years to be informed as to what had been taking place at the other trading-post and in the eastern part of the estuary.

An outline of the development, which was destined to assume the most formidable proportions in relation to all the trade at Hayle, is noted by Gilbert thus —

"An opinion, or rather a feeling, had prevailed in Cornwall that the copper ores should be smelted at home, and not sent to the opposite coast of Wales. Nothing could be more erroneous. About three times the quantity of coal is required to smelt any given weight of copper ore; and the importation of

46

coal from Swansea being very large, the conveyance of copper ore there produced alternate cargoes. The whole scheme seems to have originated in mistaken analogies drawn from ordinary operations.

"A plan so injudicious and adopted without estimate or consideration must have failed, and would have done so at once, but for the counteracting power of individual ability, in the person of Mr. John Edwards; a young man of Ludgvan, who had been recommended at a very early age to some situation requiring talent, by our celebrated historian Doctor William Borlase[1]. Mr. Edwards speedily acquired the entire management and direction of the whole concern" or, as he puts it elsewhere "soon forced himself into the chief management"

The latter cogent comment is worth noting for its bearing on future events and a further remark that "he obtained an ascendency over most persons on all occasions". The concern in which this forceful John Edwards so soon got himself appointed as managing partner was the Cornish Copper Company, which started smelting the local ore in the neighbourhood of Camborne in 1754, the year after the unlucky Thomas Pascoe had gained his lease at Carnsew. The initial success which the Company gained was hampered by costs and difficulties of transport to the coast. This they overcame by securing a site on the Hayle estuary where Welsh coal could be delivered direct to their works, the whole of which they moved in 1758. The place, then known as Ventonleague but since as Hayle Copperhouse, was situated at the extreme eastern end of the lesser lobe of the estuary in the parish of Phillack, most of which was then part of the great Cornish estates of Lord Arundell of Wardour.[2]

Here the Company re-erected their furnaces, built a quay, and acquired their own shipping. The small stream which I have called (in anticipation) the Copperhouse River ran by their works, but they were a mile further from the sea than merchant Curnow & Co. and this arm of the lagoon was as much subject to the sand bugbear as the other.

At the outset, the Company was faced by a still more dangerous threat to

[1] Rector of Ludgvan and author of *The Antiquities of Cornwall*, etc.
[2] Lord Arundell owned the land on both sides of this arm of the estuary, comprising the estate of Penpol on the south and Riviere on the north (perhaps a corruption of the old Cornish Rovear) with manorial rights over the foreshore and much of the actual bed of the estuary, claiming, as will be seen that of the Penpol River. Ventonleague was a separate tenement and, though it was at such an inconvenient distance from the sea they were probably able to acquire a site for their works there more easily.

its existence than the problems already named. This came from its brother copper-smelters in distant parts. They were a long-established and close-knit fraternity who had always acted together to drive hard bargains with the Cornish miners, whose prices they had largely been able to control to their own advantage. They had been consistently opposed to earlier efforts to produce pure metallic copper in the Duchy, and the failure of those enterprises must have been partly due to their machinations; and they now did all in their power to thwart the plans of the Cornish Copper Company which was, however, strongly backed by capital as well as by local enthusiasm, in addition to being led by that very determined John Edwards.

After having been settled on the estuary for a whole decade, the C.C.C. made its first effort to improve the navigation by getting leave from Lord Arundell to form a canal from their works down to the narrows and the upper end of the Curnow quays. They dug it a hundred feet wide in the sands and muds along the edge of the south shore, which was almost straight the whole way. At the same time, they erected floodgates and sluices at the Ventonleague end, whereby water could be impounded at the high tide and released at the lowest of the ebb. This had the effect of scouring sand out of the bed of the canal and possibly some part of the channel beyond. It was a device which had been employed successfully elsewhere and was used by Smeaton in his construction of Ramsgate harbour.

Nothing important is reported from Hayle for another eleven years and then, in 1780, quite a lot of things happened all at once that were to have a profound influence on the place and, eventually to carry its name all over the world.

III

RIGHTS IN THE PENPOL RIVER

SUCH COMPLICATED DETAILS OF LAND TENURE AS prevailed at Carnsew must make rather dull reading, but I feel they are essential to know in relation to future events and the unique history of Hayle harbour. Many points in the foregoing I have extracted from particulars of a lawsuit held at Bodmin during the Summer Assizes in 1828, when counsel for the plaintiffs had questioned a number of old men about what they could remember in their early days. One of them recalled that it was he who, in 1779, took John Harvey's furniture in a waggon, belonging to his master, a farmer of St. Erth, from Gwinear to Hayle, and remembered "one Margaret Berriman living in the same house at Carnsew which Mr. Harvey first lived in".

This must have been the lady who had gained the strip of ground across the northern part of Carnsew except for the quay and buildings and "Mr. Ellis's House" (which seems to have been actually located in her territory) and, there being no other dwelling in that part except the Honeychurch cottage, was providing general hospitality.

The ground which Harvey had secured for his foundry lay to the south of Mrs. Berriman's part and had been carved out of the Hearle third. It consisted of nine acres of land and equal rights on the foreshore with other under-tenants of Carnsew except, of course, that small portion of it that was now occupied by the quay and its buildings. It was bounded on the south and west by the Hearle property, now occupied by Francis Paynter, on the north by the Berriman strip, while to the east, it was open to the foreshore as far as the Penpol River, which took a very erratic zig-zag course in that part.

John and his wife, Anne, brought their family of seven children with

49

them—Joanna (aged 22), John (19), William (17), Francis (11), Anne (9), Jane (7), Henry (4), and Elizabeth (newly born). There is no record as to how this first enterprising Cornish ironfounder set about erecting his works or how, and from whence, he got his equipment. We have heard already that he was, himself, an expert stonemason and bricklayer as well as a smith and his two bigger boys were of an age to give much help. We can't tell what other labour he employed but probably Arthur Woolf, the carpenter, who had worked with him under Trevithick when the Carloose engine was moved to Dolcoath, was one of the party, and very likely William West, the young mines engineer, lent a hand, for he was an admirer of John's eldest daughter.

The necessary buildings to be tackled immediately were the foundry, itself, where he would have to install a reverbatory, or "air", furnace for melting Welsh pig-iron to run into moulds for his castings, sheds for workshops and storage, and a boring-mill. The whole undertaking was a large one for a man of very limited capital who, on having made this outlay, would have to bear constant calls on his purse for the raw materials of his trade, while his customers were not likely to be over ready in their responses, for the finances of mine adventurers fluctuated notoriously with the fortunes of their mines, from month to month. Over and above these considerations were the enormous problems of transport by land, sea, and sand.

There is nothing to say in what month Harvey arrived at Carnsew, but the quay and its facilities must have already been bespoken by Messrs Dunkin and Thomas Ellis, for their lease was signed in December of that year. Harvey's only means of sea communication, therefore, was the tidal gully of the Penpol River — such as it was, or what could be made of it — and he was soon negotiating with the agent of the Arundell estate for leave to deepen its bed. This was granted with more dispatch than usual, the deed being dated September the 9th, 1780.

The Arundell lease has a pleasant opening, saying that it is being given "for encouraging so useful an undertaking". It grants John permission "to make and bring up from the River Hayle a level or canal for the use of the Foundry" and, furthermore, "free Liberty, Licence, and Authority to take and use the running water in the said Wastrell and to pound and pool the same above the road (from Camborne) for such use and uses as he shall think proper and may well be without damage to the road". The ending is worth noting for future reference —"that he (J. H.) shall, and lawfully, peaceably, and quietly have, hold, and enjoy the Liberty and Authority hereby granted without the lawful Lett, Suit, Molestation, Interruption, or Denyal of him (Lord A.) or of any other person or persons whatsoever". The lease was for the usual ninety-nine years on three lives — John's children, Joanna, John, and William. No doubt his lordship was really impressed by the boldness of the blacksmith's enterprise for he only charged a yearly rent of 10s. 6d.

While these things were going on on the southern shore of the estuary — Harvey and his sons feverishly active, Dunkin and Ellis biding their time pending the partnership agreement which would bring in the additional capital they needed, old merchant Curnow died. Immediately after, the Cornish Copper Company acquired the whole of his business interests at Hayle together with his two quays. John Curnow had, for some time before his death, survived or bought out all his partners and got his mine-merchant trade entirely into his own hands. He had added considerably to his fortune and had bought two mansions, one of them the big house at Penpol where he finally lived. His heirs were three daughters, one of whom had married a partner of the C.C.C. named Robert Oke Millet, who, through his wife, inherited the Penpol estate and, on his father-in-law's death, he went to live at Penpol House. This alliance, coupled with their other gains, suddenly raised the Copper Company from a precarious situation to a place of power. It gave them control of nearly the whole of the eastern shore of the estuary and placed in their hands a secondary trade which was in a flourishing condition, that of mine-merchant.

Besides their struggle to keep their smelting works going on the fundamentally uneconomic basis pointed out by Gilbert and their unprofitable efforts to beat the ban laid on them by the Welsh and Bristol smelters, they had had to meet a new menace in the shape of a totally unexpected find of copper in the far off isle of Anglesey. The ore was not of such high quality as that in Cornwall but it occurred in a singularly massive formation. The whole heart of the hill was made of it. It could be worked more like a quarry than a mine — by opencast. The drainage problem, so costly in Cornwall, was such that it could be mastered by a single windmill, and labour in Anglesey could be had for half the price of that in Cornwall. At the foot of the hill was the little port of Amlwch which had a deep water harbour, from whence the ore could be quickly transported to Liverpool. The company had had the good fortune to engage a manager — Thomas Williams — who was quite the equal in wits and

51

go-getting to John Edwards, and he had been able to bypass the malice of the old-established smelters by getting his company to establish a smelting works of their own near Liverpool and also a rolling mill and copper wire works at Holywell on the Dee.

The opening of the Parys Mine had an almost immediate effect on the price of Cornish copper which it continued to depress until, by 1780, it had sunk from £7 6s. 6d., the hundredweight, to £3 13s. 0d. This baleful influence on the market continued until the end of the century, at which time Thomas Williams died and the mine was practically worked out. For Cornishmen, the nature of the case must also have rankled, as the discovery had come about in the most haphazard way. An Anglesey landowner would only let a small mine elsewhere in North Wales to an English mining company on condition that they kept a prospecting party on that hill at Amlwch where he believed, merely on the strength of an old local tradition, that a vast hoard of copper was concealed. To this proviso the English company only yielded with the utmost reluctance. They had no faith in Welsh prophets but they were compelled to detail a foreman and six men to go. This detachment kept an unprofitable vigil for three years, by the end of which time they had given up hope and were preparing to pack up. As a last resort, the foreman promised a bottle of whisky to anyone who would strike copper in a final attempt—and one man did, within seven feet of the surface. His prize cost the Duchy half a century of woe[1].

It may well be imagined that, after these set-backs, John Edwards's appetite for profit-making in the newly acquired business of mine-merchant was whetted, and he cast a jaundiced eye towards the competitors in Carnsew who were about to rehabilitate that much decayed trading post. As for John Harvey's little foundry, it could hardly bring anything but good to the mining community and perhaps be of some benefit to the Copper Company.

Messrs. Dunkin, Harris, Grenfell, Richards, and Ellis set to work with a will to repair dilapidations and improve facilities on their newly acquired premises. It has been said that it was they who first dug the Carnsew

---

[1] The satisfaction of that foreman, Johnathan Roose, is expressed on his tombstone in Amlwch churchyard.

> He first yon mountain's wondrous riches found,
> First drew its minerals blushing from the ground.
> He heard the miners first exulting shout,
> Then toiled near fifty years to guide its treasures out.

Channel through the sands, but this I have taken the liberty to doubt for reasons given on page 45. What they certainly did do was to revet the western bank of the channel to help keep it open, a work they carried out by putting down foundations of gorse and brushwood, on which they piled a training wall of rubble. Probably the crumbled defences of the old prehistoric fort close by provided a convenient source of material for that purpose.

Success in the mine-merchant trade depended on two things. First, one must find one's customers. To secure them it was essential for the merchant to be an adventurer, or shareholder in several mines. In the second place, he must be able to sell his goods as cheaply as possible which would depend on what bargains he could make at the source and what he would have to pay in freight charges. If he owned or chartered vessels and they had to return empty—in ballast—often with long delays due to adverse winds and the tide at Hayle, he would make no profits. The outward cargo, with rare exceptions would be copper ore. The lower grades (formerly rejected) were now being calcined at the mines and exported as *regulus*. Of this kind there was an abundance for shipment—if one were favoured with good business connections on both sides of the Bristol Channel.

Blewett's success at Carnsew may have been partly due to his having joined forces with Humphrey Mackworth Praed. This gentleman's father was the subject of Gilbert's "Singular story", which tells how the last of the Praed family of Trevethow got into financial difficulties "till meeting with a gentleman of the family of Mackworth, in Glamorganshire, bred to the higher department in the law, he arranged with this gentleman, that on being freed from all pecuniary difficulties, and receiving a certain annuity for life, the whole Cornish estate should be transferred to Mr. Mackworth: on the further condition of his taking the name of Praed, and what seems almost ludicrous, of his engaging, so far as the consent of one party could be sufficient, to marry Miss Penrose, of Penrose, near Helston, the heiress-in-law of Mr. Praed's estate".

All these conditions except one having been fulfilled on the death of the old Cornish squire, John Mackworth (now John Mackworth Praed) went to pay his addresses to Miss Penrose but, says Gilbert, "so far from obtaining success, he found some difficulty in escaping with his life". Furthermore, the lady sued him for the possession of the Trevethow estate, but lost the action. Now, it seems fairly certain that John Mackworth was a very near relative of the famous Sir Humphrey Mackworth of Neath, Deputy-

Governor of the Mine Adventurers Company, and the largest smelter in South Wales at the end of the seventeenth century — and one of the largest coal-owners. One may see in this connection a family link helpful to trade and the profitable loading of two-way cargoes.

I have not come across any record indicating what the early doings of the newcomers at the Carnsew cellars were. They were clearly not men of the same calibre as the founders of the quay, and they had against them an entirely novel factor from the outset of their venture in a determined local opposition. The Cornish Copper Company, not content with their own large gains in the trade of the estuary, had set their minds on getting the monopoly of it.

IV

THE CORNISH COPPER COMPANY

O F THE NEXT DECADE (1781-91) THERE IS ONLY incidental information about what was happening at Hayle Foundry. But those were eventful years in more ways than one. Within that short time John Harvey lost his three elder boys. Besides the grief which the whole family must have suffered when each of these hopeful young members was taken, the successive blows must have fallen very hard on the father who, no doubt, had fully reckoned on their support in his plans, both present and future, for the development of the newly created works at Carnsew. John, the eldest, died in '83, William in '88. Both funerals went to the parish church of their old home at Gwinear, in whose registers the interments are duly noted though not the nature of the illnesses which carried them off. Two years later, Francis was killed in an accident at the Foundry. The only other boy remaining was Henry, and he was but fifteen years of age.

There was, however, one happy event in the family annals, the marriage in 1784 of Joanna Harvey to that young mines-engineer already mentioned, William West. The bride was then just turned twenty-seven and the groom thirty-three years old. It was to prove an excellent match from which not only did Joanna gain a good husband for herself but an exceedingly good and useful son-in-law for her father.

William West was of a kindred trade to John Harvey and owned a smithy at Helston. He was probably attracted to the more specialised business of mines-engineer in the first place by doing smith's work for Richard Trevithick, whose son, the younger Richard, became his boon companion. Despite the difference in age between the two they were kindred spirits, children by adoption of the new age of power, one the "born" inventor, the other the "born" mechanic.

At the time of William's marriage, steam engines had become much more numerous in the Cornish mining area and the new patent, one produced by Boulton and Watt of Birmingham, had been gaining ground over the long-established Newcomen "fire-engine" since the first was installed at Chacewater seven years before. All these machines had to be assembled at the mine out of parts imported from various foundries and be made to fit together and then kept running by the mines-engineer, whose qualifications for the work must often have been very doubtful. But William West had both experience in mine engine work and also the natural bent of a good craftsman, while, in disposition, he was unassuming, a hard worker, and utterly reliable. John Harvey took him into the Foundry and one thinks he could hardly have found a better man to share the burden and difficulties of the enterprise.

The project had indeed succeeded beyond expectations, but the difficulties of carrying it on increased in equal ratio. There was endless trouble and expense in getting deliveries of coal and pig-iron for the foundry which must either come in specially chartered vessels from Wales or by arrangement with the Cornish Copper Company or Messrs. Harris and Ellis. But the activities of the latter party were being progressively and systematically curtailed by the former, who were now using every possible means of driving them out of business. This they did by the time-honoured device of price-cutting and then by buying out members of the partnership. In 1787 John Harvey was determined to free himself of intermediaries and bought a vessel of his own, the sloop[1] *Providence*, which he placed in charge of a very dependable master mariner, Captain Sampson. This at once roused the suspicions of the C.C.C. that the iron-founder, having gained his own sea transport, might find it profitable to supply the mines with coal (and other necessities) as well as his foundry and break their monopoly in the Hayle estuary which they were so near winning. So the keen John Edwards immediately came to terms with the widow Berriman (who was now the widow Carbis) and secured her strip of Carnsew which came between the Foundry and the Carnsew Quay and Cellars. This contained the house of John and Thomas Ellis where they were, however, allowed to remain as tenants of the Copper Company. Thomas Ellis was the last of the old trading concern which must, by now, have ceased to be a menace to any rival, but he held on to his lease of the quay till the C.C.C. agreed to give

[1] The sloop was a single masted fore-and-aft rigged vessel which differed only from a cutter in having a single head sail run up on a stay instead of being set "flying" as with the cutter's gib.

him an annuity of £40 a year. The bargain was struck two years later and the lease surrendered.

Thus, in 1789 all Carnsew north of the Foundry wall was in the hands of the Copper Company who claimed, moreover, the exclusive right to the foreshore — the waste and wastrel — contiguous to their holding, leaving Harvey with no access to the sea except at very high tides when his sloop might get up the Penpol River as far as the Foundry. This, they imagined, would effectively discourage him from entering the mine-merchant trade. Harvey, however, maintained that the foreshore rights of Carnsew had always been held in common by all three owners, no boundaries had ever been drawn thereon, no act of ownership in any particular part had ever been declared, and in every lease the use of "the waste and wastrel" was granted without qualification.

If Harvey had admitted the claim of the C.C.C. he would not only have had to abandon any idea of becoming mine-merchant but he could not even have continued in the foundry business except on terms of sufferance, as it was only on comparatively rare occasions that his sloop could reach the foundry. At other times she had to discharge her cargo where the tide served, which would generally be on a sand-bank some distance away, from which it would have to be delivered by cart or pack-mule over a long stretch of that debatable ground. But Harvey did not admit the claim, neither did he fear the consequences of taking that very step which the C.C.C. tried to prevent. He became mine-merchant.

On the eve of taking possession of the Carnsew Quay, the Copper Company had undertaken a work at their other depot calculated to make a most important improvement to their shipping facilities, not only at the old Curnow wharves but also at the smelting-house at Ventonleague. It will be remembered that they had linked the two places by a canal, and installed floodgates at the upper end, behind which water could be impounded on the high tide and released through a sluice at the ebb, which had the effect of scouring sand out of the canal and perhaps exerting itself to a limited extent, beyond. They now erected floodgates and a sluice at the lower end of the canal — in the narrows. This enabled them to pen up tidal water over the whole expanse of the eastern lobe of the lagoon. The force of this large area of water, released at every low tide, and directed by a training-wall of heavy slag from the copper works, was capable of making a profound difference in the depth of the old channel towards the sea and also in rendering the canal navigable for much longer periods, all of which

THE CORNISH COPPER COMPANY

was, of course, a good thing for Hayle Harbour as a whole, and not without (quite unintentional) benefit to Foundry shipping as well.

Among the numerous and varied archives of Harvey & Co. is one relic which claims particular attention, if not romantic interest. It is a folio volume of good hand-made paper, bound in white vellum, bearing the title "Henry Harvey, his Cyphering Book — March 14th 1787". It was the school exercise-book of John Harvey's youngest son, aged twelve. The opening pages have, at the top of each, an arithmetical rule given in model copperplate handwriting with large Gothic headings. All have a strictly commercial application such as —

> "DOUBLE FELLOWSHIP OR FELLOWSHIP WITH TIME" Example "Three Merchants, A. B. & C. enter into partnership. A. puts in £107 16s. for 9 months, B. puts in £100 for 10 months and C. puts in £79 19s. for 16 months. Now I demand to know each one's part after gain in proportion to his Stock and Time".

Blank spaces following each rule are filled with sums worked by the pupil and initialled by him. Perhaps they are fair copies after trials had been wrestled with on the slate, but the results show that the cypherer was not lacking in application and industry. Turning the pages, where fourteen of these mathematical riddles are set out, one suddenly finds writing in the same hand but upside-down, the book has been put to another use and re-started from the far end under another title-page "LETTER BOOK. Begun 1st August, 1791". Henry was now sixteen, no longer a schoolboy but a man of business, clerk to Hayle Foundry.

This book, the first detailed record of the firm, contains copies of all (or most of) the out-going letters from August 1791 to February 1796 and, with a few exceptions, they all appear to be in Henry's handwriting and give a clear indication of the state of things at the Foundry and the steady progress, from year to year, which the business was making. They also give us an intimate glimpse into the character and abilities of that young man who was destined, in his lifetime, to raise up his father's small and insecure foundation into one of the foremost companies of engineer constructors in the world, and to possess the land of his enemies.

The letters appear to be Henry's own composition, phrased in the formal business manner (which he must have picked up astonishingly quickly) salted occasionally with a little breezy Cornish. They show how, in spite of the manoeuvres of the Copper Company, Harvey's foundry business was prospering and he was also fairly launched on his merchanting enterprise, supplying not only the mines but traders in the neighbourhood and private individuals. There was more to do than the sloop Providence (45 tons burden, old measurement) could cope with. He was already chartering and taking space for part cargo in other vessels. For the foundry, he was shipping pig-iron from Coalbrookdale. This had to be sent down the Severn to Bristol and deposited with a wharfinger who stored it till it could be fetched. Pig-iron was also being got from Messrs. Lewis, Tait and Guest who owned the furnaces at Pentyrch and Dowlais, and shipped at Cardiff. Wrought-iron and faggot-iron (for producing the same) came from Bristol. Much of the wrought-iron, as well as coal, which came in frequent shiploads from Cardiff would be for the mines.

A long list of articles for disposal outside the foundry included tools, grindstones, screws, nails (and nail-rods for making them), wire, fire-grates (some "with suitable mantelpieces"), and other domestic fittings, soap, olive oil, linseed oil, red lead, pig-lead — all from Bristol. Slate for roofing and other purposes, including tombstones, from the Delabole quarries, fetched from Port Isaac. Tiles from Bridgwater and also bricks — the latter were even got from as afar afield as Hawarden on the River Dee. There was an increasing demand for iron "potts", kettles, and pudding-basins. These utensils, made to suit the more primitive hearths, were rather different from what is understood at the present time. "The name of pot" says the contemporary dictionary of Dr. Johnson "is given to the boiler that grows narrower towards the top, and of kettle that which grows wider". These pots were undoubtedly cauldrons which had legs to stand on and a hoop handle for suspension over the fire. Abraham Darby had taken out a patent for his method of casting them in dry sand, and all three vessels were a speciality of the Coalbrookdale works and were ordered from there.

In the early days Harvey does not seem to have imported a great deal of timber, though this was much in demand at the mines, due, perhaps, to difficulties in transferring it from ship to foundry over the sands. Nor are there any orders for the raw materials for rope-making before 1796, indicating that the rope-walk was not yet in being.

Payments were usually made by bills of exchange to mature at near or distant dates, though something would generally be saved by ready money, if that could be found. Payments to the Foundry were notoriously longer in coming than those the other way. Reminders had constantly to be sent. When these failed "bearer" was dispatched. Thus Captain Sampson of the

Providence went to collect a sum outstanding for three years, armed with the ominous note "if you don't pay the bearer the amount, shall proceed another way immediately".

With a limited capital to meet such considerable outgoings needful for his two trades it is wonderful how Harvey managed to make ends meet, but it is clear from the letters that he was more punctual in his payments than his debtors. Yet he often had to ask for postponements.

A case in point. On May the 13th, 1793, Henry writes to William Lewis, of Lewis, Tait, and Guest, ordering forty tons of "dark grey melting pig-iron" for shipment by the *Providence*. On June the 23rd he writes, enclosing two bills value £166 9s. 1d., "In about a month shall have a remittance for the balance of your acc. The affairs in Cornwall are very gloomy. We must crave next cargo 3 months for payment. Father expects to see you soon". He is as good as his word for, on July the 13th, he sends the balance — £130 10s. 11d. "Should have sent you the amount sooner but cash is so scarce in this country we have trouble to get it for the goods without taking bills of 60 days". And he gives a further order for forty more tons of the same.

At that time his father had already set out on a long exploratory expedition to Shropshire, South Wales, and as far north as Liverpool, and must have needed a fair stock of cash to take with him. He had, by now, gained sufficient confidence in his youngest son to leave him in charge of the administrative affairs of the Foundry, while William West looked after the works[1]. Nor were the trading expenses the only liabilities for, in the same year, he had been able to renew his lease of the premises, already occupied, for ninety-nine years on three lives (Henry, Anne, and Elizabeth Harvey) and also to take the remainder of the Hearle portion, abutting to the south, for ninety-seven years (on the lives named in the Blewett lease). This bold venture portending much enlargement of his premises had been made in spite of the now open hostility of the Copper Company and the present tightness of money.

The letters show that John Harvey had another source of revenue. He was investing what he could spare in mining adventures. In these doubtful speculations his sound judgment was vindicated by good returns. Apart from such gains, it was essential for the mine-merchant to have a stake in the mines in order to secure their custom.

[1] Letters from H. H. to J. H. are given in Appendix II.

PERRAN FOUNDRY STARTED

The Hayle Foundry was no longer the only one in Cornwall. Another had been started in 1791 on the Perran creek of the Fal estuary "conducted by Messrs. Fox, a family distinguished for ability, exertion, and liberality, from generation to generation" says Davies Gilbert. They were rich Quakers and built on a scale commensurate with their means — as may be seen from the original gateways still standing at Perranarworthal. They had the further advantage of being able to load and discharge vessels at a good tidal quay alongside the works. In the year following the erection of the foundry, the Foxes and their partners acquired important interests in South Wales, at Neath, including mines of ironstone and coal and a copper-smelting house. They were, however, getting pig-iron from the Coalbrookdale partners who were also eminent Quakers. It was not unknown that this spiritual brotherhood acted together in worldly matters and Henry Harvey wrote to William Reynolds of the Dale Company to complain of preferential treatment. Enclosing a bill for £205 4s. 5d., he remarks —

> Remainder of your acct. we'll remit you soon, but before we order for another cargo of your Iron would wish to know your price per Ton as we are Informed from the Foxes Foundry that you sold it to them (before we had the last cargo) for 10/- per Ton less than you charged us, and as the price of your goods is so considerably fallen 'twill be hard on the Founders in this County if the price of Iron do not lower in proportion. However, we hope you will not charge us more than any other person. Your answer per turn of post will much oblige my father, for whom I am &c."

Among the earlier letters (1792) are three to Jonathan Hornblower (the younger). A few words should be said about this remarkable family of engineers. The grandfather, Joseph Hornblower, came to Cornwall from Staffordshire in, or about, 1725, apparently under the instructions of Thomas Newcomen, himself, to erect the second of the inventor's engines in the Duchy at Wheal Rose. His son, Jonathan (the elder), settled at Chacewater and is said to have erected more than forty Newcomen engines between 1745 and '75. He had a family of thirteen children, every one of which he took the fancy to christen with names beginning with "J", finding a fruitful source in the Bible, which supplied him with such curiosities as Jecholia, Jedidiah, and Jerusha (his brother, Josiah, was the first to introduce the steam engine into America). Both Jabez, the eldest, and Jonathan, the sixth child of the all-J family were prominent among the mines engineers; and it is to this Jonathan who is given the credit of having invented the compound engine (of which, more later) which Henry's letters are addressed.

Two of the letters relate to pumps and other castings which Harvey was supplying for Jonathan at Tincroft, Wheal Unity, and Poldice mines. The third is in answer to one seeking advice on the making of brass. Henry gives this on behalf of his father and adds "you cannot mix the metal so well in pots (crucibles) as we can in the Air (reverbatory) furnace".

This is an interesting sidelight, showing that John Harvey was skilled not only in ironfounding but was an authority on the manufacture of alloys from the local raw materials of tin and copper. And there exists a very fine example of his work in that line—the nine hundredweight tenor bell in the parish church at Stithians. It bears the legend in bold Roman capitals JOHN HARVEY FECIT 1790. It had caused wonder that he should have learned how to cast iron pipes, but to turn from blacksmith to bellfounder in so short a time was surely a much greater *tour de force*! How to shape the moulds and pour in the appropriate mixture of copper and tin so nicely that, when cooled and struck, the note of "G" will be sounded? Perhaps it was, in fact, an older bell re-cast. If that were so, the achievement is still a remarkable one. In 1956 the Stithians peal was re-hung in a modern frame by Taylor of Loughborough and the tenor bell slightly re-tuned. Nothing else had been done to it, and it remains a testimonial to the thorough workmanship and the versatility of its maker.

By 1792 the Foundry was not only making castings but complete steam engines for, at the end of that year Henry writes "Another fire-engine to be built in the foundery immediately". It would be on the Newcomen principle, constructed from drawings by the engineer of the mine for which it was intended. The Watt patent, covering the separate condenser, prevented would-be inventors from making any improvement in engines working on low pressure steam and as, at that stage, the Foundry did not produce designs of its own, it was preserved from getting involved in the endless lawsuits over the rights of that patent. Watt does appear to have given Harvey a few orders for parts of his engines in Cornwall, but he did not continue his custom and wrote to his partner to say that Harvey was too slow and charged too much. This was very likely true, as John insisted on doing things thoroughly and with the best obtainable materials. But Watt disliked and distrusted anything Cornish, sentiments which were fully returned by Cornishmen. They had to admit, however, that his Watt engine consumed only half the fuel of the earlier one and paid its way in spite of the exorbitant royalty that was charged. It was mainly adopted by the eastern mines while those in the neighbourhood of Hayle stuck to the old "fire-engine".

While engaged on these larger undertakings, the Foundry was doing all manner of odd jobs. A Mr. Bodelly of Guernsey calls and orders two screws for tobacco presses. The captain of one of the Post Office packets, running between Falmouth and Lisbon, orders a fully fitted-up caboose (kitchen) for his vessel and is told "We have made out a draft of your Cook room & through the strictest computation thinks the time you mentioned is not sufficient to compleat such article as there is a great deal of work hid from an outward view". The work took thirteen weeks "Price roughly £24, but not to include carriage". A tailor at Padstow orders a set of clothiers' press-plates, a troublesome and unremunerative commission but conscientiously carried out. "Should have cast your press plates before this but you ordered them so thin that we mist two to one that we have cast". But so much painstaking was not rewarded by prompt payment. After repeated applications "bearer" (John Harvey, himself) proceeds to Padstow to collect the debt — a journey of some sixty miles, there and back.

Meanwhile, the Cornish Copper Company, having tried all ordinary ways of obstructing their obnoxious but flourishing rival, began to step up their campaign. On October the 21st, 1793, Henry writes to Francis Paynter, the agent for the Trelissick estate, whom he has been supplying with some domestic fittings —

> Have this day forwarded to Mrs River's (the carrier's depot), Truro, your stove grate & Casement fastners, desiring her to take care of the same and send you word immediately. Mr Edwards have deny'd father (use) of the Channel & beg you'll sett him your right from the Cock Pool & under Treliseck hedges in the wastrel.

The Cock Pool was on another branch of the Hayle River which came up on the north-west side of Carnsew and might be used as an alternative channel to the other two for high tide landings though it was much more remote from the Foundry. It was close to dry land belonging to the Trelissick estate and there could be no argument there about common or exclusive rights on that foreshore. But how had John Edwards ventured to deny Harvey the use of the channel formed by the Penpol River, for the right to deepen which he was paying Lord Arundell an annual rent? The answer of the C.C.C. was that Mr. Oke Millett of Penpol House (their partner) had now acquired the freehold of the Penpol estate, and they said there was nothing in the conveyance to allow Harvey to enjoy any right in the river. Yet he was still paying the agreed rent to Lord Arundell.

THE CORNISH COPPER COMPANY

There is no more news of the dispute until the 24th of May, 1794, when Henry writes to Lord Arundell's agent —

These few lines are to inform you of Father's proceedings concerning his Channel in this place. About 5 weeks since he began to open it & last week Mr John Edwards sent his men & fill'd it so that we can't bring in our goods. The water that was turned out by them some time since we have brought in its old course, which they turn out and we turn in. Father waited on Mr Edwards to know his reason for so doing & he said Lord Arundel had no right to it. We beg you'll order Capn Paul Penrose immediately to inspect it; & father begs you'll write my Lord the consequence of the Business, that he may not lose his right, nor father his bargain. It is a great disadvantage to us & have lost already between 30 & 40 £. We hope you'll not fail to do so. A few lines by turn of post will greatly oblige my Father, John Harvey.

He is speaking of another stratagem when he says "the water was turned out some time since". It was the diversion of the Penpol River, achieved by cutting a short canal for it to run into the head of the Carnsew Channel. Yet, far from being cowed and dismayed by these open hostilities on the part of his powerful neighbour Harvey was about to give the order for the building of a new and much larger vessel. The *Providence* had been laid up for repairs since January in Mr. Clibbetts's yard at Bideford, where Captain Sampson was also located, keeping a sharp eye on the work and receiving constant exhortations from Hayle to speed it up.

The new vessel was to be a brig[1] called the *Henry*. Her keel was laid some time in August. It is interesting to note that the shipwright only played a limited part in the construction of the vessel. John Tyack, the famous smith of Camborne, was to make some of the wrought-iron work and the anchors. Captain Sampson was instructed to get the studding-sail boom irons made by a Bideford smith "as we can't tell the size you'll have them". He was also to employ a local carpenter to do the cabin work. The sails and rigging were being made in Cornwall.

By the end of December the new ship was nearly ready and Mr. William Clibbetts applied for a further instalment of pay. He was answered —

Cannot comply with your request at present as father is from home and I have no time to go in search of any [ready money] neither do us draw any bills. Hope it will make no material difference for a short time as we shall be there when she is launched and will bring it with us, only desire Capn Sampson to let us know the day when she will launch some time before hand. You may expect the sloop up on the rising of the next spring tide.

A few days later he writes to Sampson with two bills value £41 12s.

[1] Brig; a two masted vessel, square rigged except for the gaff-mainsail.

64

1d. —

which you'll pay the Builder if you think it safe to do so, but if you think all of it is too much, pay him so much as you think proper. He have had already towards two payments £201 10s. 0d. before these two bills now sent & let him send us a receipt for what you now send him. We shall get everything reddy this week (i.e. sails, rigging, anchors & et.) & if the wind is fair the sloop will sail the beginning of next.

He writes again to Sampson (January 16th, 1795) disagreeing with the shipwright's intention of rigging the vessel on the stocks —

We think it to[o] great a risk & if anything should happen, it is a question whether or not the Builder would stand to it, as being rigged before launched, therefore we would wish him to get her off the stocks as soon as possible, leaving us know the day per turn of post. We have put everything in the sloop & she is now ready in St Ives waiting for a fair wind — it is now N.E.

John Harvey's absence from home, as mentioned above, can probably be accounted for. He was determined to get his rights in the lease he had taken for deepening the Penpol River vindicated. He found it useless to argue with agents and set off to see Lord Arundell himself at his home in Wiltshire. He succeeded in doing so and was well received, Lord Arundell promising to instruct his agent to issue a writ on the Copper Company. But it seems the matter was quietly dropped.

It is not certain when the party succeeded in reaching Bideford as the only note on the occasion is the settlement of a bill of £5 5s. 0d. for "Launching feast". This, and the final payment to the shipbuilder of £111 18s. 6d., was made some time later and, in the accompanying letter, Henry was not above rising to a pun. He says "Our Dear Brig (for so we may call her as she cost, £150 more than we expected she would) brought down a cargo of coals from Swansea & is now in Bristol. We like the Vessel very well but she cost too much money". Her tonnage is given as 80 (old measurement).

The Copper Company's next move was made by R. O. Millett. When Harvey was still in favour he had given him leave to make a leat through a very small portion of the waste ground at the edge of his domain to carry off the water which worked the wheels at the boring mill. This permission he now withdrew, threatening to fill up the leat if Harvey did not immediately find some other means of disposing of the water. What then happened is told by Henry in a letter to Francis Paynter (January 22nd, 1795) —

Mr Edwards have been to his word in filling up the leat which have stopped the Boring mill and poold up the water over the road and part of Trelissick

65

Lands, which made it impassable and not his right to do. People of all ranks think that father is left very Cold with the Lords [of Trelissick] in not having it settled, as we have been striving to keep the property to no use. We hope you have an answer from Esqr Rodd concerning the plot under Trelisic Hedges or some place in your right to land our goods, if not please press him for the same, otherwise Father's industry must go to wreck. If the weather permits Father intends waiting on you in a few days.

In the Memorandum (page 340) it is recalled how John first tried the expedient of raising the axles of the wheels three feet to give the paddles a clearance above the impedence of the waste water. That proving ineffective — as also his landlords — he defied the ban and cleared the rubbish out of the leat. So, a little more than a fortnight later Henry writes to Paynter again —

The present is to inform you that yesterday Messrs Edwards & Millett again sent their men and filled up the leat, which pool'd up the water higher than it was before so that people cannot pass with safety, and are now taking of the timber from the Platt where the Lighter stands & have gave us 9 days notice to take of [f] the Lighter also, which if not done they will take her down themselves. After we have laid those things before [you] we beg you'll take what steps you think proper so soon as possible as some of our Works are Idle, & a few lines by turn of Post will oblige my father.

The lighter was being built to serve the new ship whose increased tonnage and draft would not permit her to come up the Penpol River unless that channel were deepened a good deal more, even on the highest tides. The idea was to save the expense of carriage over the sands by cart or pack-mule, and the lighter was being built on part of the wastrel adjoining land covered by the two new leases of 1793 taken from the lords of Trelissick (the old Hearle third) — a plot that was not in dispute. Only eight days later, Henry writes to Paynter again —

Contrary to your Opinion in your last, Mr. Millett & Capn Prideaux with about 40 men Came and took down the Lighter. In our letter before we mentioned concerning the Oak and other timber they had taken from a place in the Trelisick right and put it to a place where the Tide flows, & this morning the Sea carried off a great many pieces which is a great loss. In your last you recommended Mr. Grylls to have the Hearing of it but believe he is not come from London. Father have had some talk with Mr. Edwards who would have him pay some acknowledgement for the standing of the lighter. Father told him he would have no objection if the plats were his, if not he could not expect it. Mr E. farther told him that Mr Grylls said that all the plats were his and the Ellises confirm the same by saying they enjoyed them 30 years. Father will wait on him to your desire when he returns. In the meanwhile he think you have no time to lose and let us know our rights, they not hearing from you in this Business Encourages them to go on more rapid. The foundry stands next in danger which (the talk is among the people) they mean to take down likewise. We beg to hear per turn of Post your opinion on how to proceed.

Thomas Grylls was Sir John St. Aubyn's steward. The word of the defeated Ellises could be discounted. They had doubtless been browbeaten by the masterful John Edwards and shortly afterwards Thomas Ellis is discovered as a clerk in the offices of the C.C.C. In spite of the appeal at the end of the last letter no answer was received. Henry wrote again —

> In your last you desired to hear from us if any further Steps should be taken on the part of Mr Edwards (in answer to which) we sent a letter 10 days since Informing you of their taking down the lighter & as we have not heard from you since fear it miscarried. Father, to your request, waited on Mr Grylls who would wish you would call on him and bring with you the Original Deed of Carrnzews (Carnsew) & he would come with you on the Spot and try to settle the Business. Hope you'll not be backwards as we have sustained a Great loss in not having the rights ascertained. Your sending a few lines per turn of Post, saying when you could make it convenient to come that father may be at home, will greatly Oblige him, for whom I am &c. . .

There is nothing in the letter-book to indicate what happened either then or later in causes of friction between the two parties, though entries continue to be made for a further twelve months. But it is clear that none of Harvey's landlords exerted themselves on his behalf as further incidents of high-handedness are noted in the Memorandum (page 341). The limekiln on Carnsew Quay still stands intact — an ancient monument to those early days of strife which I hope will be preserved.[1] The remaining letters in the book show a steady advance in the Foundry's trading. Captain Sampson was promoted skipper of the brig Henry and Captain Jasper Williams was given charge of the sloop *Providence*.

In the family there had been another marriage. In 1794 Anne Harvey, now aged twenty-four, had given her hand to a namesake of her father's, John Harvey of Helston. He is thought to have been a distant cousin, though the relationship has not been established. Very little is known about him except that he was a well-to-do cabinet-maker, and that, in the year after the marriage, he entered into partnership with a mercer of the same town and like surname, Nicholas Harvey. But, at least, we know what he looked like, as a well executed miniature of him has been handed down in the family. The union was auspicious for the fortunes of the Foundry, to which it gave a line of able leaders in succeeding generations. With the last entry under February the 12th, 1796, the sequence of letter-books is lost for

[1] Since demolished

thirteen years and we are again left with only incidental information about the doings at the Foundry. It is most probable that we owe the survival of that precious early record to sentiment, in that its first purpose was to serve Henry as his school exercise-book.

V

RICHARD TREVITHICK THE YOUNGER

IN 1797, RICHARD TREVITHICK DIED. HE HAD, SAYS Gilbert in a letter to J. S. Enys "the reputation of being the best informed and most skillful Captain in all the Western Mines". His son, of the same name, but much more widely known today, was immediately elected in his stead as leading engineer in the district. He was just turned twenty-six.

It may be noted in passing that in that seagirt peninsula of Cornwall nautical terms had gained more currency ashore than elsewhere. A mine, like a ship, was given feminine gender, as were its engines. Depths and distances are universally spoken of in fathoms and not feet and yards, and managers of mines, and sometimes their engineers, are given the honorific title of Captain. Henry Harvey, though he was neither of these things, is affectionately remembered as the "Little Cap'n".

The younger Trevithick had already had many dealings with Hayle Foundry, where his close friend, William West, was employed and had become a member of the Harvey family and, in the same year that the elder Richard died, the younger married another of John Harvey's daughters — Jane.

Most people have heard of this Richard Trevithick, who made the first practical self-propelled road carriage and also the first railway locomotive. A two-volume life of him was written by his son, Francis, and at least two other biographies have appeared within recent years. They cannot give us more than a shadowy impression of that unique figure whose sensitive intellect combined the perspicacity of a poet, the prescience of a prophet, and the logic of a judge, seated in a physique as robust as that of Samson. The marriage augured the perfect pooling of talent. John Harvey was a producer only. He worked to other people's designs and ideas. Trevithick was both designer and inventor as well as a practical mechanic. But both

John and Richard cherished personal independence and their business relationship never became closer than that of manufacturer and customer. It is out of character for a genius to be muscular, but Trevithick's feats of strength gained such repute as to attract the attention of the Royal College of Surgeons, who begged him to submit himself to their examination, on which, they declared they had "never before seen muscle so finely developed"[1]. On the other hand, it is quite in character that a genius should be a dunce at school, and the opinion given by his master at the little Camborne seminary was that he was "a disobedient, slow, obstinate, spoiled boy, frequently absent, and very inattentive". The mine captains came to hold a very different view of his capabilities for, at the age of twenty-one he was entrusted with the task of testing the duty of a new kind of steam engine at Tincroft Mine, for the purpose of comparing its efficiency with another at the same place installed by Boulton and Watt. This was work which required that the consultant should be reliably accurate and entirely disinterested in the tests. That young Trevithick should have been engaged to carry them out was a tribute both to his skill and reliability.

To ascertain the *duty* of a steam engine, that is, its efficiency in terms of fuel consumption, had become a matter of the utmost importance since the introduction of the Watt engine in 1777, as it was on that basis that the Birmingham firm charged royalties (in addition to the price of purchase and erection) on the running of their engines. This duty was calculated on the number of pounds of water which could be raised one foot on a single bushel of coal. When Boulton and Watt installed one of their engines in place of an old "common fire-engine" (of Newcomen type) they gauged how much coal would be saved by the new engine above the old, and fixed their royalty at one third of that price, to be paid annually during the life of the patent.

The new engine in question had been erected by Jonathan Hornblower, the younger, on the lines of a patent he had taken out ten years before (in 1781), and was designed primarily to circumvent the nearly all-embracing coverage of the Watt patent with its separate condenser. But it was, in fact, an important departure, for it introduced a new principal which, in later years, would be adopted with great advantage in the matter of saving of fuel, namely, that of using more than one stage of expansion. This compound engine had two cylinders of different sizes. Steam entered the

---

[1] Francis Trevithick *Life of Richard Trevithick*.

smaller, where it was allowed to expend only part of its force and then passed on to the larger cylinder. Here the remainder of its force was used up and the steam condensed by a jet of cold water, as in the old fire-engine.

The result of the trial showed that the engine did a duty about equal to that of Watt though it was a good deal more cumbersome. But it gave Hornblower a number of new orders, for the Cornish adventurer much preferred a home-made to the Birmingham import, and they were finding the Watt royalties both unfair and oppressive. The Birmingham competitors, however, dismissed the novelty and virtue of the principle of two expansions and saw only the attempt to evade their patent which, they declared had failed because the second cylinder was nothing more than a *separate condenser*, and they began proceedings for infringement against Jonathan.

The cause, Boulton and Watt v. Hornblower and Maberley, came on in 1796, the year before Trevithick's marriage to Jane Harvey. The court found for Boulton and Watt, but the defendants appealed. The hearing had an important side-issue for Trevithick as he met there, for the first time, Davies Gilbert (Giddy)[1], who was also called as witness for the defence. Gilbert has been quoted several times in this account, but only in his capacity as a local historian. His dominant interests were for natural science and mathematics. In both these departments he was the most distinguished amateur in the whole country, eventually gaining the chief honour in the scientific world of being made President of the Royal Society. The two men took to each other immediately and, in Gilbert, Richard found a friend and consultant who advised and supported him in all his multifarious schemes throughout his life.

After their marriage, the Trevithicks went to live first at Redruth and, shortly afterwards, at Camborne. This stormy petrel had chosen for a wife a woman hardly less remarkable than himself, though different in many ways. She was of a singularly equable temperament and, in the many trials she had to sustain during her husband's life, she remained absolutely loyal and constant.

At the Foundry, the landlords remained unhelpful, and friction with the Copper Company continued. John Harvey had dug a new leat from the boring-mill down to a lower place in the Penpol River so that it all lay within the parish of St. Erth. He had again deepened his channel in the river to enable lighters to bring cargoes from his vessels up to the foundry.

[1] See Todd A C, *Beyond the Blaze*, Barton, Truro, 1967

This was countered by the C.C.C. by dumping heavy slag over a ford at the lower end of the channel. This ford linked the more northerly track across the sands towards Penzance with an ancient road which passed through Ventonleague and (the present) Copperhouse. It was on the route which Celia Fiennes had intended taking but found herself baulked by a spring tide[1]. The Copper Company maintained that they had taken this measure because Harvey's dredging operations had interfered with the public highway over the ford. This was untrue. He had only deepened his channel down to that point. Now he was, for the time being, unable to use his lighters for direct transhipment even on the highest tide. No doubt he quickly took measures to clear the passage, but how and when is not recorded. It was not by any means the last time that this trick was to be played.

About this time, something else was going on at the Foundry, outside the ordinary routine of business. William West was making a model for his friend, Trevithick. It was to demonstrate a theory which the latter had been revolving in his mind perhaps ever since the Hornblower trial — the use of what he called *strong* steam. If it worked, it would, amongst other things, deliver the Cornish engineers from the long bondage of the Watt patent (though that was now due to expire very shortly) — it needed no separate condenser. The idea must seem to us as obvious as it was simple, yet it had never been given a fair trial.

The Watt engine, like its Newcomen predecessor, was essentially an atmospheric engine. It was supplied with steam only at a low pressure (2 to 3 lbs. per square inch). Its power was derived from the condensation of the steam and the ensuing weight of the air when a vacuum was formed. Trevithick proposed to raise the boiler pressure to 65 lbs., or more, and let the steam go free into the air without bothering about the vacuum. Watt had been fully aware of the application of "strong steam" but said it was much too dangerous to tamper with and preferred to stick to his speciality. One reason for this was that no boiler then being made was capable of resisting more than a low pressure.

West's model was duly delivered to his sister-in-law's new home and a distinguished company assembled to witness its trial. There was Davies

---

[1] Cary's road-book (1812 ed.) notes the road over the sands and says it "is passable at 12 o'clock, either by Night or Day; but at any other time the Passage depends on the Tide". Spring tides on that coast are never full at the times mentioned and high neap tides at those hours would not make the fords impassable.

Gilbert (who had previously been consulted about the daring innovation, and approved it) and Francis Basset of Tehidy, the squire of Illogan, who had just been created Lord de Dunstanville, with his wife. The boiler is said to have been made "like a strong iron kettle", the machinery of brass. It was placed on the kitchen fire and Gilbert raised steam with a pair of bellows. Lady de Dunstanville was given the honour of turning the cock to start "the first high-pressure steam-engine".[1]

The experiment was a success, and Trevithick went on to apply the principle in all manner of ways — to winding-gear at the mines (replacing the old horse whim), to his plunger-pole pumps, and to locomotion. For the latter, William West was kept at it making models. At the same time, Trevithick designed boilers capable of withstanding pressures up to more than 100 lbs. (notably the well-known Cornish boiler).

What was learned from the models was consolidated in a full-scale self-propelled road vehicle which was ready to run its trials on Christmas Eve, 1801. It was erected at John Tyack's smithy at Camborne, the castings having been made at Hayle by John Harvey. Typical Cornish mid-winter weather prevailed with sheets of rain, and it was getting near dusk, when the father of all motor cars sallied forth into an excited crowd. Showing that complete confidence he always had in his ideas, even before they were tried, he made a start by setting the machine to climb a hill with a gradient of about 1 in 20, while seven or eight people clung on where they could get a footing. The only fault found was a difficulty in keeping up steam at the required working pressure.

After some necessary adjustments had been made it was planned to take the "fire-carriage" (as its maker called it) on a state visit to Tehidy Park, three miles away, to show its paces to the Basset family. Davies Gilbert (who had acted as stoker for the embryo model) was informed of this intention and he not only rode over from Tredrea the day before but went to the front gate at the predicted hour and waited there to give the party an ovation. The carriage started in great style, with Andrew Vivian (who was to be Trevithick's partner in the pending patent) at the helm. But Gilbert had to wait in vain, for an obstruction in the road dashed the tiller out of Vivian's hand and the vehicle was ditched.

The finale of the adventure was recalled by Gilbert some years later in a letter to J. S. Enys —

[1] Francis Trevithick *Life*.

The travelling Engine took its departure from Camborne Church Town for Tehidy on the 28th of Deer. 1801, where I was waiting to receive [it]. The carriage, however, broke down after travelling very well, and up an ascent, in all about three or four hundred yards, Then, after the overturn, The carriage was forced under some shelter, and the Parties adjourned to the Hotel, & comforted their Hearts with a Roast Goose & proper drinks, when, forgetful of the Engine, its Water boiled away, the Iron became red hot, and nothing that was combustible remained of the Engine or the House.

The taste of this good Christmas cheer cost the loss of two years work and seventy-two odd pounds, as may be seen by the entries in Trevithick's account-book reproduced in his son's life. But Trevithick never repined at losses in time or money. He had not been born with any strong sense of values in those respects. Nature had endowed him, instead, with irrepressible optimism, and a genius for invention more flexible and universal than that of James Watt.

In the extract from that account-book, just mentioned, there appears the name of Arthur Woolf. He had been employed by Trevithick in earlier work and, as we shall hear of him later in close connection with Hayle Foundry, he may be briefly introduced at this juncture. He was the son of Arthur Woolf, the mine-carpenter at Dolcoath, who had worked under the elder Trevithick and had been one of the party engaged in the re-erection of the Carloose engine noted in Appendix I.

The younger Arthur had been brought up to his father's trade, but his bent was towards things mechanical and he went off to London where he found work in the establishment of Joseph Bramah the millwright, inventor of the hydraulic press. In 1796 he is discovered with Jonathan Hornblower at Newbottle in County Durham, helping to erect winding engines of the Hornblower compound type. When Boulton and Watt finally won their case for infringement, Jonathan's activities here and elsewhere were stopped. Woolf then appears to have returned to Cornwall, for Trevithick was employing him in 1800 to deliver and manage one of his small portable high pressure engines. The incident is noted in his account-book as "To Arthur Woolf going to London as engine fireman with Shetland engine, at £302 a year". It must have been shortly after that that he was enlisted by Meux's Brewery as their engineer, though he is noticed again by Trevithick the following year as doing an errand for him to Coalbrookdale.

The Watt patent had expired in 1800 after a long life of thirty-one years, and in 1802 the patent for the high pressure carriage engine was taken out by Trevithick and Andrew Vivian, after some lobbying and friendly intervention by Basset and Gilbert, and William West was busy at Hayle making castings and a wrought-iron boiler for a second automobile designed to cut a dash in the streets of London. This phoenix was a much more finished and improved creation than its predecessor. A large body was being made for it by William Felton, the coachbuilder of Leather Lane, who was also the author of the first standard work on carriages. It was made to hold eight inside passengers (stage-coaches held six, mail-coaches four). When preparations were sufficiently under way William West was spared from the Foundry for some months to help assemble the machine in the coachbuilder's yard. The engine had all the characteristic Trevithick improvements over previous steam engines. The boiler was heated internally by a U-shaped fire-tube, the hot gasses in the flue returning into the chimney at the same end as the grate. One of Watt's improvements had been that he retained heat in the cylinder by surrounding it with a steam jacket, Trevithick went one better by inserting the whole of the cylinder in the boiler (at the other end).

The carriage ran some most successful trips in the streets of London and then ventured a short way out into the country where the only "incident" on record occurred. John Vivian, a young cousin of Andrew's, then serving in the Navy, was appropriately given the tiller. He said afterwards —

> One day they started about four o'clock in the morning, and went along Tottenham Court Road, and the New Road, or City Road: there was a canal by one side of the road at one place, for he was thinking how deep it was if they should run into it. They kept going on for four or five miles, and sometimes at the rate of eight or nine miles an hour. I was steering, and Captain Trevithick and someone else were attending to the engine. Captain Dick came alongside of me and said, "She is going all right". "Yes", I said, "I think we had better go on to Cornwall". She was going along five or six miles an hour, and Captain Dick called out, "Put the helm down, John!" and before I could tell what was up, Captain Dick's foot was upon the steering-wheel handle, and we were tearing down six or seven yards of railing from a garden wall. A person put his head from a window, and called out, "What the devil are you doing there! What the devil is that thing!"

These exploits were intended as a public demonstration of what the high pressure engine could do, especially as adapted to the entirely new expedient of locomotion. One may imagine what a new sensation the appearance of the first motor car in the streets of London must have caused! Yet the journalists of the day seem to have thought it quite beneath their notice. Not a single mention of the trials appeared in the London press. The costs of the experiment came to nearly a thousand pounds, out of which nothing is put down for West's expenses in time and his long sojourn in London, nor credited to John Harvey for the work done at Hayle Foundry. But West was given a share in the patent rights of the high pressure engine which he held until these expired, though lack of funds compelled Trevithick and Andrew Vivian to sell theirs prematurely. Arthur Woolf, now engineer of Meux's Brewery, went several times to see the carriage during its construction in Leather Lane and during its trials.

It was probably not until the late summer of 1803 that William West got back from his long absence in London to his home at Hayle, where he now had a family of four children, two boys and two girls. He must have had wonderful stories to tell. Though news of the horseless carriage had failed to impress the public, it must have greatly interested John Harvey, at whose works and under whose eye all the essentials of its power had been made. Whether even such a practical and far-seeing man as he was realised what a great revolution in steam engine practice had been brought about by his son-in-law one cannot tell. He had lived to witness all the stages of growth of that chief instrument of industrial power and had fought hard to found and keep going the establishment where its latest triumph had been brought about. But he was now in the late evening of his days and, in October of the same year, he died and was taken to the old church at Gwinear to lie by his three elder sons. Henry was left alone to face problems of a difficult trade, rendered more uncertain than ever by the renewal of the Napoleonic wars, and an implacable enemy on the home front.

Two years before his death, John had entered into a deed of partnership with his son for the term of his natural life transferring to him one half of the "cellars[1], quays, wharves, erections and Furnaces, used and necessary for carrying out the Trades of Merchant and Ironfounder" and a half interest in the two ships, *Providence* and *Henry*; sealing the "bargain" legally by receiving from Henry ten shillings of "good lawful money of Great Britain".

---

[1] The word "cellar" was formerly used for any place of storage, whether above or below ground. The first meaning is intended in this context.

VI

HENRY HARVEY

ENRY HARVEY, AT THE AGE OF TWENTY-EIGHT, WAS left sole proprietor of Hayle Foundry. Very little in the way of records or even legends has been handed down on which to base a clear character study. Something is gained from the contents of the early letter-book which shows him to be meticulous as to detail, checking cargoes by weight to the last pound and never letting any short measure or damaged goods, or such as were inferior in quality pass without an immediate challenge. When only a mere boy he had been found competent to take charge of the office in the absence of his father. We can credit him with industry, acumen, and high principles in business honesty and we know that he shared his father's ideal in the matter of service to his customers, insisting on first class workmanship out of materials of the best quality. He says in his Memorandum that he had not so much patience as his father, but his future conduct shows that he had that gift in full measure, though he could be roused to a pitch of wrath on occasions which his father would not have been capable of.

Gilbert only once makes mention of the two men when he says, "Mr. (John) Edwards experienced rivalship in trade of a very able and enterprising individual, Mr. John Harvey, and after his decease, still more powerfully of his son". The best testimony to Henry's powers as an administrator lies in the conduct of the works during the remaining forty-seven years of his life and the great achievement he left to his successors. As to what he looked like, we are left with two sketches, both drawn about 1840 when Henry was in his sixty-fourth year. The one wearing a hat and a Napoleonic look is from the lithograph of a drawing by a visiting artist named Hubbard. The attribution of the other rests on tradition but could well be a more "speaking likeness".

There could hardly be a greater contrast in temperaments than those of

77

Henry and his brother-in-law, Richard Trevithick, though, in different degrees, both shared one trait in common, that of enterprise. With Trevithick it was an almost ungovernable impulse, carrying him in search of betterment of ideas from one thing to another. With Henry, it was a cautious but persistent probing after a betterment in markets and the finer qualities both in goods and men. He had been brought up on the administrative side and continued to guide the business from that angle, leaving the technical conduct of the Foundry to his subordinates, though he kept a firm hand on all that was going on. He knew his limitations but said of himself characteristically, "I have always made it a rule, wherever I find myself deficient, to endeavour to make it up by industry and perseverence".

Within a year or two of his father's death Henry added a third ship to his fleet —another sloop, but more capacious in draught and tonnage than the *Providence*. There is a short reference to the event in the Brief prepared by counsel for the trial of 1829. The note is made immediately after the reference to John Harvey's death and runs —

> During this time Mr Henry Harvey built another Vessel called the Elizabeth and two other lighters, and every obstacle was thrown in the way of his launching the Vessel [by the C.C.C.] by throwing stones under the Vessel's weighs, but he at last succeeded.

By "weighs" we are to understand launching ways, and the Custom House Registers of St. Ives confirm that the new ship was actually built at the Foundry and not in a shipwright's yard.

Things seem to have gone on at the Foundry much as before until 1809, when there was an entirely new departure. It appears that one Hannibal Curnow Blewett, a merchant and speculator, had given his word to the Crowan United Mines to keep them supplied with coal throughout the following winter and was under a penalty of £20,000 if he failed to do so. He found himself in a predicament over his bargain and approached Henry Harvey who happened to have a supply of 14,000 bushels on hand. The bushel was a measure which still varied locally, as did the wey, but the quantity just mentioned would have been about a hundred tons. It was not likely that Henry would wish to part with the hard-gotten store he had accumulated and he rejected the proposal. Blewett was pressing, and Henry was starved for capital. He conceived a bold plan for meeting both needs and at the same time gaining a measure of ascendancy over his persistent enemy.

Harvey now offered to sell the whole of his premises and stock to a co-partnership in which he and Blewett should be members, Blewett to have five-eighths of the shares and Harvey three-eighths. This seems to have been agreed to quickly. Buildings and stock were valued and three other partners were brought in, each taking up a fraction of Blewett's shares. They were Andrew Vivian, one-eighth, Thomas Ellis, one-sixteenth, and Philip Richards, one-sixteenth The capital represented was £28,000 and the new venture was named *The United Mining Company*, a style that seems hardly ever to have been used, as all correspondence and financial transactions were subscribed *Blewett, Harvey, Vivian & Co.*

I have not been able to trace any relationship between this Hannibal Curnow and George Blewett, about whom so much was said in earlier pages. He is not named by Gilbert unless, when speaking of George's self-made wealth he writes "the property went to a nephew, and the whole has been dissipated". The cap would seem to fit! Nor do I know if this Thomas Ellis was the same as the former member of Harris, Ellis & Co. of Carnsew Cellars. He is described as partner in a brewery at Helston which makes it appear that he was somebody else of the same name. He was elected Treasurer of the new company and made cashier and book-keeper. It is perhaps just an odd coincidence that the other Thomas Ellis, after the breakdown in his affairs at Carnsew, had been employed by the Cornish Copper Company as a clerk from 1798 to 1808. Of the part played by Philip Richards, except as a shareholder, very little is heard. Henry Harvey, though now reduced from proprietor of Hayle Foundry to the second place in its government was still in charge of the general management of its affairs.

A provisional agreement of co-partnership, which was to remain in force for twenty-one years, was drawn up on September the 30th, 1809, but it was neither signed nor engrossed as there were some points on which Henry could not be brought to agree with his capitalist colleague, and blanks were left in the instrument to be filled in at more leisure when concurrence might be reached. A month later a new set of letter-books was opened with a handsome first volume looking much more like real business than the old school-book of eighteen years ago. And the partnership certainly meant business, as the opening letters of the new series show. One addresses a Bristol iron-merchant, "We beg leave to mention that this Iron is for a new concern, the partners that have joined Mr. Harvey are much respected in the mines therefore we expect that our orders will be much larger than it was [with] Mr. Harvey". Refreshed with so much new capital, to say nothing of Blewett optimism, they intended to more than reduplicate the scale and scope of their trade. At the outset, four orders are sent out simultaneously for cargoes of bricks to four different brickfields, two of them up in Flintshire.

Bricks and slates for sale had been imported by John Harvey from the days when he first started trading as a merchant. But this large influx was evidently intended for the firm's own building purposes. A large increase in the working population was forecast and new housing was doubtless being provided for speedily. In three months time they were advertising in the Bristol press for a foreman-moulder at £80 a year "with house provided".

Apart from the requirements of the Foundry, a large building programme must have set in both at Hayle and the neighbouring mines, for repeated orders for shiploads of bricks and pantiles continue to be sent out during this and the years closely following. There were far more orders for pantiles than slates, though on buildings now standing these are rarely seen. The Delabole slates are always called *heling stones*, and a particular size which is long and narrow is called *scantle*, examples of which may still be seen on some of the older buildings.

These letters are not comprehensive like the older ones. They deal only with those administrative matters with which Thomas Ellis was concerned — orders for raw material and finance. Even so, they are not inclusive, and there are as yet no "in" letters to match them. So we only have inferential news of what was going on in the iron foundry. In February, 1810, timber is ordered for the building of another lighter, whose construction is undertaken by a local shipwright. The brig, Henry, and the sloop, *Elizabeth*, are in constant commission, but there is no mention of the *Providence*. I have not discovered whether she had been disposed of or met the fate of so many vessels of her class. In a letter dated March the 17th of that year it is said "We have just commenced making cordage", after which, orders for hemp and tar begin, and then sales of rope to the mines and also visiting shipping. A map of Carnsew dated 1810 shows the ropewalk in being.

The Cornish Copper Company seem to have maintained their hostility in spite of the greatly augmented strength gained by the partnership. John Edwards had died in 1807, but his successor, as managing partner, Joseph Carne, was scarcely less vindictive. The Brief says, "the parties seemed equally determined, and many sharp battles were fought between the men employed by the two Companies, to the great terror and alarm of

Map 2. Hayle Harbour, 1810

Copied from one surveyed and drawn by David Palmer

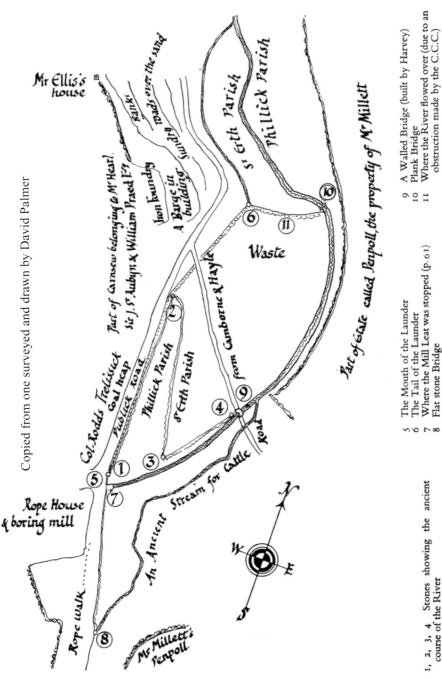

Mr Ellis's house

Part of Carnsew belonging to Mr Heart.

Sir J, St Aubyn & William Praed Es.

Banks

wads over the sand

Iron Foundry

A Barge in building

St Erth Parish

Thillick Parish

Col. Rodds Trelissick Coal heap

Publick Road

Thillick Parish

St Erth Parish

Waste

from Camborne & Hayle

Part of Estate called Penpoll, the property of Mr Millett

Road

Stream for Cattle

An Ancient

Rope House & boring mill

Rope walk

Mr Millett's Penpoll

5   The Mouth of the Launder
6   The Tail of the Launder
7   Where the Mill Leat was stopped (p. 61)
8   Flat stone Bridge

9   A Walled Bridge (built by Harvey)
10   Plank Bridge
11   Where the River flowed over (due to an obstruction made by the C.C.C.)

1, 2, 3, 4   Stones showing the ancient course of the River

81

the neighbourhood". There had, however, been a short armistice in which agents of the Carnsew landlords and solicitors of the C.C.C. got together and tried to settle that moot point of law about the foreshore rights, but no agreement was reached. The weakness of the Copper Company's claim seems to be shown by the odd fact that, during the whole time of their long struggle to demonstrate it, they never took the matter to court to test it but relied wholly on provocation and violence. After the failure of the armistice there was another clash. A letter of February the 11th, 1811, mentions "the Rioters" and early the next month Thomas Ellis writes to Francis Paynter & Son, the firm's solicitors, "our Mr. Harvey & Mr. Blewett (who are now in London) have received notice by Mr. Joseph Edwards[1] of Trial about 10 days back ... & I wish to be informed of the names of our Labourers that you may think proper to attend the assize". This relates to an action for assault by Blewett, Harvey, Vivian & Co. against the C.C.C. which, however, never came to trial.

Meanwhile, in the United Mining Company, there were already certain unhappy signs of disunion. Early in the first full year of the partnership there is no money available to meet accepted bills of exchange for more than £1600 due for maturity, and Ellis writes to H. C. Blewett, "I am quite at a loss what answer to make ... as I can see no way of paying them anything at the time limited". In the middle of the year he is writing to J. E. Blewett, H.C.B's. nephew and head of a business house in London, "We are sorry you should have had so much trouble respecting your debt due from us . . . On the 15th last Mo. there was a Resolution made by the majority of the Company that your debt should be discharged by our acceptances at two, four, and six months. The reason you was not made acquainted with this was we were daily in expectation of receiving from Mr. H. C. Blewett & Mr. And*w* Vivian the proportion of capital which they are deficient which would then have enabled us to pay your debit by Bills of a shorter date, but we have stil waited without success & *have not yet received anything from the above named*". He goes on to suggest a scheme of deferred payments "this being the only method we can at present liquidate your acct. which is by reason of our partners not coming forward as they ought". He writes again on the eve of the next Company meeting "We cannot admit you our acceptance before we have the assent of our partners who we shall immediately call on for this purpose, therefore you may expect to hear

[1] A lawyer; son of John Edwards.

from us again in the course of a post or two". But, when the meeting was held, neither H.C.B. nor Vivian turned up.

The Copper Company had now fallen back on the more subtle strategy of price-cutting in respect of all goods supplied to the mines. In December, 1810, Ellis writes to the adventurers of Trevenen Mine about rope for their whims, "We do not consent to have our Bills cut to the Copper House prices, as all other Ropers now Charges 76/- per cwt.". More galling still was it when Ellis had to write to his own partner, Andrew Vivian, shortly after that meeting which he had failed to attend, "We have a very bad account with the bank . .. and we cannot help saying that you have treated us very unhandsome by taking Coal from the Cornish Copper Co. & paying them money for it, & sending here for Coal for your burning Ho.s &ct. on Credit".

Reprehensible as that must seem, it is known that Andrew had been in financial difficulties, himself, for some time and had had reluctantly to part with his share of the patent he had taken out with Trevithick in 1802. He was purser for four mines which had also been out of luck and perhaps, on their behalf, he may have felt bound to get the essentials to keep them going by any available means, whatever his personal feelings were.

Blewett, however, had no such excuse for the step he was about to take. For him the Cornish mines were only a field for speculation and his gambling had met with reverses. Early in 1812 he judged it necessary to recoup by a bid to regain the capital which he had locked up in the United Mining Company, and he proceeded to take an action in the Court of Chancery for a dissolution of the partnership which was otherwise due to remain in force for a further eighteen years. It cannot be doubted that Henry Harvey was any less anxious to be liberated, but he found himself, as the second largest shareholder, in the position of defendant and bound to justify his conduct of affairs before the Lord Chancellor against a series of monstrous charges which the plaintiff had trumped up.

Blewett complained that Harvey and Ellis had let the other partners down by bad management and obstructive practices; that through their fault bills of exchange had been dishonoured and ships arrested in ports for debt, to the ruin of the firm's good name; that Thomas Ellis had kept the books irregularly and that he H.C.B. had never been permitted to examine them.

The other side, in addition to rebutting these charges, produced some curious evidence. It has been mentioned that a provisional agreement of co-partnership was drawn up in 1810 in which certain blank spaces were left to be filled in later. In January, 1811, a meeting was arranged at a solicitor's office at which the partners were to foregather and agree on the completion of the document, and have it engrossed. Blewett failed to attend that meeting. In July of that year, when Harvey was away from the Foundry, Blewett arrived at the office bringing his copy of the agreement with all the blanks filled in by himself and his signature appended. But to those amendments Harvey still would not agree. There were several deals which Blewett had made for his own profit in the name of the firm, though unauthorised by all partners. Lately, he had bought the ropewalk of Messrs Gluyas of Marazion[1] and then had hemp and tar to the value of £900 pounds transferred there from the premises of Hayle Foundry.

The plea for dissolution, made by both sides, was granted, with a judgement in favour of Henry Harvey. In the letter-book there are no entries between September the 5th and December the 14th. On the 19th, Thomas Ellis writes to the Coalbrookdale Company —

> Your letters of the 22nd September and 24th Ulto was not opened til the 14th Instant which was in consequence of a Chancery suit between the partrs which occasioned an Injunction to be served that put a stop to all proceedings for three months this only has been the reason you had not heard from us in due time. Our Mr Henry Harvey is now appointed by the Court Receiver & Manager of all the Coys business so that you may expect our future payment in due time.

And Henry writes to Andrew Vivian —

> Having previous to my Appointment as Manager and Receiver of the Partnership Effects at Hayle Foundry, entered into Recognaizance for faithfully discharging that office & collecting the Partnership debts, I have to request you will without delay Settle with me the amount of the debt due from you in your private capacity, and also the several sums due from you as Purser of Binner downs, Wheal Strawberry, Wheal Trenoweth, and the United Hills. I request your immediate answer to this letter.

And to Hannibal Curnow Blewett, after a similar preamble —

> I have to request that you will without delay settle with me the Debt due from you in your private capacity and also the sums due from the Marazion Co (Messrs Gluyas's ropewalk) & Casks of Tallow delivered by your order to Capt. Andrew Vivian. We are now about taking Stock & the Books are open to your Inspection which *they have always* been previous to the Injunction being served.

There is an amusing sidelight on the latter days of the abortive

---

[1] Note on Gluyas, Appendix II, letter to Van Cappelen.

partnership which shows the feelings of the principals towards each other and how one of them is trying to curry favour by a time-honoured manoeuvre. It is told by Francis Trevithick in the *Life* of his father, as follows. "Blewett sent a handsome silver teapot to Miss Betsy Harvey, who kept her brother's house, called Foundry House. Trevithick was sitting with them when the box was brought in and opened. Mr. Henry Harvey was indignant at Mr. Blewett at sending a bribe or make-peace to his sister, and threw the silver teapot under the fireplace. Trevithick, however, quietly picked it up, pointed out the dinge it had received, wrapped his pocket handkerchief around it, and saying, if it causes bad feeling here it will do for Jane, marched away home with the pot".

It may well be imagined that the C.C.C. had watched the decline of the United Mining Company with close interest and with the hope that in its fall it would bring about the collapse of the House of Harvey. But John and Henry's investments in the mines had turned out particularly rewarding and Henry, in winding up the Company, found himself in a position to pay off the capital which his partners had put into it and still carry on the business. The position of Thomas Ellis was unaltered. He remained as partner and continued to keep the books, which as anyone who examines them today will sec, had, all along, been meticulously posted in beautiful copperplate handwriting, amply refuting the abuse which H.C.B. had hurled at him before the Lord Chancellor. But the winding-up took some time and letters continue to be signed Blewett, Harvey, Vivian & Co., until the end of January, 1816, when they go out in the name of Harvey & Co. This Company is then augmented by two less ambitious but more trusted partners, Elizabeth, Henry's sister, and William West.

But in the family circle there had been two losses. Henry's sister, Anne, who had married John Harvey of Helston, died in 1808, and her husband, the next year. They left six children whom Henry and Elizabeth took into their home at Foundry House and cared for. Jane Trevithick with her good nature and equable temper, had shared the extremes of fortune with her genius husband and stood the test with fortitude and devotion. Though Richard's dealings with his brother-in-law's firm were always sporadic and transacted when it suited his own convenience, the basic ideas which he evolved were of lasting value to that Company and contributed to the great success it was to achieve long after the inventor's death, so a brief sketch of Trevithick's doings between the days of the Camborne and London "fire-carriages" and the dissolution of the United Mining Company in 1812 is thought to be not out of place.

Trevithick's early experiments with "strong steam" had proved to him its many advantages over the low pressure system, to which Watt still pinned his faith, maintaining that anything higher than six or eight pounds to the square inch was culpably dangerous. When, in 1803, one of Trevithick's high pressure boilers burst, killing three men and fatally injuring a fourth, the Birmingham makers could hardly conceal their exultation—"We told you so!" Although the cause of the accident was shown to be due to the fact that the boy who tended the engine went off fishing for eels and handed over to a labourer who got frightened when its pace accelerated and stopped it, though keeping the safety-valve locked, the setback might well have discouraged anyone less confident of his own powers than Richard. But the next year we find him directing the construction of nearly fifty high pressure rotary engines that were being made at several works in different parts of the country.

These compact little machines were designed for a wide variety of uses — winding at the mines, turning the stones of grist mills, giving forced draught to blast furnaces. It was a commission for the latter which brought Richard to the Penydarren Iron Works in South Wales. Its proprietor, Samuel Homfray, was greatly impressed by the new engine. He was a go-ahead fellow and had taken a leading part in the construction of the Glamorgan Canal. He was also a strong supporter of local race-meetings, and he bet a neighbouring ironmaster five hundred guineas that he would haul ten tons of iron from his works to the canal wharf, along his railway, by the power of steam, a distance just short of ten miles. The wager was accepted, and Trevithick rose to the occasion. To win this impromptu stake for his patron he gave the world its first railway locomotive.

The faithful Gilbert made a special journey to attend the trial, which took place successfully in February, 1804. In addition to the weight of iron specified, "about seventy persons" swarmed on to the train. The only hitch was that the rails were not up to the weight of the engine and several of them broke as it passed over. It was, in fact, the earlier form of line, a *plate-way*, laid with angle-irons turned outwards, made for wheels that were smooth-tyred and not flanged. They ran on the horizontal section of the irons and were guided by the vertical. The experiment settled a doubt that nearly everyone had entertained except the inventor, namely, that, with a heavy train attached to it, the engine, with its smooth tyres on the iron rails, would move forward and not stand still with spinning wheels.

Andrew Vivian was so convinced that this would happen that he insisted on a clause being inserted in the patent specification, providing for the use of studded wheels in the case of railroad locomotion.

Harveys had no part in the manufacture of the Penydarren engine, all the parts were made at Coalbrookdale. The next year, the owner of the Wylam Colliery in Northumberland ordered another railway engine. The work was put in hand at Gateshead, just across the Tyne. While it was in progress, Trevithick made the acquaintance of George Stephenson, a young man of twenty-four who was then in charge of the steam pumping engines at Killingworth Colliery, close by. They seem to have met frequently when Richard was in the north.

While all these works were going on, Trevithick was approached by several notables who wanted to know whether his invention could be applied to drive a fire-ship into the flotilla of landing craft which Napoleon was assembling in the harbour of Boulogne. The Marquis of Stafford sent for him, to whom he unfolded the plan he had, at once, evolved. The Marquis thought the idea excellent and passed him on to the Navy Board. "I was at the admiraltrie office and was ordered to wait a few days before they could say to mee what they wanted. I called 5 or 6 days foll'ing and never received a satisfactory answere, only to still wait longer" so "I left them".

In 1806 Trevithick is discovered converting an old brig-of-war into a bucket-dredger for raising ballast which had accumulated in the bed of the Thames, by means of his engine, now classed universally as a *puffer*, because of the noise it made exhausting its steam into the atmosphere. The device worked, but the engine of six horse-power, though sufficient for dredging mud, was found not strong enough for lifting the heavier material. The inventor proposed to install an engine of six times the power (cost, £5,000) and to be allowed an additional 3d. per ton on ballast raised. But this was above the rate permitted by the Ballast Act for the much slower process of dredging by man-power, so the contract lapsed.

In 1807 Trevithick was in charge of the works of a private Company for making a tunnel under the Thames from Limehouse to Rotherhithe. With the limited experience available at that time, the proposal was one to daunt the most highly trained civil engineer. Trevithick was chosen on the reputation he had gained for underground work in the Cornish mines. This assignment was likely to last some years and Trevithick wished his family to join him in London. Henry Harvey, who well knew his brother-in-law's weaker points and the kind of accommodation he was likely to find for Jane in that part of London adjoining the work, advised her strongly not to go until things were more settled. But Jane put her husband first, and made the long journey of several days over bad roads by post-chaise with her four infants aged ten, eight, six, and two.

The new home in the squalid neighbourhood of the Limehouse Reach cannot have been congenial to the Cornish-bred woman and, on arrival, she discovered that two of her last letters were still unopened. "You know, Jane", explained her husband, "your notes were full of reasons for not coming to London, and I had not the heart to read any more of them". If Jane accepted that excuse I doubt if the reader will.

After overcoming extraordinary unlooked-for difficulties in penetrating the strata of clay, gravel, hard rock, and loose sand under the river, pilot drift-ways, put through from either bank, were nearly meeting, when the company suspended operations. After deliberating for some months as to whether the added expense, proved necessary by the pilot excavations, could be justified for attempting the full-sized tunnel of a double carriageway, the project was abandoned. The period of indecision lasted for nearly a year, during which time Trevithick remained in London. Those idle days he occupied by a small private enterprise of his own. He hired a plot of ground close to the entrance of the present Euston Station and built thereon a circular plate-way track, fenced it round, and installed a pay-gate entrance.

A new locomotive was made (whether at Hayle or Coalbrookdale or elsewhere is not recorded) and a train of wagons for carrying passengers. The whole thing appears to have been ready as a public spectacle shortly after mid-summer, 1808. The engine was called *Catch me who can*[1]. It would seem that the early days of the show were spent in giving patrons a ride, and the fare was perhaps included in the gate-money which was a shilling. Later, the sporting element was included once more and, now the press took more interest than they had done in the fire-carriage. On September the 18th, the following appeared in the columns of the *Observer*

EXTRAORDINARY WAGER. It has been some time announced that the NEW MACHINE for travelling without horses, being impelled entirely by STEAM, was matched to run twenty-four hours against any horse in the kingdom. This bet, so novel in the sporting world, will be decided on Wednesday and

[1] The 1808 locomotive was built at Bridgnorth.

Thursday next. The machine is to start at two o'clock on Wednesday, on its ground in the fields near Russel-square, to demonstrate the extent of its speed and continuance. It is calculated that the machine, though weighing eight tuns, will travel 240 miles, at least, within the time limited. Very large sums are depending on the issue.

But the showman was not a winner. He had spent all his available cash on promoting the demonstration which was probably mainly intended to advertise the patent, but we find that in the same year he parted with all his own share in it, though it was not due to expire for a further eight years. Meanwhile he had taken out another patent in conjunction with a new partner, Robert Dickinson. Like the steam dredger, it was a device to save man-power and called the *Nautical Labourer* — a self-propelled floating crane which would load and discharge cargoes from ships, and also act as a tug-boat. Dock labour protest, voiced by the Society of Coal Whippers, succeeded in whipping the Nautical Labourer off the seas.

Then the two inventors heard of a sunken wreck lying at Margate and made an offer to the owners to raise her. A bargain was struck, and they went to work. The method employed, then used for the first time, was to sink iron tanks on either side of the vessel, to which they were braced, pump the water out of them and so refloat her by their buoyancy. The owners had joined them to witness the experiment, which turned out successful. It was then attempted to bring the vessel inshore and beach her. But the owners began to haggle over the agreed price for the rescue and Trevithick, in a passion, cut the tanks adrift, on which the wreck returned to the bottom.

In the same year, and early in 1810, two other patents were applied for by the partners, covering a variety of original ideas, notably iron tanks for ships. These were to be used for drinking water in place of the wooden casks, then universally in service, and notoriously subject to contamination on long voyages. They were also to take in water-ballast in place of the unwieldy rubble that had to be loaded and discharged when a ship sailed light. They were specially shaped to lie snugly in the bilges, and a small factory was established to produce them. But funds ran out and, early in 1810, Richard went down to Cornwall to try to raise money on his mine shares and property.

On his return to London, his son says, bailiffs were put into the house who "siezed everything belonging to him and he had to retire to a sponging-house in a street of refuge for debtors". Here the Cornish giant was suddenly laid low by a desperate illness, described as typhus and gastric fever. The plight of Jane and her young family must have been frightful, but she contrived somehow to survive the long ordeal, to nurse her husband and keep her own health and that of the children. The one letter relating to this time is recorded by Francis in his book. It is from Henry Harvey to his sister, dated June the 1st, offering to do whatever he could to ease the situation (which, no doubt, he had already been doing), advising "you must not say anything to him about his business, that is likely to hurry his mind, until he gets better" and "If he is not likely to do well where you are, do you think he would consent to return to Cornwall—if not to settle, for a little while? His native air might be a means of getting him about". It seems that by then both Jane and Henry had discovered that the partner, Robert Dickinson was a rascal who had been robbing Trevithick all along.

In September the invalid was sufficiently recovered to be moved and, with his family, was put on board the *Falmouth Packet*. Trevithick appears to have had an extraordinary capacity for attracting not only bad luck but dramatic situations, so that it seems natural to read how, on the last lap of the London adventure, the little packet was chased by a French ship of war and only narrowly escaped capture. The good Cornish air did what was expected of it, and Richard's strong constitution rallied. He had to bear the news the following February that he had been declared bankrupt. There is no doubt that the blame lay with his late partner. But he went to London to face his examination, and then returned to Cornwall, fully determined to challenge Fate by making a new start on the old home grounds of the mining area.[1]

[1] In the "*Life*", Francis Trevithick places his father's bankruptcy before his illness, suggesting that it was a contributory cause; but H. W. Dickinson (on the evidence of dates) points out that it must have been the other way round.

VII

ARTHUR WOOLF

W HEN LOOKING INTO THE PAST IT IS ALWAYS tempting to speculate as to what would have happened if men of marked personality had reacted differently towards each other, if turning-points had been recognised when reached, and opportunities taken when presented. In 1812, on the dissolution of the Blewett partnership, Henry Harvey had come into his own again but at such a cost that there must have been grave doubts as to whether his business could continue. At the same time Richard Trevithick had recovered his health and mental vigour and received his discharge in bankruptcy; but he had lost that financial independence which had enabled him to range freely, picking up orders for his new ideas and having them carried out in distant foundries of his own choice where, doubtless, manufacturing machinery and mechanical skill were more advanced than in Cornwall. Now, as in the game of snakes and ladders, he had to make a fresh start where he had first begun and limit his operations to the sphere of the mines in the neighbourhood of his old home.

Looking back at conditions as they were in that time, one must wonder how it was that two such gifted men as Henry and Richard could not have acted together at that juncture. Though Hayle Foundry was admittedly backward in equipment and skill as compared with other works in Britain, its proprietors had shown such resolution in holding their ground under difficulties that would have daunted most men that its future was full of promise. The talents of the two men were exactly complementary, and they were tied by a family alliance that might have been of benefit to both sides, for Jane was an exceptional woman who might have kept disparities in balance. Locomotive power was the very thing that the rapidly expanding world of industry needed most and they held the master key to this problem. Although Trevithick's patent had expired, if they had joined forces in 1812 and made improvements on the first trial engines which were logical and almost inevitable, they could have taken the lead in what the inventor, himself, had clearly foreseen would be the coming thing as soon as the prejudice against high-pressure steam, sedulously inculcated by Watt, had been overcome. The three seeds he had sown — on the Penydarren tramway, the circular track in London, and the Tyneside engine slept in secret for some time and then germinated eleven years later, in 1822, when George Stephenson bought ground in Newcastle for the establishment of a locomotive manufactory. Thenceforward, our railway system began to grow out of the north and not the west.

But it is doubtful if either Henry or Richard were fitted to run in double harness. Both were strong individualists. Henry's cardinal virtues were his steadfastness in purpose and his scrupulousness in money and business matters. He stood firmly by decisions he had made, and loyally defended the judgements of his subordinates even if, as was sometimes the case, they were proved wrong. Richard had a weakness for distractions and would move from one bright idea to another without consolidating. As a man of action and a great creative artist, his contempt for money and business method were not surprising but, in another way, his nature was contradictory. Vigorous, buoyant, genial, open-handed, an arresting talker, he was immensely popular; yet when absorbed in his own affairs, he was capable of showing complete indifference to the claims of his wife and family and the feelings of his friends.

Under the present circumstances the two parties were thrown much together and Hayle Foundry saw a good deal more of Trevithick than it had for a long while. Immediately on his recovery he returned to his old love, "strong steam", and was bent on developing it a stage further than in the small "puffer" or portable engines on which he had previously concentrated. These he had made for his road-carriages, railway locomotives, winding machines at the mines (whims), and for mill-work. They were all fitted with the boiler he had designed to give a greater and more efficient heating-surface for the raising of high-pressure steam. All the older boilers used by Newcomen and improved successively by Trevithick's father, Smeaton, and Watt had been heated externally (like the domestic kettle), whereas the younger Richard's model was a fire-tube boiler, using an internal flue which was "U" shaped. This carried the flame in an outward direction through the water and then back to the chimney which was placed near the fire-door [1].

Trevithick now wished to extend this principle to boilers for working the much larger pumping-engines at the mines and increase at once their power and economy by running them on high-pressure steam. His first important step in this direction was taken on familiar ground, at the Dolcoath Mine. He had succeeded in persuading the Adventurers to give a trial to "strong steam" and to cast out the existing boilers in favour of his own. He had, in fact, made the same proposal before, as far back as 1806, but it had been over-ruled. The boilers were long cylindrical vessels built with wrought iron plates rivetted at the joints. They had a fire-tube which extended from the grate to the far end. Here the hot gases were passed back again under the boiler (between its shell and the surrounding brickwork) and then returned forward through similar flues on either side, escaping after this three-way circuit up the chimney. The dimensions were quoted by an old man in 1858 who had been employed on the work forty-eight years before. He said "they were 18 feet long, 5 feet diameter, having an oval tube 3 feet 4 inches in the largest diameter at the fire end; the other or chimney end of the tube was somewhat smaller. They were found too small for the work to be done, and another boiler was built immediately, 22 feet long, 6 feet 2 inches diameter, and [he believed] a 4 foot tube"[2].

This achievement by Trevithick was equally important for the advancement of one branch of steam power as the Penydarren locomotive had been for another, for it marked a turning-point in the development of the *stationary* engine. The type, which came to be known as the "Cornish boiler", has persisted down to our own times with no material alteration to the design, its only rival in the fire-tube class having been the "Lancashire boiler", a mere variety of the species with two tubes instead of one.

The object of installing the new boilers at Dolcoath was to work the engines already there by high pressure. They were a mixed trio. There was the venerable 45-inch[3] Newcomen atmospheric which, it will be remembered, Richard's father had transported from Carloose in 1775 and which was now approaching its century of age. It had been titivated from time to time by both father and son and, in 1799, it had been moved to a new location in the mine and at the same time had been given a cylinder-

[1] (Opposite) Fortunately one of those portable engines has survived almost intact. It was built for Sir Christopher Hawkins in 1812 to drive a thrashing-machine and was at work until 1879. It is now in the Science Museum at South Kensington.
[2] Francis Trevithick *Life*.
[3] The diameter of the cylinder. This is understood in such descriptions as "70 inch engine".

cover (all Newcomens were originally open-topped). The other two were low-pressure engines, each with 63 inch cylinders, one was a single-acting[1], the other, double — one of Boulton and Watt's latest models before the expiry of the patent.

While Trevithick was confident of success, the adventurers must have had qualms as to whether these engines could digest the stronger meat. Their engine-men decided in advance that they should not be so imposed on. They suffered from the generally held belief that high-pressure boilers would explode and they were aware that in the new method of firing more attention and much more care would be required in placing the fuel in the grates. For the first plea there was some justification as the technique of making rivets tight in the boiler-plates had not yet been perfected and, when pressure rose they were apt to leak with a hideous noise and to keep the boiler-house filled with steam. So the men carefully disregarded Trevithick's instructions, the engines worked sullenly, and the water in the mine began to rise. The adventurers were greatly alarmed. Trevithick, who quickly guessed where the cause of failure lay, insisted that the men who were firing the boilers should be removed and replaced by a team of his own whom he superintended in person, on which, the water again receded. His predictions were fulfilled: more power had been gained and for less consumption of coal than formerly.

The fact that these old engines could not only be rejuvenated by the elixir of strong steam but could be made to work harder with less fuel was a step forward in the problem of mine drainage. But what had been done at Dolcoath was only a part of the plan in the engineer's mind. The final thing was to make a new engine to match the new boiler, and on this work he was already engaged at Hayle Foundry. It was not a new invention but the adaptation of what was already in existence — the condensing engine geared to high-pressure steam used *expansively*, meaning that steam would be cut off at an early part of the stroke, leaving it to be completed by the expansion of what had already been admitted to the cylinder. Watt had been well aware of this property and had claimed to make use of it in his later engines, but as they worked at such low pressures it had not been very

---

[1] Single-acting means steam on one side of the piston and vacuum on the other during one stroke of work (usually downwards with recovery by the weight of the pump-rods) double-acting means that the piston is powered both up and down. Terms commonly used were single or double engine as distinguished from a compound which was called a combined engine.

effective. Hornblower's two cylinder compound engine was expressly designed to work on the expansive principle. Yet it was not on that ground that Boulton and Watt succeeded in getting it suppressed, but because they persuaded the court that the machine was nothing new and that the second, and larger, cylinder (in which the steam was condensed) had only been added to evade their patent of the separate condenser.

But now the Watt patents were all dead (having expired in 1800) and there was no bar to the use of a separate condenser. In his new engine, Trevithick did not scorn to embody this and other features of the Watt design. Its sole novelty lay in its adaptation for work with high-pressure steam used expansively. It was a small experimental affair built round a second-hand cylinder of only 24 inches diameter and was erected at Wheal Prosper Mine early in 1812, with a boiler to match, giving it steam at 40 pounds pressure per square inch. There was nothing spectacular about this engine; indeed it seems to have attracted so little attention that it isn't even mentioned by Francis in the *Life*. Yet it was the prototype of a line of engines that would become world-famous and, in the perfecting of which, Henry's Foundry would take a leading and profitable part. Others would share in the gains, but not Richard. Even his name was not commemorated in what came to be known as the "Cornish engine".

It is odd that Francis Trevithick, who published his book in 1872 should have neglected to give credit to his father in this instance when Dr. Pole had done so in his work which appeared in 1844[1], calling the Wheal Prosper experiment "the first Cornish engine ever erected" — a verdict endorsed in recent times by H. W. Dickinson[2] who gives full details in his memoir. But it was more than two decades later that the Cornish engine came to maturity in the same place where it had first been made — the shops and furnaces of Hayle Foundry. We shall be hearing more about it then.

That small engine was not the only one which Trevithick was having made for Wheal Prosper (also with boilers to match) and at the same time. The second was on a novel, if not an entirely new, principle — that of the *plunger-pole*.

The plunger-pole must first be thought of as a water-raising pump and not a prime-mover. Its use as such is recorded as early as the reign of Charles II when Sir Samuel Morland, mathematician and Fellow of

[1] *A treatise on the Cornish Pumping Engine*, William Pole, F.R.S., Professor of Civil Engineering, London Univ.
[2] *Richard Trevithick* by Dickinson H. W. and Titley A. 1935.

Magdalene College, Cambridge, was granted a patent for it in 1674 and, in the following year, applied it to raise water at Windsor Castle. It differed from the ordinary bucket-pump (which works by suction when the bucket is drawn upwards) by having the action of a ram which, when descending into the pump-barrel, forced the water out of it. In earlier days when pumps, like pipes, were mainly made of wood, the plunger type would have been harder and more costly to construct and, in any case, conservative bias was always weighted against any new thing. But the idea seems to have lingered on into the second half of the eighteenth century or to have been re-born. At any rate, Trevithick had taken it up again enthusiastically some time before his illness. By then, the introduction of a means for making iron castings readily available and the general improvement in turning out metal fittings had made the principle both easier and cheaper to apply.

Trevithick's pump was formed with two cast-iron pipes, one (the *pole*) having a less diameter than the other (the *pole-case*). The pole was closed at the bottom and turned in the lathe to pass up and down through a stuffing-box in the top of the pole-case. Sufficient room was left between the two to allow for a free passage of water. When the pole was lifted, water followed it by suction and filled the pole-case, where it was held by the closing of a foot-valve. When the pole was thrust downwards the water was displaced by it and forced upwards past a valve in the delivery-pipe, where it was again held till the pole made its next plunge, when it was pushed on another stage —and so on till it reached the point of discharge at the adit level.

This pump had three advantages over the old bucket variety. It was cheaper to make because only the pole required to be machined — the pole-case could be left rough, as cast (since it had not to be mechanically in contact with any moving part), and to turn a solid cylinder needed less skill and trouble than boring a hollow one. Also, it was less liable to jamb with grit than the bucket with its leather cup packing or, if damaged, it was easier to repair. The third was that it was kinder to the engine and the pump-rods. The bucket-pump worked like the village or domestic pump where, when you pushed the handle *down* it brought the bucket up, the water following it by suction. So the engine beam operated like the pump handle and was powered on the down stroke, while the pull on the pump was upwards. Thus it not only had to lift the heavy pump-rods but also the water which the bucket was then forcing up against the resistance of the column above it in the "rising main". The weight of the pump-rods was more than sufficient to draw the piston back in the cylinder for the next stroke — so much more, in fact, that it had to be offset by a counterpoise in the shape of a small pivoted beam called a "balance-bob"[1] which has one end attached to the pump-rod while, at the other, was a large box which could be filled with stones to any required weight.

The pump-rods were made of large square timbers strapped and bolted together to form one continuous length from the end of the main engine-beam to the bottom of the shaft. The column of water was raised to the surface in a series of lifts by a pump at each stage, usually accompanied by a balance-bob, while the pump-rods worked all at the same time. As the plunger-pole acted in the downward direction the work of the engine was more evenly divided, as it then had only to contend with the weight of the rods on the steam-stroke while, on the return stroke, the same weight was sufficient to force the water up in the pumps. Under those conditions the pump-rods could be made lighter and less cumbersome.

Trevithick's adoption of the plunger in the early days of his fame had been sufficient to popularise it and it had been taken up widely in the mining area while he, himself, had gone on to make another use of the same idea, but in reverse, if, instead of using the pole for displacing water in the pole-case you treated it as a piston and powered it with water at high pressure, you could turn it into a hydraulic engine and do away with the large steam engine, its high stone house, and all its paraphernalia. This, of course could only apply when there was running water at a higher level than the top of the mine shaft, which was rare. Roskear Mine had that advantage, and there, in 1798, Trevithick erected the first plunger-pole engine to act as prime mover and work by water pressure. It is said to have worked satisfactorily for seventeen years before needing repairs. On this machine he made many modifications before producing yet a third trick out of the same hat.

The latest idea was to work a plunger-pole unit by steam instead of by water. That was the other engine, already mentioned, which was being made (probably at Hayle also) for Wheal Prosper at the same time as the small Cornish engine. It was to work at a pressure quite unheard of in those days — 100 pounds to the square inch — but the area of the pole

[1] The action of the main beam projecting from the upper storey of an engine-house over the head of the shaft and continually dropping curtseys must have suggested the happy word "bob" which has always been used in Cornwall for that beam or the smaller one with counterbalance, both in common talk and the official language of letters and specifications.

was small compared with that of one of the regular engines. It had an 8 foot stroke and, like the other engine, worked expansively with an early cut-off of steam; and it had a surface-condenser.

Richard, who was never bound by any inflexible rule, either traditional or self-made, designed two particularly attenuated boilers to raise and maintain the hundred pound pressure on the pole engine. They were cigar-shaped, forty feet long, with a diameter of only three; and this time they were heated externally. The fire was made to go first under the bottom, then back along the sides and, finally, forward again over the top (acting as superheater) to the chimney. One of Trevithick's pupils called Samuel Grose was in charge of the erection of these boilers. In later years he became famous not only as a mines engineer but as a designer of the Cornish engine.

The inventor seems to have been particularly happy about his pole steamer for, a few months later, he wrote to J. U. Rastrick about it. "The new engine you saw near the seaside, with me, is now lifting forty millions [of pounds of water, see page 100]. which is very nearly double the duty that is done by any other engine in the county". Rastrick was at that time a partner in the Bridgnorth iron works of Hazeldine* and Rastrick where Trevithick placed many of his orders, to the mortification of the home foundries at Hayle and Perran. Later, he became proprietor of the important works at Stourbridge and played a leading part in the introduction of railways and locomotive traction and was one of the judges at the Rainhill trials which awarded the prize to Stephenson's "Rocket". He was a true friend to Trevithick and a strong backer of his ideas.

Some time in 1812, when events just related were in progress, a man arrived on the scene who provided a somewhat disconcerting interlude. This was Arthur Woolf, the son of the Dolcoath Mine carpenter whom we last heard of exactly ten years earlier. It will be remembered that he had been employed by Trevithick and sent to London as fireman with one of his portable engines. Here he had got himself attached to Meux's Brewery and, it was noted, that in 1802 he was present at the trials of the London road-carriage. Still earlier, he had been engaged by Jonathan Hornblower in Durham to assist in the erection of his compound engines but had left him some years before Hornblower was successfully prosecuted by Boulton and Watt for infringement of the condenser patent. When, therefore, he went to

---

* In both contemporary and modern usage the spellings Hazeldine and Hazledine appear equally valid and were used interchangeably.

the Brewery he knew all that there was to be known about Hornblower's abortive invention and the possibilities of Trevithick's revolutionary ideas on high pressure steam, and was no doubt turning over in his own mind what could be made of the two notions if they were put together.

With his experience and natural aptitude as (for that day) a very finished mechanic, Woolf soon got himself appointed engineer-in-charge at the Brewery and persuaded the management to allow him to convert one of their simple engines into a compound. In 1803 he took out a patent for a compound engine, together with a boiler for the production of high pressure steam. It was the boiler rather than the engine which was a new invention, being an early form of the kind now well known as water-tube — the opposite principle to the fire-tube as exemplified in the Cornish boiler. It consisted of a number of cast-iron pipes situated below two cylindrical shells which formed the main storage of the boiler. Circulation was maintained between all these members by a number of intercommunicating tubes. The fire-grate was placed at the bottom and the flame and hot gases played among the tubes thereby presenting a large heating-surface to the water. Woolf then tried to get his masters to adopt his new engine, but the cautious brewers, who were probably infected with the anti-strong-steam complex wished first to take outside advice and called in the great John Rennie. Whether he was really not impressed by the engine itself or biased through his long association with James Watt, he shook his head over Woolf's engine and Messrs. Meux turned it down.

By those who knew him or were acquainted with those who did, Woolf is always noted as being an irascible and opinionated fellow with a singularly rough tongue. Many years later William Pole, the exponent of the Cornish engine, spoke of him as having "a peculiar unconciliating temperament and disposition". He now took umbrage at the adverse decision and left the Brewery. His next move was to enter into partnership with a Lambeth millwright called Humphrey Edwards for the purpose of putting his engine and boiler into marketable shape and having them manufactured. This collaboration lasted until 1811 when a disagreement occurred and the partnership was dissolved. Edwards continued to manufacture the engine but found that there was a greater demand in France than at home. He therefore went to Paris and presently procured a French patent. His business flourished. He became partner in a French firm of ironfounders and, before his death, had established a wide vogue for the compound engine in France.

After his rupture with Edwards, Woolf's thoughts turned to his old home in Cornwall with which he must have kept in touch during his years of exile. He had no doubt learned of a very interesting movement which had been started there by the mines engineers. When the Boulton and Watt patent rights came to an end in 1800 the firm recalled their agent and mechanics who had been located in the district for the past twenty-two years to maintain and repair their engines. As the Watt engines grew older and were less cared for, there was a general tendency of the owners of non-Watt engines to lose interest in the efficiency of their machines which they had formerly pitted against the Birmingham models. An age of mechanical decadence seemed to be setting in.

It was very sensibly suggested that matters could be improved by a regular system based on the revival of emulation. The idea was to have impartial monthly tests made of as many engines as possible over a period of time and the results published. Those reports could be studied by all, improvements noted, and the spirit of competition would be certain to vanquish that of *laisser faire*. Money was promised by some adventurers to fee a "Registrar and Reporter" and in August, 1810, the post was offered to Andrew Vivian at a salary of £150 a year. Vivian told Henry Harvey that he was too busy to undertake the work and suggested Trevithick. Henry passed this news on to Jane in London, where Richard was still lying very ill. Although he had just suffered the complete loss of his financial resources he turned down the offer at once, having the honesty to admit that he was no routinist.

I don't think either of the men would have filled the place so well as the one who finally took it. This was Captain Joel Lean. The tables which he began to issue (about 1810 or '11) gave details of the engines, the depth of each shaft from which the water was pumped, the number of gallons raised per minute, and other points. But, in each case, the criterion of efficiency (called the *duty* of the engine) was the amount of water which an engine could raise one foot high with the consumption of a single bushel of coal (94 lbs.). This was expressed in millions of pounds ("foot-pounds" in modern usage).

The results of this competitive "showing up" were very remarkable. They kept both engineers and manufacturers on the alert to take advantage of every slight improvement that could be heard of or discovered. When doubts were expressed about the reliability of the Record, a disinterested committee of engineers was at once called in to re-try the case. In particular, the evolution of the Cornish engine towards near perfection owed much to the monthly reports. Joel was succeeded by his son, Thomas, who published a general account of the system in book form in 1839[1] which included tables for three significant years — 1814, 1825, and 1835.

One imagines that it was news of this renaissance that persuaded Arthur Woolf to return to the Cornish mines and put forward the claims of his compound engine and water-tube boiler. He seems to have adopted a very confident attitude about this from the moment of his arrival, as will be judged by the following sidelight. This was given by Captain Samuel Grose to Francis Trevithick when he was collecting reminiscences of his father in Cornwall some time in the 'sixties of the last century. Grose was then an old man. He had become celebrated in the Duchy both as an engineer and an engine designer. He had a reputation for reliability and is unlikely to have borne false witness. He said of Trevithick "When he had returned from London to Cornwall, he employed me to look after the erection of the Wheal Prosper high-pressure engine. Oats, Captain Trevithick's head boiler-maker, was constructing the boilers; Woolf came into the yard and examined them. 'What do'st thee want here'; asked Oats. 'Damn thee, I'll soon make boilers that shall turn thee out of a job!' was Woolf's reply. He was a roughish man."

Woolf's boast, as will be seen, was not to be justified in the long run, but the unpleasant fact was that this former employee had returned in no friendly spirit but as an avowed competitor with his old master. He was, however, a potential customer of the Hayle Foundry, and likely to be an important one. Henry Harvey probably recognised this, and more. He had a keen flair for detecting quality both in things and men and he probably divined that there were finer things in Woolf behind the mask of his boorish manners. They appear to have been on good terms at the time and were destined to have a closer association with each other than had ever been possible between Henry and his brother-in-law, but that was not to happen for another four years.

Meanwhile, as the summer of 1812 advanced, things cannot have been happy at the Foundry where there must have been much uneasy speculation as to what would be the outcome of the chancery suit that was being argued in London. On September the 5th news of the injunction arrived whereby the court ordered the closing of the works until the Lord Chancellor's

[1] *Historical statement of the improvements made in the duty by Steam Engines in Cornwall. Reprinted by Barton, Truro, 1969.*

judgement was made known. For the principals, this meant an end to all business and, for the workmen, the sudden blow of unemployment for an indefinite period. It must have been a terribly trying time for all concerned and feelings must have been greatly embittered by the knowledge that the Cornish Copper Company was probably looking on with undisguised glee and in high hopes of seeing an end to the Harvey enterprise.

The injunction hit Trevithick in what must have been a particularly sore spot, for he had just received an export commission which, though small, was promising. This was for one of his portable engines to work a sugar mill at St. Kitt's (estimated at 12 mule-power), and he had placed the order for the castings with Harvey. It could not now be carried out and he had to re-order from the Bridgnorth Foundry (at his own expense). The engine was finished too late for the customer who had probably got what he wanted from Boulton and Watt, and a likely introduction to a similar trade in the West Indies was lost for Hayle and closely followed up by Birmingham.

VIII

SLAG IN THE PENPOL RIVER

THE PARALYSIS WHICH ENSUED ON THE LORD chancellor's injunction lasted exactly one hundred days. The ban was not lifted until the 14th of December. All that time the Foundry, forges and ancillary shops, the timber-yard, coal-yard, granary, rope-walk, and the two ships were idle. The only thing which appears to have been untouched by the spell was the farm. This was part of Henry's private property which had been kept out of the agreement, though it served the Company and was leased to it for £110 a year.

The chief importance of the farm was that it provided transport facilities in the shape of horses and waggons for carrying cargoes over the sands and delivering goods to customers. Its arable and pasture land produced food for its animals and some grain to supplement the much larger quantities which were imported for sale. For the plough, it maintained yokes of oxen and steers. In the early years there was much outside hiring of carts and pack-mules, and the tax returns for 1813 show that there were then only nine draft — and one saddle-horse available and an average of about £40 a month was being paid to outside carriers for the transport of coal alone from lighters to coal-plots. But the stables were gradually enlarged until hiring was practically eliminated.

When restrictions ended on that 14th of December, 1812, with the court's decision that Henry was appointed to be Receiver and Manager in winding up the affairs of the United Mining Company he could take credit for a personal triumph. But the new problems he faced were very great, namely, to keep the iron works and the merchanting side of the business going as fully as possible whilst paying off the capital of his late partners. In fact, the task of settlement was protracted for three years, and it was not until January the 29th, 1816, that the style "Harvey & Co." could be used on letters and documents in place of "Blewett, Harvey, & Vivian" and

Hannibal Curnow Blewett could be sent the final instalment of £2000 in full discharge of his capital.

But it must have been exceedingly vexing to the C.C.C. to observe in the New Year of 1813 renewed activities at Carnsew, with chimneys smoking, sea-borne cargoes arriving, and carts once more plying over the debatable wastrel. They began to prepare for a Spring offensive.

With the passing of the equinoctial gales and the return of finer weather Harvey once more set about the old operation of deepening the channel in the Penpol River between the Foundry and the lower ford. This ford, it will be remembered (which Cecilia Fiennes had aimed at crossing), intervened between the coast road from the east and the long track across the sands to another ford over the River Hayle and thence to Penzance. The ford was by a public house now called the Royal Standard, then known by the name of its tenant landlord as Millwood's House. At that point the Penpol River had a firm gravelly bed and could be crossed on horseback or in a wheeled vehicle when the tide was out, though between it and the Foundry the river bed was a mixture of soft sand and mud. As the river divided the parishes of Phillack and St. Erth, the waywardens of neither had ever attempted to mend or improve the ford, nor was it any more necessary than trying to mend the track over the sands. Harvey made no attempt to interfere with the ford, his digging was done to the south of it in implementing his father's agreement with Lord Arundell. This was the shoal part of the river which prevented ships coming up to the Foundry.

The first step taken by the C.C.C. in their new drive on the intruder was to send a note on the 14th of May directed "To Messrs Blewett, Harvey, Vivian & Co., and to Mr Henry Harvey" signed by Joseph Carne, Managing Partner of the Copper Company. It ran —

> I do hereby as Agent of the Cornish Copper Co. and on their behalf require you to remove from *that part of the Tenement* of Carnsew winch adjoins the outer wall of your Foundery yard on the North and North West, all the Coal, Iron, Iron dross and other rubbish which you have caused to be placed there. And I do hereby give you Notice, that if the same be not removed within one Week from the day of the date hereof an Action of Trespass will be immediately afterwards commenced against you.

This was an entirely new point of attack. It was aimed against a small piece of foreshore which had been reclaimed by John Harvey more than twenty years ago and though his rights elsewhere on the wastrel had been hotly contested, he and his son had remained in undisputed possession of this corner for all that time.

One of the inherent drawbacks of the situation had always been that the firm had no proper quays, they only had portions of levelled ground adjoining the river where consignments of pig-iron and coal could be deposited — "plots" or "plats". They served well enough for these commodities but were not suitable for the reception of copper ores from the mines which the Harveys were so anxious to attract in order to provide back cargoes to the smelters in Wales in ships which brought them coal and other things. Ships which had to make a one-way passage in ballast charged a higher freight on the Hayle-bound voyage. Increased cost applied to Harvey's own vessels as well as those on charter. That corner of made ground just beyond the foundry wall, but on waste foreshore, was nearest the sea and had proved most useful for the dumping of coal and pig-iron. Lighters could reach it fairly often and even ships on the higher tides and discharge direct to the shore, while the main and larger plots lay higher up and were much more difficult of access except by the laborious intermediary of land transport.

Henry had no intention of taking the suggested action. He forwarded the Carne letter to Francis Paynter. This Francis was the son of the late agent of the Hearle and Trelissick estates to whom, as a boy, he had sent so many like complaints and threats. But only four days later, he had to write again and inform on a new development in the enemy's campaign.

I wrote you the 15th Inst, with a Copy of Mr Carrie's Notice to remove our Iron &c. on the plot to the North of the Foundery yard Wall. The C.C.Co's Lighter loaded with Slag is this day hailed up in our Channel in order to fill it up to prevent our Vessels or Barges from coming up to discharge, & we are told that there are 5 others loads at the Copper Hse. for the same purpose. If this is not immediately removed it will be the means of preventing us from laying in a sufficient quantity of Coals this summer to fulfil our engagements with the Mines, but before we begin to remove it we wish to have your advise. We therefore have to request that you will come on the spot for the purpose. You will have the goodness to drop me a line per return of post saying what day we may expect you unless you could make it convenient to come here this week which I hope will be the case; but if you cannot possibly come please let me know if we are safe in removing the Slag. I am this moment returned from denying the men from putting the Slag in the Channel, but they refuse to take denyal. They are placing it directly in the road crossing from Hayle Copper Hse. to Penzance.

All that Paynter could do was to recommend Henry to take the opinion of counsel. This advice was acted on at once and more than one learned K. C. was consulted. Their answer was that the only safe course was to indict the Copper Company for obstruction to the navigation of the

Channel. An indictment was actually prepared to present at the Summer Assizes. Meanwhile, the week named in the ultimatum respecting the plot had long expired and the C.C.C. were threatening to remove the coal and iron therefrom by force, a manoeuvre which they had successfully performed in early days when they carried off the unfinished lighter and timbers and set them down at the edge of the tide. But then the labour force at Harvey's disposal was not strong enough to resist. That was no longer the case. The enemy continued to utter threats but did not dare to use force, and time drifted on.

Meanwhile, since their re-opening, the works had been engaged on two further orders from Trevithick, one was for an engine to be used in draining the foundations of the new bridge at Exeter, the other was for a pioneer of its kind and the manufacturer must be allowed to share honours with the inventor. It was the first powered rock-boring machine. For more than a year a great work had been going forward at Plymouth. This was John Rennie's mile-long breakwater across the middle of the entrance to the Sound. Immense masses of local limestone had first of all to be dumped in deep water to form this long artificial island, and Trevithick could not resist the temptation to think of a way of reducing the arduous labour of splitting off the huge blocks of stone, and also the expense involved, by harnessing one of his "puffers" to the task.

The contractors were the Foxes of Perran Foundry and that keen and enterprising mine adventurer, John Williams of Scorrier House. Henry was in London at the end of November awaiting the result of the Chancery suit. Trevithick wrote to him about his new brainwave, and he replied promptly with some cogent and friendly advice.

> Mr Giddy [Gilbert] informs me that Mr Fox and Mr Williams are to have 2/6 per ton for making the breakwater at Plymouth, and he considers that they can do it for 2s. which he thought would give them 50,000£. profit. If you meet those gentlemen, I have to caution you not to LEARN THEM anything until you make a bargain, as I know Mr Williams will endeavour to learn all he can and then you may go whistle.

He goes on to work out how the inventor should earn at least five-hundred pounds a year while the work lasted.

Just before this letter arrived J. U. Rastrick went to Camborne to see Trevithick. After staying a few days with him and the hospitable Jane the two engineers made an expedition on horseback to Plymouth. The stone for the breakwater was being got from Oreston on the Cattewater where

1 John Harvey of Gwinear

2. John and Ann Harvey of Helston

3. Henry Harvey, aged sixty-five

4. Richard and Jane Trevithick

the Admiralty had acquired twenty-five acres for the purpose. Here the two visitors arrived but were not at all favourably impressed by the way things were being done. Rastrick commented to Samuel Goodrich "The method in which they get the Stones and convey them to the Quays; the Construction of the Vessells, the way of Loading and discharging is in my Oppinion, the *very very worst* that could be thought of by the greatest Bungler that ever was . . . On the whole it is the worst conducted Public Work I ever saw"[1].

This visit fired Trevithick with fresh ardour and in January, the Foundry having been re-started, he wrote to Robert Fox —

I have been making trial on boring lumps of Plymouth limestone at Hayle Foundry, and find that I can bore holes five times as fast with a borer turned round than by a blow or jumping — down in the usual way, and the edge of the boring bit was scarcely worn or injured by grinding against the stone, as might have been expected. I think the engine that is preparing for this purpose will bore ten holes of 2½ inches in diameter 4 feet deep per hour. Now suppose the engine to stand on top of the cliff, or on any level surface, and a row of holes bored, 4 feet from the edge of the cliff, 4 feet deep, and about 12 inches from hole to hole for the width of the piece to be brought down at one time, and wedges driven into the holes to split the rock in the same way as they cleave moorstone [granite] . . .

A week later, after a personal talk with Fox and further experiments he writes again —

I am convinced to a certainty that the engine at Hayle will bore as many holes in one day as will be sufficient to split above 100 tons of limestone, and would draw that 100 tons of stone from the spot and put them into the ship's hold in one other day. The engine would burn in two days 15 bushels of coal, four men would be sufficient to attend on the engine, cleave the stone, and put it into the ship's hold. I think it would not amount to above 9d. per ton, every expense included.

By March the 14th the machine was ready and had been taken to Redruth to await an opportunity for the inventor to conduct it in person to Plymouth. Unfortunately there is no further record of its future career, but Dickinson points out that as, shortly afterwards, the cost of getting the stone and putting it on board was more than halved, it must have performed the service intended.

At Hayle, the atmosphere of rivalry between the two companies remained tense throughout the summer. The debatable plot was left unmolested and

[1] Goodrich Papers, Science Museum, South Kensington.

entries in the cash-book, month by month, for expenditure on "Channel and improvements to plots" show that Henry had not been deterred from deepening the river though, for the time being, leaving the obstructive slag on the ford untouched. The C.C.C. were now loudly proclaiming their action as something which had been taken in the public interest, giving out that what Harvey had destroyed they had made good at their own charges. However, towards the end of August, Henry had made up his mind not to trust the delays and uncertainties of a court action. He took the law into his own hands and sent his men to remove the slag. Joseph Carne reacted with another notice served by one of his officials on September the 9th —

> I do hereby, as the Agent of the Cornish Copper Company, as well as individually, give you Notice that unless you immediately desist from breaking up, carrying off, and injuring the public road from Hayle to St Ives and Penzance you will be prosecuted for the same.

Henry paid no more attention to this than he had to the previous threat and continued to clear the obstruction till it was all gone. As to the impending prosecution, no more was heard of it but, not long afterwards, an unfortunate accident happened. A girl was riding over the ford at low tide, when her horse stumbled and she fell into the shallow water. She was carried to a house where she began to throw violent fits. A doctor was called and it was reported that he took a grave view of the case. A few days later the moral of the story was pointed by a local attorney who wrote to Harvey, drawing his attention to the accident which, he declared, had been caused by his interference with the ford and calling on the Company to do "what humanity, to say nothing of legal obligation would prescribe". Henry had, however, ascertained that the doctor was a son of that potentate of the Copper Company, R. O. Millet, and he knew that this man had been regularly posted with others to watch the removal of the slag with the obvious intention of being called as witnesses if need be. So he drew what were probably the right inferences.

That plan was not a very good one but, as it provoked no acknowledgment of repentance from the other side, a much more drastic one was tried. It will be remembered that nineteen years before, Millet had forcibly filled in the leat which carried off the water from the foundry boring-mill and compelled John Harvey to dig another within the bounds of his own undisputed territory. In spite of that it was now planned to intercept the leat again by cutting a trench and building a wall across it. The C.C.C.

sent a strong force to undertake this work. Harvey turned out all his people and they tackled the enemy so vigorously that the magistrates were called to quell the disturbance . . . "In consequence of this" says the Brief "an Indictment was preferred and found against Mr. Harvey and another at the next sessions for an Assault. The defendants removed it by *Certiorari* into the Court of King's Bench, and when ripe for Trial in March 1815 was abandoned by the Cornish Copper Company". Odd indeed! Having at last mobilised the law after so many false starts, why were proceedings dropped. One can only conclude that all along they were uncertain of the legality of their several claims and shunned the acid test of a court case. They did not attempt to "repair" the ford again and this latest campaign of frightfulness which had failed at every point was not renewed.

It may be mentioned that the slag dumped on the ford was the dross of copper ores eliminated in their reduction. Much use was made of it by running it into moulds to make building blocks.[1] The material was highly resistant to the weather and much of it may be seen in the neighbourhood today looking quite fresh. The road leading up from the shore to Lelant village is entirely walled by these blocks with shaped coping-stones. It is exceedingly heavy and its removal from the ford must have been hard work. By a strange turn of fate this same slag is almost the only memorial relic which remains to be seen today of the once extensive works of the C.C.C.

Except for continued price-cutting, there was a lull in offensives which lasted some time. In 1814 Arthur Woolf had got one of his compound engines and water-tube boilers installed at Wheal Abraham and was taking orders for others. I imagine that these machines were being made at Hayle Foundry. Some of Trevithick's plunger-pole pumps were also being made there. The rivalry between the two engineers was becoming keen. Richard had turned his attention to the possibilities of the compound and was engaged on applying this theory to something quite different from that of Woolf.

The new idea was to marry one of his plunger-pole steamers to an existing Watt low-pressure engine and pass the partially expanded steam

[1] John Wesley made a memorable comment on its architectural properties in his journal for 1785. "About nine I preached at the Copper-works, near the Hayle, in the new preaching-house. I suppose such another is not in England, nor in Europe, nor in the world. It is round, and all the walls are brass; that is brazen slags. It seems nothing can destroy this, till heaven and earth pass away."

from one to the other. This development came rather later but, by the spring of 1816, he had nine of these hybridised compounds working. Meanwhile, he had concentrated on the simple plunger-pole steam engine and had taken out a patent for it. The results were so gratifying that he actually challenged Woolf with a bet of £10 to £500 that he would beat the duty of his best engine "but that party refuses to accept the challenge".

No doubt this unlooked for competition with an old employee was exasperating to Trevithick and may have helped him to make up his mind to follow a tempting lure which had been distracting him for some time. A brief outline must be given of those events which led to his departure and a long break with the Hayle connection.

The story begins in 1811 when certain merchants of Lima, the capital of Peru, bethought them of re-opening the long disused silver mines at Cerro de Pasco situated more than 14,000 feet up in the Andes and some hundred-and-sixty miles away. The leading spirit in these talks was a Swiss called Uville. What his status was in Lima society is not clear. The mines were derelict and full of water. Rumours of the new power of steam which had been developed in England had reached them and Uville was commissioned to go to England and make enquiries. He carried an introduction to a member of the East India Company who told him that Boulton and Watt were the best engineers in Europe and he should proceed to Birmingham. This he did. He called on Messrs. Boulton and Watt who had the honesty to confess that their engines, which depended mainly on atmospheric pressure would not work properly at that altitude. When Uville further explained that the only approach to the mines was by a mule-track in the mountain side that was barely more than two and-a-half feet wide in places and that all machinery would have to be made so as to be conveyed on the backs of those animals they said it was quite out of the question to make any engines so small.

Uville therefore considered that his mission was a failure. But, in visiting London, on his way back he happened to pass a small shop, in the window of which he saw the model of an engine. On entering he heard that it worked by high pressure and was the invention of a Mr. Trevithick. Either he did not ask, or the shopman did not know, the inventor's address, for he left the shop without learning it but not without the model, for which he paid twenty guineas. Its origin is unknown and one cannot help wondering if it was one of those made in the early days by William West.

Uville returned with his treasure which was duly taken up to the old mines and tested in the rarified atmosphere with success. There seemed to be nothing for it but to send Uville all the way to England again to search for the maker. He made a roundabout passage, for his ship having doubled Cape Horn, went north to the West Indies.

Uville fell ill and was put ashore in Jamaica where he had to spend some time recovering. This was the terminal of the principal link between America and England by the mail packets running between Kingston and Falmouth. In one of these, Uville eventually embarked. When he came to speak of his mission to one of the passengers and of the problem he would have to solve in searching for this Mr. Trevithick he found he was talking to a cousin of the engineer, who told him that Robert lived only a few miles from the port to which they were bound. Uville arrived at Falmouth in May, 1813 but had to take to his bed again, where he received Trevithick, who lost no time in riding over as soon as he heard of his visitor.

This unexpected call on his genius from the far off New World must have touched Richard deeply in the sources of his professional pride and his Celtic imagination, for it had all the romantic quality of a Cornish fairy-tale. Despite his preoccupations in the home mines, he had organised, in less than a month's time, an entire production plan for making a start in re-opening the old treasure-houses of the Incas, namely, to complete the orders he had received for six engines. One he had already on hand — the reject made for the St. Kitts sugar-mills. On June the 2nd he writes to his patron —

> I drop you this note just to inform you that I have begun your job. Yesterday I engaged a great many smiths and boiler-builders who set to work this morning. I have also engaged all the boiler-plates in the county, which will be sent to-day to the different workmen. The master-smiths that I have engaged are the best in the kingdom. I have obligated them to put the best quality of iron, and to be delivered at Falmouth within four months. I have been obliged to give them a greater price than I expected, otherwise they would not turn aside their usual business employment for a short job of four months.

By giving such an extensive order Uville had already exceeded the instructions of his Peruvian co-partners (only two engines had been envisaged) and found a difficulty in raising even a small part of the money required to pay for the work in hand from the London agents. Trevithick, however, divined his usual ready way out — he to pay a large percentage of the bills in return for being given a fifth share in the adventure.

The order for the castings and much of the additional material had been placed with Hazeldine and Rastrick of Bridgnorth, and Rastrick had personally seen to it that the first consignment was accompanied by a free gift of Shropshire ale and clay pipes for the workmen. But the Cornish foundries were not offered any share in the order and Richard was naturally in their bad books again. The reason had probably nothing to do with the Woolf complex but haste in getting delivery — Hayle Foundry was rather noted for putting thoroughness before speed. A huge effort was being made to get the machinery ready before the end of August, when a Peruvian warship was due to sail from England. Security in transit across the Atlantic was regarded as particularly important because this country had just become involved in its second war with its old American colonies and their privateers were busy.

Unfortunately it was not a propitious moment to get work done at Bridgnorth as the foundry was much engaged on the construction of Rastrick's iron bridge at Chepstow. What with delays there and money shortages the departure of the warship was handsomely missed and there was nothing else available until Uville obtained a passage home on a South Seas whaler in September, 1814. By then, three more steam engines and three more machines had been added to the cargo and the bill had risen to more than £16,000. Trevithick had to sell some of his newly-acquired shares to English speculators to help meet the creditors. In the same ship with Uville and his acquisitions went three Cornishmen to put the machinery to work at the other end. They were Captain Henry Vivian, a mines engineer, brother of Andrew, and Richard's brother-in-law, an assistant called Bull, and Thomas Trevarthen who had had long experience in pit-work. Trevithick had misgivings about letting Vivian go. He admitted that he was a good man but that he had the "one failing of making too free with an evening glass" and he feared that if anything happened to him (which, in fact, it did) he would be blamed by the family — the old friendship with Andrew was already badly strained.

News of the expedition did not get back to Cornwall until well into the following year, when Uville wrote to say that only one engine had been started, the one which had been made for St. Kitts. It had been put to work in the mint at Lima and was not at all satisfactory. Apparently this was due to the use of wood fuel instead of coal for the boilers. Richard wrote to his men to tell them how to make the proper adjustment. He had already made up his mind that he must follow them and see to things himself and told them that he was coming. He said that if he could not get a passage to Lima he would go to Buenos Aires and make his way across the whole breadth of the continent. In the end he did not attempt this daring feat but more than a year passed before he was able to leave.

While that independent spirit had been preoccupied with his own tumultuous affairs the quiet Henry Harvey had made a remarkable venture. It was one which I think shows most clearly how, while by nature he was exceedingly cautious and careful, he was also capable of bold enterprise when well-considered foresight called for it. In 1814, in spite of the pressing financial burdens, he ordered a new ship, another brig, twice the size of the *Henry*. His fleet had, for some time, consisted of two vessels only, the brig and the sloop *Elizabeth*. The earlier sloop, *Providence*, is lost trace of in that gap in the records between 1796 and 1809; nor is there any mention after that interval of the admirable Captain Sampson. It must be feared that both suffered the fate of so many contemporaries on that dangerous coast. After gaining information from various builders in the Bristol Channel, Henry ordered from Bideford again — not from Mr. Clibbetts this time but Messrs. Chapman and Ellis. The contract was signed on August the 11th, 1814. Two watch-dogs were stationed there to keep the builders on their toes and have an eye to materials and prices. They were Captain Frank Cundy, who acted as expert adviser and through whom payments were made, and Captain William Curtis, the future commander of the vessel. Again, the shipwright was not allowed to do all the fitting-out in his yard. Where money could be saved, parts were procured from elsewhere. Rigging and cordage were sent from the home rope-walk, the lower masts from the timber-yard, and the sails made by a local sailmaker, but dead-eyes for the standing rigging were had from Swansea. The builders were permitted to supply topmasts and spars. Payments were made in five instalments, completed by the day of launching, which took place in the Spring of 1815. The shipyard bill (apart from the imported gear and the pay of the two captains) amounted to £1,252 19s. 10d. She was nearly twice the burden of the *Henry* and a fair amount deeper in draught, an indication of confidence on the part of the owner that he would have his way in clearing the Penpol Channel. The new ship was named the *Fame*.

IX

THE BATTLE OF THE SANDS

THE YEAR 1816 WAS AN EVENTFUL ONE, BOTH IN THE world now freed from the long menace of Napoleon, and at Hayle. On January the 22nd the last "out" letter subscribed "Blewett, Harvey & Vivian" is found in the letter-book. The next for the 29th, is signed "Harvey & Co." (to appear over the offices of the Company until 1985). But the scribe was so accustomed to the old style that he wrote the first name and had to scratch it out. The Company, thus announced, was of a more reliable character than the late one. Thomas Ellis stayed on in partnership and the salary he had enjoyed before (£200 a year with £12 for his horse) was continued. The two new partners were members of the family, Elizabeth Harvey, Henry's sister, and William West, his brother-in-law. The unobtrusive but hard-working William was turned sixty-five years old when he was elevated to the boardroom. Who should take his place in the iron-works which he had supervised since the earliest days? The choice fell on Arthur Woolf.

Woolf's exact connection with Harvey & Co. remains obscure. He was called Superintendent of the Foundry, but he kept remunerative positions he had already gained as Engineer at several of the mines. As a salary for what must have been part-time work at the Foundry there is no note of his having been paid more than £50 a year[1], but he had another source of income from pupils which he trained at the Foundry. It is said that one reason for getting him to associate himself with the company was that Woolf had seriously considered setting up a foundry of his own but was persuaded by Henry to give up the idea and join the existing concern. If, as was said, Woolf's object was to produce and market his engine and boiler the prospects would not have been bright. Sales could never have matched

[1] Entry in Cash-book for March 31st, 1824 "for his attention to the interest of the Co. 8 years to this day; £400".

116

costs and, as it turned out eventually, both articles were failures, as the inventor, himself, had to admit.

Woolf was valued by Henry not as an inventor but a technician. His skill as a craftsman and in the use of special tools was of a high order. William Pole says that he had heard that Woolf's engines were "more like ornaments for a show-room than machines for draining a mine"[1]. The results of this co-operation were apparent before the end of the year in the building and fitting-up of an entirely new foundry.

During this year, for the first time, the Copper Company entirely refrained from hostilities and began to put out feelers for peace-talks. Presently an armistice was signed by both parties which purported to give mutual advantages. The C.C.C. had always scored by having wharves which were suitable to receive copper ores in transit between the mines and South Wales. The supply was always greatly in excess of those they needed for their own smelting furnaces. The ores were sorted in heaps placed on mats woven out of the marram grass which grew on that vast range of sandhills, the Towans. Here sampling could be done conveniently, after which, the parcels could be put straight on board ships, which were able to lie alongside old Merchant Curnow's quay. By these means the Copper Company were able to get back-freights to Wales which reduced the cost of freight on coal imported by the same ships.

Harvey, on the other hand, had nowhere fit for copper ores to lie and could not therefore attract back freights even from mines in which he held large shares. Ships bringing him coal and iron had to return empty and to this higher cost was added that of having to discharge by cart and pack-mule. At the same time, he had to keep his selling price uneconomically low to beat the prices of the C.C.C. They, in turn, were put out, though to a less extent, by having to cut their profits on coal to beat Harveys. They now sought to limit Harvey's imports of coal while offering him, in return, freights of copper ore at their quays. But the agreement was that Harvey should only use his own ships and not, as hitherto, charter additional vessels. The Foundry ships were to take the turns due to them at the quays. The document was duly signed by Henry and Joseph Carne. It had some advantages for the former, in spite of the limiting clause, but the balance was certainly in favour of the C.C.C.

I remember, some time ago, when travelling along the main Swansea-

[1] W. Pole, *Treatise on the Cornish Engine.*

Carmarthen road which runs near the coast between Kidwelly and St. Ishmaels noticing that a long succession of field-gates had their posts made of granite, a rock not found in those parts. When I sought for the meaning of this I was told that, in the old days, captains of small sailing ships, taking coal from Wales to Cornwall, but having to return empty, brought these posts over as ballast and sold them to the farmers. They could be raised from the Lelant quarries for a matter of only 4d. or 6d. a-piece and the masters of the vessels would no doubt be entitled to the profits as "captains' privilege". Welshmen have long memories for things of that kind, and I dare say most of those gate-posts came in Henry's ships in the hard times when he could not secure back-cargoes.

Those times returned only too soon, for the truce did not last long. Henry found that his ships were not being allowed to take their rightful turns at the berths, but were often kept waiting and missing tides in favour of those in which the Copper Company were more interested. So he gave notice that, as the agreement was being regularly broken, he felt no longer bound by it, and went back to the old tedious mode of carting over the sand; but he was once more free to get what stocks of coal he could sell by chartering additional ships. The incident is vouched for in the Brief, but the months in which it was made and ended are not given. One may imagine that the breakdown was particularly vexing when the new ship, *Fame*, had just come into commission, for the difficulties of getting her up the Penpol channel would have been much greater than with the two smaller vessels.

It was not until October, 1816, that Richard Trevithick was able to get a passage direct to Callao (the port for Lima). On the 20th of that month he sailed from Penzance in the *Asp*, a South Seas Whaler. Although his departure had been delayed a good deal longer than he had expected he had been far from idle. Among the ideas he had been concentrating on were an aerophile engine (to work by jet propulsion) and a screw propeller for ships. The latter invention he had been nursing since 1812. At last, in the autumn of 1815, he applied for a patent and at the same time ordered the necessary castings for engine and propeller (8 feet, 10 inches, diameter) from Hazeldine and Rastrick . . . These were to be sent to a millwright in London, who was to provide the hull. There were the usual delays and the ship was still fitting out when Richard left for Peru and could not supervise her construction, a feat which, apparently, the millwright never succeeding in achieving. So this radical improvement on the paddle-wheel made no headway until 1836 when Sir Francis Pettit Smith took out a fresh patent and demonstrated it in his ship *Archimedes*. I. K. Brunel was so much impressed by her performance that he altered his design for his new Atlantic liner, *Great Britain*, then three parts built, from paddle-wheels to screw. Yet Smith took all the honours and in the Dictionary of National Biography he is named as "inventor of screw-propeller for steamships".

Trevithick must have borne all the expenses of this last abortive experiment, as of so many others, and have been quite out-of-pocket on the eve of his departure for, on the very day before he sailed, he surrendered half his rights in the plunger-pole steam engine to William Sims for £200. Sims was the principal engineer of the Eastern mines and agent of John Williams who controlled the most important of them. He was left to look after the invention, make what he could out of its profits, and pay Trevithick a quarter share of what it earned by its "duty" (a royalty based on its savings in fuel similar to that introduced by Watt).

The building of the new foundry at Hayle must have been completed by the Autumn as the principal bills for its construction were settled in November, and there was yet another new development in the business, for Henry had decided to set up as a tin-smelter and his smelting-house was built and in production by October. Late in that month he was writing to merchants with whom he had long dealings, explaining his reasons for this new departure and canvassing for orders —

> Being concerned in an extensive Mine which Produces Tin of very superior quality it has induced us to erect a Furnace. We have now commenced smelting and shall be happy to supply you with any quantity of Fine Tin you may want, and shall feel obliged if you can take some & your price and mode of payment. You may rely on its being very good and we will render it on as good terms as you can get it from any other House. Should it not suit you to deal in this article will you have the goodness to recommend us to a safe House.

The mine alluded to was Wheal Vor, long famous for its age as well as its size. Situated in the parish of Breage, it had early associations with the Godolphin family and its story (could it ever be all found out) would surely be one of the most remarkable of any of the great subterranean adventures. It is said that the first steam engine ever to be worked in Cornwall was erected here — by Newcomen, it is believed; but some go so far as to hold that it was by Savery.

The mine had lain disused and derelict for a long while in spite of the local belief among the old men that great wealth still lay hidden beyond its flooded workings, and it was a local family named Gundry — Captain

John Gundry of Goldsithney and his brothers — who took the risk of restarting it, doubtless at very great expense, though they seem to have been well supported by shareholders and Henry Harvey was one of the more prominent adventurers. Captain John set to work in 1814 and, in 1816, Arthur Woolf fixed here the second of his compound engines. The old men proved right, for the richest lode of tin ever struck in Cornwall was discovered, but just too late to benefit the enterprising promoter. John Gundry had become bankrupt through unlucky speculations elsewhere.

The enterprise gave promise from the start and Henry wisely undertook to provide facilities for smelting at his works, where he could also arrange for shipment to pewterers at Bristol and tin-platers in Wales direct. But tin was the only one of the many metals found in Cornwall which had to have a royal due paid on it before it could be offered for sale, a time-honoured grant to the Duke of Cornwall, eldest son of the reigning sovereign. This was enforced and collected by the Stannaries authority at one of five "coinage towns" — Liskeard, Lostwithiel, Truro, Helston, and Penzance. That entailed land transport over bad roads, taking ore from the mine to the smelting-house, where the fused metal was run into moulds and made into rectangular blocks. As "block-tin" it was then taken to a hall in the town where a quarterly coinage was being held. Here an official of the Stannaries chipped off one corner of each block, assayed its quality, affixed the Stannaries mark, and finally collected the due payable. Only after this process could the tin be offered for sale.

Henry's first consignment was ready and coined at Helston before the end of that year, 1816. It consisted of 32 blocks, weighing in all 5 tons, 12 pounds. Dues amounted to £20 1s. 0d., with carriage £1 16s. 0d. His coal-bill for smelting (anthracite, 18 tons, 1 cwt. 6 qrs.) was £42 12s. 6d. The two qualities, "refined" and "common" are priced for sale at 94/- and 90/- per cwt. respectively for ready money and 2/6d. extra for a bill at six months. Coinages were not only essential to the Duchy for the collection of dues, they were also convenient foregatherings of the smelters who could arrange among themselves what selling prices should be adopted by all and at the next meeting a further 7/6d. per cwt. was proposed. For the moment things were prospering in this quarter. Ironmasters and coal-owners were also trying to control prices by forming associations, though without much success, and prices in those markets continued to vary from source to source. The letter-books show how keen Henry was to probe the current situation and get the quality he demanded at the lowest price with the lowest freight charges.

The end of the year saw Harvey & Co. more established on its rightful *terra firma* whilst being greatly enlarged both in buildings and appliances. But the old difficulties remained — the disputed rights in the use of the foreshore and the lack of a proper quay and access by water to the Foundry. These grievances must have appeared in a more glaring light since the scope in production and its manifest usefulness to the neighbourhood had grown with the new facilities for serving it. The attempted but unprofitable peace with the C.C.C. which had either failed or was on the point of giving up, must have been an added irritant. Under Henry's tactful management, however, Woolf, in spite of his "peculiar unconciliating temperament and disposition" had proved useful both in what he was doing in the works and in his association with the mines. But what a pity that the greatest inventive genius of his time had been allowed to sail off into the blue!

The year 1817 turned out to be even a more crucial one in the history of the company, though the really dramatic event did not occur until nearly the end of it. At the outset, however, there was an interesting development. Looking through the records of the parish church of St. Erth I came across the following entry in the Vestry Book for Relieving the Poor —

> At the Vestry held this 20th day of January, 1817, at the house of John Morgan in St Erth.
> Resolved that the sum of two hundred pounds be borrowed for the purpose of enabling Mr Henry Harvey and Capt. Richard Hodge for prosecuting the mine commonly called Wh. Squire and for the particular purpose of subsisting the labouring poor of this parish employed in the said mine, and that the interest thereon shall be paid by the parish.

Rather a surprising arrangement! From whom did the parish borrow the money? Could it have been from James Halse? He certainly took a lively interest in Harvey's reconstitution of this mine, for, in the course of the year he paid him upwards of £500 in connection with it and early the following year he received a dividend from it of £200 — an indication of how quickly and effectively the new work had been undertaken. The ore was bought by Henry for his smelting-house. He was already buying ore from other mines besides this and Wheal Vor and production figures were steadily mounting.

James Halse was M.P. for St. Ives, and Gilbert says of him "This gentleman is amongst the most enterprising and successful adventurers in mines of the present day". But there was a still stronger bond between him and Henry than the mining interest. Henry's new partners, unlike his late ones, had not supported the business with large capital and he was very much in need of it. He probably wished to remain in sole control of this now compact family concern and ruled out the idea of taking more partners for the sake of their money. He had resolved, instead to borrow, on mortgage or note-of-hand, from neighbours who had gained sufficient confidence in him. James Halse was one of these. A cash-book entry for March the 31st, 1819, records "Paid James Halse Esqr. one year's Interest on our note for £1,000 due the 25th Instant £50".

The next important development (already foreshadowed) took place in the Autumn, due to the demise of Hugh Edwards who died on November the 6th. He was the sole survivor of the "three lives" named in the leases covering both the Praed and the Hearle thirds of Carnsew. It will be recalled that the most important part of this land, the Carnsew Quay and Cellars, had been sublet to the Cornish Copper Company twenty-eight years earlier. Now their tenure was at an end.

The then owners of Carnsew were a younger generation. Unlike their predecessors, of whom John Harvey had complained about being "left very Cold with the Lords" they were kindly disposed towards Henry and had even become backers of the Foundry faction so that, although the C.C.C. made strenuous efforts to secure a renewal of the leases, their applications were not granted. Henry had received secret assurances from the landlords in advance that he should be the next tenant, and they kept their word. He thus became master of two thirds of the whole of Carnsew, in addition to part of Trelissick estate which was occupied by his farm. The Copper Company were left with only a small footing in their old domain, an unoccupied piece of ground to the west of the Quay and Cellars, part of the St. Aubyn third. That lease had thirty-five years to run and there was a surviving "life" to support it. This was James Pascoe who must have been in or near his 'seventies, for the lease had now run for sixty-four years.

The landlords were, in fact, exceptional men, in touch with contemporary ideas in the world beyond the Tamar and not by any means behind their times. William Praed, the second son of Humphrey Mackworth, and now owner of one of the thirds, was Member for St. Ives more than once. He played a leading part in the promotion of England's most important inland waterway, the Grand Junction Canal. The other third which had been jointly owned by the three heiresses of John Hearle had come by marriages to Francis Hearle Rodd, the Rev. Henry Hawkins Tremayne, and Samuel Stephens. Rodd was a large landowner and, besides his link with the Hearle family, he was also, by another marriage with the Paynters, the heir to part of the Trelissick estate which included the mansion of that name and the land held by Harvey in Carnsew and Mellanear, which was mainly occupied by his farm.

Tremayne managed to earn one of Davies Gilbert's most unstinted eulogies — "possessed of good abilities, of sound understanding, of practical knowledge of business, and of the utmost kindness of heart, he became the father of his neighbourhood, reconciling all disputes, adjusting all differences, and tempering the administration of justice with lenity and forbearance". Samuel Stephens must have been a man of taste, for he sent for the celebrated architect of Bath, John Wood the younger, to build him his house at St. Ives, Tregenna Castle — now a hotel which keeps the same name. He inherited his portion through his mother and grandmother, Harriet Hearle, who married a well-known naval officer, Captain Wallis, the discoverer of many islands in the South Pacific, where his name is still remembered in the Wallis Archipelago. These men who were now so helpful at a critical juncture were to back Henry up again in a still more vital contest with the C.C.C.

The enemy had never carried out one of his most formidable threats — the forcible clearance of the plot beyond the boundary wall, and now that wall was no longer the boundary. When Henry crossed it, unopposed, to take possession of the old establishment that had first been laid down by George Blewett, the forceful Marazion merchant, and improved and added to by Harris, Ellis & Co., he found everything in a state of complete dilapidation — cellars (warehouses), office buildings, and timber-pool. The Carnsew Quay and its lime-kilns were presumably undecayed, but the Carnsew channel, which gave it communication with the sea, was silted up and unusable. The truth was that the Copper Company had never had any use for the place. Their situation on the Curnow property fulfilled their needs. They had taken it in the first instance to squeeze the Ellises out of business and retained it in the hopes of ruining the Harveys also.

As John Harvey had dreamed for long about what he would do if he got a footing in Carnsew, so Henry had had similar visions of what he would do if he ever got possession of this particular quarter of it. They were to straighten and deepen the channel of the Penpol River and build beside it an immensely long quay which would reach even beyond the lower ford to the deep water near the entrance of the river. This plan he began to put into operation as soon as the rough weather of the winter was over. Expenses for work on the channel are first shown in the accounts for May, 1818.

If the C.C.C. were still prepared to abide by their long and aggressively paraded theory relating to the foreshore rights, namely, that they belonged exclusively to tenements immediately adjoining the wastrel, versus the claim for equal-sharing for all tenants of Carnsew, no fault could possibly be found with the works now contemplated by Harveys. So, about the beginning of May, twenty men with picks and shovels were detailed to re-start the now time-honoured excavations in the channel. It is likely that they had an additional object to that of deepening it, which would be to probe for foundations for the projected wharf.

The native rock here is killas (the old word used for sedimentary strata surrounding the granite masses) with a general north-south strike and a steep dip — a common reef-making formation. In between two such reefs lay the hollow of sand and black silt that was the bed of the Penpol River. The presence of such a reef confining the river on its western bank, but lying at some depth under drifted sand, must have been known or, at least, surmised and could now be proved.

Doubtless the Copper Company watched the advance of Harvey & Co. into their old preserve with no kindly eye, but they offered no protest or showed any sign of resistance. Now they would observe the working-party vigorously digging. How could that be challenged! They, themselves, had maintained that the tenant of Carnsew Quay had an exclusive right there.

They took no action for several weeks. Then, one day, Henry heard that the enemy was going to send a strong force to undo the work his men were engaged on. He at once took the precaution of adding greatly to the digging party. Shortly afterwards, at nine o'clock in the morning, the invaders appeared, armed, every man, with a shovel. They immediately set to work to throw back the sand and mud as the other side dug it out. In this process the opposing parties seemed to have avoided coming to blows but, the Brief says, that the possibility of that happening terrorised the neighbourhood. When dusk fell the Copperhouse men had succeeded in neutralising that day's work on the part of the diggers.

Meanwhile, Henry had thought out a plan which was quite Napoleonic in its logical simplicity, fraught with the element of surprise. At nightfall he enlisted an additional band of labourers and secured horses and carts from every available carrier and farmer prepared to hire. Soon after daylight the next day, the Copperhouse contingent duly arrived, augmented in strength.

5. Foundry Square

6. Hayle Harbour

7. Hayle Harbour from the air, 1960

But this time Harvey's men threw their shovelfulls into the string of waiting carts which drove off quickly to an inland dump and rattled back again for more. The day ended in a victory for the Foundry so complete that the invading force did not make a third attempt to interrupt the work on the channel. It is odd that tempers remained so controlled that no physical violence seems to have been attempted. Possibly the Copperhouse men had had positive instructions not to come to blows lest the magistrates should be called in again to the disadvantage of their masters.

This curious episode must have taken place about the middle of the summer of 1818 and the Copper Company were already defending their action by a most brazen and barefaced justification. They were giving out that as they were still tenants of one third of Carnsew, although remote from the scene of contest, they were entitled by customary right (the thirds being undivided) to have equal rights with other tenants on the whole of the foreshore. If the Foundry chose to dig they had an equal right to fill in. If they chose to build, they had equal right to dismantle — a plea on the part of the Harveys which they had persistently and furiously rejected for years.

The trial of strength having thus ended so quickly and favourably, Henry continued to deepen the channel south of the ford until, it is said, vessels up to 150 tons burden could pass up it to the Foundry on a high tide. He then began work on his great wharf.

We must take notice at this point of what had happened in the Penpol River after the C.C.C. had made their lock-gates and sluices in the narrows between the lagoon and its eastern lobe. This was done in 1788. Up to that time, the river, after crossing the ford, but before reaching its mouth, had taken a fairly sharp turn to the east and emptied itself into the main stream just below the pool called the Bristolman's Dock by which merchant Curnow had built the quays which he sold to the Copper Company. This turn in the river was caused by a bank of sand which had accumulated in the course of time. The confluence, in fact, occurred exactly opposite a small inn on the far bank called after its tenant Burt's House. The daily sluicing at the gates when the tide was out to scour the channel in the main stream had had the effect of washing away the sandbank and the river now flowed out at a point considerably to the west of Burt's House. This diversion had caused a deposit of sand to be built up over its old course which formed a projection on its eastern margin roughly the shape of a triangle. As the river, taking its original course, had formed the boundary between the parishes of St. Erth and Phillack, the old demarcation had been obliterated though, in law, it would be held to have remained as before. Henry had taken good note of this, for it meant that the promontory was rightfully in St. Erth parish and therefore part of the Carnsew foreshore.

When the work on the Foundry channel was completed and also (presumably) the prospecting for foundations along the rocky reef, Henry started building his wharf and, at the same time, he placed boundary stones along the base of the triangular projection where he remembered that the Penpol River used to run. As the work on the wharf progressed, the C.C.C. realised that it was going to be a far bigger undertaking than they had ever imagined and although at this time (to quote again from the Brief) Harveys "received every facility and encouragement from the Lords and the good wishes of all the country, and were congratulated on their success so far against the Cornish Copper Company" the latter "threatened indictment against Messrs. Harvey & Co. and their people for a riot & assault with actions for trespass, and with Bills in Chancery and Injunctions to stay their proceedings". The threats, however, as formerly, were empty ones and tactics were suddenly changed. "A meeting was proposed by the Cornish Copper Company's Solicitor [Joseph Edwards] to discuss the rights. This failed of taking place or of success, and Messrs. Harvey & Co. proceeding with the erection of their Quay on a scale far beyond anything the Cornish Copper Co. had ever dreamt of or anticipated, they resolved as a last effort to endeavour to counteract or defeat Messrs. Harvey & Co's. views by proceeding to build a Quay close to Messrs. Harvey & Co's. new Quay, and thus effectually stop up the Channel & render their Quay of no avail".

There is more in this last statement than meets the eye. Harvey's quay can be seen today exactly as he planned, except for the archway which he had made by the upper ford to give through passage between it and the track to Penzance over the sands. That arch has been filled up long since. The quay is 440 yards long — a full quarter of a mile. Opposite the far end, and overlapping it by about sixty yards, stands the new Copper House quay, just referred to, also unaltered. But there is a gap of forty-four yards between the two and it can hardly be believed that such a distance would form an effective obstruction to vessels coming to the Foundry, even when the other wharf was fully berthed with ships tied up alongside it.

There can have been no need whatever for the C.C.C. to build their new wharf as there was ample room at the quays they already owned on either

128

Map 3. Hayle Harbour, c 1828

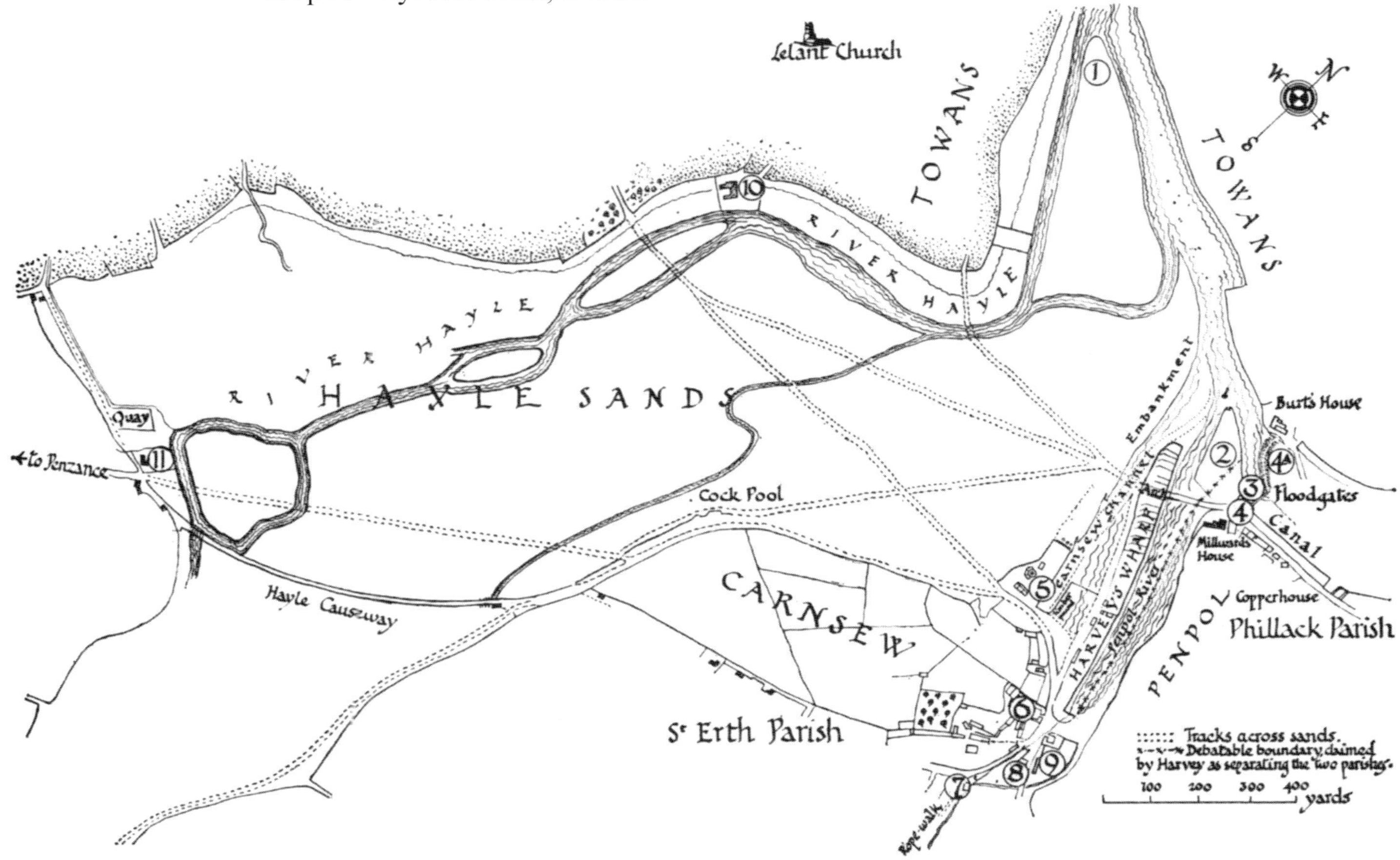

Key:

1   Norwayman's Dock
4,4a   Merchant Curnow's quays
5   Carnsew Quay
8   Old White Hart Hotel
9   Tin smelting-house

Legend:
...... Tracks across sands
~~~~ Debatable boundary claimed
by Harvey as separating the two parishes.

0   100   200   300   400   yards

Map labels:
TOWANS
TOWANS
Lelant Church
RIVER HAYLE
HAYLE SANDS
RIVER HAYLE
Quay
to Penzance
Hayle Causeway
Cock Pool
St Erth Parish
CARNSEW
Carnsew Channel
HARVEY'S WHARF
Penpol River
Embankment
Rope walk
Williams's House
Copperhouse
PENPOL
Phillack Parish
Canal
Floodgates
Burt's House

129

side of the Bristolman's Dock to serve their purpose. It was an undertaking that was reckoned to have cost at least £5000 — a very expensive "last effort" to counteract Henry's "views"! What, in fact, was the idea?

The summer had passed with one assault on the part of the enemy that narrowly avoided being a riot, and one overture of peace, both of which had failed. In the Autumn a new storm was gathering. It broke on the 16th of November — a Sunday, the day of rest and off-guard. There is one eye-witness of what happened. His account is revealing, both as to the incident and the motive behind it. It is given in the verbatim report of the arbitration held at Hayle twelve years later (p. 172). At this, the witness, Charles Anthony Harvey, answered questions before the Arbitrator put by counsel. Charles was the son of a brother of John Harvey and therefore first cousin once removed to Henry. He had joined the firm as confidential clerk to Henry in August, 1812, and was a very intelligent and reliable young man with all his wits about him.

He said "The particular period to which I allude was of a Sunday night — begun between 9 and 10 o'clock and was continued until or after midnight ... I was sitting down in my cousin's parlour [at Foundry House] when one of the men came in and said there was a movement on that ground by the Copper House people and we went out to see what it was". By "that ground" Charles meant the spit of sand which had accumulated near the mouth of the Penpol River after its diversion and where Henry had placed those boundary stones to stake a claim for Carnsew. The witness continued "When we found how they were engaged we rallied the men that we could on the spot and went down to resist them".

The time was well after dark and the activity — so unusual on a Sabbath night and in religious-minded Cornwall — would have been quickly noticed by the showing of a twinkling cluster of lantern lights.

Counsel: You went up on the Sunday night. You mustered about 40 men. How many men of the Copper Company did you find there?
C.A.H.: I can't state exactly. Perhaps at the moment we went down just about the same number, but then numbers increased during the night ..."
Counsel: The next morning was there any assembling?
C.A.H.: The next morning there was a vast assemblage of people waiting again to begin the dispute with reference to this spot..."
These questions were put by the counsel for the plaintiffs. The counsel for the defendants was disposed to be facetious in his cross-examination.

Counsel: How many men had you under your command?

C.A.H.: I can't tell you.

Counsel: Such a vast army that you could not number them?

C.A.H.: There were fully four hundred men employed by Harvey and Company at that time. At least I should imagine so.

Counsel: They were not I suppose all in Mr. Harvey's regular employ?

C.A.H.: Men who were sought from all parts of the country.

Counsel: Mercenary troops in fact.

C.A.H.: They were well paid for their day's work.

Counsel: What was the company — the Copper people about then — were they at work — not on a Sunday night;

C.A.H.: We went on the Sunday night but the Copper Company people happened to be there first.

Counsel: On the Monday morning you renewed the attack?

C.A.H.: On Monday morning we were prepared ... I went out and summoned more men myself that morning.

Counsel: You mustered up in a body?

C.A.H.: We came down in pretty regular order.

Counsel: Were you the General or only Lieutenant?

C.A.H.: A sort of volunteer without any particular appointment.

Counsel: Who was Generalissimo — the Field Marshall?

C.A.H.: Mr. Harvey himself — and we all acted under his orders . . .

Counsel: Mr. [Joseph] Edwards came down to you to speak about it?

C.A.H.: Mr. Edwards met Mr. Harvey about the mid way between this place and the point the men were going to and requested Mr. Harvey to go back with his men, and Mr. Harvey's reply was "Mr. Edwards go and mind your own people"!

Counsel for the plaintiffs raised the crucial point at issue.

Counsel: Now do you remember Mr. Harvey taking anything to that spot of ground where the Copper Company Quay is now built?

C.A.H.: Taking anything to it?

Counsel: Putting anything there?

C.A.H.: I remember Mr. Harvey putting stones on the lower part of it near the edge of the river.

Counsel: Do you know what the stones were put there for?

C.A.H.: Mr. Harvey put them there to take possession of the spot.

Counsel: After Mr. Harvey had done that did the Cornish Copper Company take anything there?

C.A.H.: The Cornish Copper Company attempted to dispossess Mr. Harvey of the same spot by taking stones which they had brought for the purpose of erecting their Quay — by rolling stones from the other part down — they rolled those stones down by men employed by them to do so. The men employed by Mr. Harvey resisted them and attempted to roll them back.

In this reply Charles had not made his meaning at all clear. What stones were rolled to and fro; "The same spot" was where Harvey had staked his claim across the river and one set of stones must have been those he had placed there. Then there were stones which he says the C.C.C. had on hand ready for building their quay. Were they rolled down to the beach to obliterate the site with premature foundations and footings — to make a *fait accompli*? What, then were the stones from "the other part"? Does that mean from the uncompleted part of Harvey's own quay? Charles had said elsewhere that the enemy "had reinforced themselves by a number of one-horse carts" which sounds as if they had taken a tip from their opponents and were robbing Henry's quay in such a way that he could not regain the material. They had given out that if the foreshore was shared they had as much right to dismantle as the other party had to build. But now they would be contradicting themselves again. The tide must, of course, have been out at the time of both forays or the lower ford would have been unusable.

After the first skirmish on the Sunday night Henry had foreseen that what must follow on the Monday, in broad daylight, would be a much more determined struggle, when it would become impossible to restrain the party zeal of men on either side and would end in bloodshed, if not homicide. Early on Monday morning, therefore, he dispatched two messengers post haste, one to call the nearest magistrate, who was Samuel Stephens, vicar of St. Erth, the other to summon Samuel John, a solicitor of Penzance. Both men responded promptly and reached the scene of action before noon. One may hazard the guess that in his judicial capacity the vicar would ride over supported by his parish constable carrying his impressive truncheon of office on which would appear in bright paint the lion and unicorn and royal cypher — it was before the days of our police force. But there is no account of what happened immediately on the arrival of the magistrate, how he intervened on reaching the scene or, whether or not, he read the Riot Act. It is only noted that an ugly situation was developing when he appeared, and that he was successful in disengaging the parties.

It may, however, be observed that before this intervention Henry, himself, in leading the advance, had actually been knocked down by one of the opponents — a point given in other evidence.

Having thus achieved what he had been called on to do, Stephens was by no means content to let everyone depart in peace. He collected the leaders of both sides, together with their legal advisers, at the most convenient neutral point which was the inn called Millwood's House (already noted, now the Royal Standard). Here he demanded that a treaty of non-interference should be drawn up, there and then, between the parties and signed in his presence.

This impromptu conference remained in session for the greater part of the day. One would think that the vicar would be at some disadvantage in argument as Henry was now one of his most prominent parishioners and was regarded with so much favour by the parish vestry as to have been helped to that £200 pounds in the Wheal Squire adventure. But a breach of the King's peace had been narrowly avoided, now and in the past, for which the Copper Company was to blame, and that was a strong card for a magistrate to hold when dictating a settlement. The C.C.C., on their part, for all their threats had studiously avoided a court action to decide the question of the foreshore rights and, to suit their own convenience, they had recently come round to the view that they had formerly rejected. Their last action showed that they were not ready to abide by any rule except that of force.

When the meeting finally broke up the Rev. Samuel Stephens had worked a miracle. He had got an agreement signed by Harvey and the formidable Joseph Carne, Managing Partner of the Copper Company, which effectively put a stop to the kind of persecution that had gone on unremittingly for so long, yet without compromising either side on the vexed question of the wastrel. It set forth that either party should be at liberty to complete their quays without molestation from the other "without prejudice to their claims with respect to their undivided part of the Tenement of Carnsew" and that nothing contained in the agreement "shall be considered as affecting the right of either of the said Companies to do any act which may be advised to be necessary or proper for trying the title of the other to the Lands whereon the Quays are respectively to be built".

This admirable document was taken charge of by Samuel Gurney, to be retained by him as invigilator of its full observance. Charles Harvey had the good sense to make an exact copy shortly afterwards in the Vicarage parlour under the eye of the vicar [1].

No doubt the timely and able handling of the crisis by the parson-magistrate prevented the breaking of many heads and perhaps some loss of life — the long Cornish shovel makes a ghastly weapon of offence. But if it had not been for Henry Harvey's forethought he could never have got there in time to save bloodshed among the men or to make such a peace with their principals. And probably the innkeeper of Millwood's House was not the least pleased with the result of the long session.

That long quay wall, built under such trying conditions and on such apparently insubstantial foundations, has endured to serve the present day shipping in Hayle harbour. It has a feature which I have not heard of being found elsewhere. The wall is not lineally straight but fronts the Penpol Channel in a succession of wide arcs. It is locally said to have been designed thus so that sailing ships could cant their bowsprits outwards and therefore tie up closer to each other. But Capt. Lott, lately harbourmaster, insisted that it was to find point-to-point foundations on the submerged reef of rock. The only small bit of the wall which might have cleared matters up when it gave way three years ago was just that patchwork which had filled in the original archway over the old road across the sands and was unrevealing. So the visitor is left to make his own guess at the riddle.

[1] Excerpt from the agreement in the Appendix III.

X

THE EARLY TWENTIES

THE FULL QUARTER-MILE LENGTH OF HARVEY'S NEW quay was not completed until late in 1819, but the work was carried out without any further hindrance from his rival. He had, however, got the landward part sufficiently ready and prepared with copper-ore plots to be able to canvass the smelters for support in supplying him with those desirable back-cargoes to Wales and Bristol which would reduce the price of inward freights on coal, iron, timber, and the many other commodities in which he was now dealing. Letters of that time show his eagerness to offer prospective clients every inducement to give him their custom in preference to that of the Copper Company.

One letter, dated the 12th of September, 1818, contains an oft-repeated formula, as follows —

> Our wharfs are now ready to receive Copper Ores and being situated nearer the Mines than the Cornish Copper Co's wharfs are, consequently it can be carried for less money. There are also other advantages by your encouraging a competition in this part which you may be aware of. We shall therefore feel obliged by your ordering your ores to be lodged here & every attention in our power shall be paid to your interest.

In those days, the most direct approach to the Copper House Company's wharves from the western mines was by a rough track along a narrow strip of beach on the right bank of the Penpol River, between (and partly in) it and a line of low cliffs. This was rough going and only available at low tide. Otherwise, the ways were very roundabout. Harvey's quay was more convenient as it could be reached by road at any time and was, in fact, slightly nearer even when the tide was out. The Copper Company, however, soon after their new quay was finished, evened up their disadvantage by cutting back the cliff and building the road above the beach which the visitor will find today, occupied on one side by houses and a row of small shops overlooking the harbour.

Henry wrote more explicitly to another copper-smelter in Wales on the same day —

> Agreeable to your request last Thursday I beg to say if you will have the goodness to say if you will order your ores to be carried on our Wharfs we will engage that our vessels shall continue to sea during the Winter, and we will undertake that they shall carry it at as low freight as others. Should we attempt to lower the freight we should make the Captains our enemies which at this time we wish to avoid. This we have no doubt you will see the propriety of.

The letter is signed by Thomas Ellis "for Co & Self". A month later the same party is again addressed with a further inducement in the form of a guaranteed minimum rate for freight charges. This was a most unusual concession for Henry to make and shows how anxious he was to secure the back-cargo traffic.

> Since we wrote you the 12th Ult. we have thought it may be managed that the ores you will be pleased to lodge on our plots may be carried to Wales for less freight without interfering with the Masters of vessels. We will therefore engage to get vessels all the year, and you shall not pay above 4s. per ton freight, and our own vessels shall continue to sea during the Winter.

The latter resolve was a risky one and must have been made after some heart-searching. Henry had hitherto laid up his small fleet of three ships for the winter months and preserved them from the worst furies of the Atlantic gales. The consequence of departing from this wise rule was soon shown for, in November, the gallant little *Elizabeth* had her sails blown to ribbons, was dismasted, and lost all her standing and running rigging off the Pembrokeshire coast. Fortunately, there was no loss of life and her master, Captain Hawke, managed to get the disabled hull towed into the tiny harbour at Tenby.

What followed is of interest as showing the principles of make-do and economy on which Henry always acted. On hearing the news, he wrote to Captain Curtis of the *Fame* telling him "we have determined to send up Capt. Thos. Ninnis to give direction respecting her repairs and we have to request that you will (if possible) call at Tenby in your way down and leave with Captn. Hawke what you can spare from the *Fame*, such as Topsail, Ropes, Blocks, & Tar or anything you may think necessary".

There was no thought that the *Elizabeth*, when she was sufficiently patched up to brave a homeward voyage, should return empty. Having enquired the price of grain in Pembrokeshire, Captain Ninnis is told "a cargo [of oats] will be more than we can conveniently take, we therefore think it best to engage as much from the Farmers at Narbeth as you can

136

put in the *Elizth*, so that she may afterwards proceed to Barry for Coal. We think that by getting the old mast sawn up to make Bulk Heads [for separating the two kinds of cargo] you might find room to stow the quantity you mention, 600 lbs. . . . If you have any of the old sails less boards will do & if necessary you might get some packs [sacks;]".

Early in February, 1819, the little sloop arrived home safely at the end of her hundred-and-eighth voyage, carrying 181 bushels of oats and 14 weys[1] of coal. Here she was laid up for a thorough refit. The misfortune cost the Company at least a hundred pounds, not counting the loss sustained in having one of the valuable trio disabled for several months when urgently needed.

One of the most remarkable traits in Henry's character was that, while he was careful and thrifty to an extent that might be called cheese-paring, he could, on occasions, launch out on large and costly enterprises which must, to the unforseeing eye, have appeared as though he had thrown caution to the winds. The building of the brig, *Fame*, the enlargement of the foundry, and the construction of the great wharf had been done under such impulses when, in each case, the prospect of returns for costs must have seemed as problematical as the question of where to find the money to carry them out. Incomings habitually lagged well behind outgoings, as they had done in his father's time. Like him, he was punctual in most of his payments, while his customers at the mines were far from being so. The ships' captains he always paid on the nail for their cargoes, freight charges, and regular gratuities; suppliers were sent considerable lump sums on account when they sent in their bills, though the wages of his foremen and salaries of his office staff were often not settled for some time. This seems to have been customary. There was no thought then of a weekly pay-packet. But bonuses were paid on profits in various branches of the industry, notably the rope-walk, and some workers even made small loans to the firm, for which they were duly credited with a 5 per cent, interest.

As I have already said, although the documentary evidence of the doings of those days, in letters and office books is voluminous, there is little to shed any intimate light on the personality of the "Little Cap'n". He certainly kept the reins of government firmly in his own hands and ruled on every question of policy. But what was he really *like*? One gains the idea that under a quiet and unassuming exterior he concealed a strong will

---

[1] Approximately 42 tons.

to success which must have greatly impressed those who knew him and won their confidence. It could be shown by the acid test of the credit he could command in loans, both personal and otherwise.

One may get an inkling of this from a letter he wrote to his bankers, Messrs. Daniell & Willyams of Truro on June the 21st, 1819 —

> In reply [to your letter, we] beg to observe that having in course of the last 12 months laid out upwards of £9,000 in building wharfs &c at this place which we are happy are now nearly completed & in consequence of the depressed state of the Tin trade we were unable to discharge the loan which [you] so readily granted at the time proposed; and we beg further to observe that at this season we have to lay in Stocks of Coal, Timber &c, and shall deem it an additional favour if you would allow the present balance to remain a few months longer. Should it be inconvenient for you to comply with this request we will endeavour to liquidate it as early as possible........
>
> We will thank you to debit our account for 6 Bills drawn on your House, amt. £157 5s. 2d., particulars annexed

In fine, he never let the bankers down, nor they him.

Not only was the quay completed without "further molestation" so, at long last, was the channel, also, and Henry was able to write to a copper-smelter in Wales "The ores are never shipped by lighter, having sufficient water at the wharf for the largest vessels that ever come to Hayle". This was probably a qualified statement, meaning only such vessels in the coastwise trade which would be carrying copper ore. The large full-rigged ships which brought him timber from Scandinavia were still not attempting to approach nearer than that furthest point on the sandbanks called The Norwayman's Dock.

There was another side to Henry's character besides that of the business man—that of the benevolent patriarch. Neither he nor his sister, Elizabeth, who kept house for him, ever married, but they showed a lively care and interest in their numerous nephews and nieces. Of the West children there were two sons, William (now 32) and John (19). Their parents were both living and prosperous, their father a partner in the Company. But Henry had seen to it that the boys had been trained in the Foundry and given attractive prospects for remaining at work there.[1]

The orphaned family of John Harvey of Helston had been brought up by Henry and his sister in their own home. There were two boys, Nicholas Oliver (16) and William (14). The former was the only one of all the nephews who was not trained for a future career in the home establishment. He

---

[1] But see also Appendix X.

was apprenticed to the Eagle Foundry at Birmingham where the engineer, William Brunton, was one of the partners. Brunton was one of the foremost men in the young profession of mechanical engineer and a successful inventor. He had worked in the fitting shop of the New Lanark Mills, that important centre of the early mechanised cotton industry, associated with Arkwright, David Dale, and Robert Owen, and had gone on to be manager of Boulton and Watt's engine works at Soho in Birmingham.

No doubt Nicholas showed an early aptitude for mechanical things and was perhaps thought the most promising of all the nephews and should be trained in one of the most modern and best equipped works, where the manufacture of steam engines was a speciality. Henry had a high opinion of Brunton and, as shown by much correspondence in later years, this regard was returned.

In the Trevithick family there were four boys — Richard (21), John Harvey (13), Francis (7), and Frederick Henry (2). It could not be said that they had "lost" their father except to sight and sound. Almost all they had heard of him was from two accounts which the solicitor, Thomas Edmonds, who had drawn up the patent-sharing agreement between Richard and William Sims, had gleaned from the Lima press and sent to the Cornish papers. The first appeared the year after Trevithick sailed. It said that a second of the engines which had gone out with Uville nearly three years earlier had been got to work at last in the high Andean mines "on Friday last, and notwithstanding the great quantity of water which filtered into the mine, the engine with half its power drained the mine completely". This took place just before the *Asp* landed her passengers, the further eight engines, and the large quantity of stores, spare parts, and tools. The account goes on "what is of greater importance is the arrival of Don Ricardo Trevithick . . . This professor can, with the assistance of the workmen who accompany him, construct as many engines as are necessary in Peru without the need of sending to England for any part of these vast machines".

In fact, Richard was given a tremendous public ovation by order of the Spanish Viceroy (Peru was still a colony controlled by the home government) and it was declared that nothing less would do than that Don Ricardo should be commemorated by a statue in solid silver. But no letters from the hero arrived at his cottage home in Cornwall — and no money. He had given instructions for a life-insurance policy to be taken out just before he departed, but left nothing to pay for the policy, also he omitted to pay the annual rent for his home. To meet these expenses Jane had to sell a small property of her own. A payment or two for the shared patent for the plunger-pole steam engine are noted in the cash-book as having been paid to Henry and passed on by him to Jane. But these soon ceased, as Sims evidently preferred to busy himself with his own ideas and designs.

The next communication from Edmonds was published in *The Cornwall Gazette*[1] in 1819. It did not sound so good. "Unfortunately for Captain Trevithick, F. Uville was anxious to impress his countrymen with the opinion that it was solely owing to him that steam engines were first introduced into the silver mines of South America; and notwithstanding the obligations he was under to Captain Trevithick, he sought every opportunity, soon after Captain Trevithick's arrival at Pasco, to oppose him, in claiming to have the direction of the mines. Captain Trevithick, knowing but little of the country, and disgusted with the treatment he received from Uville and the party he had formed against him, amongst whom was a gent [R. Page] who had lately arrived from England, retired from the concern, and proceeded on other important discoveries on his own account".

R. Page was a solicitor which the London shareholders sent out in the same ship as Trevithick to look after their interests. Worse things were yet to happen. No sooner was Richard free from the plotters of Lima than he and his projects became involved in the revolt of the Spanish colonies and he was forced to become a soldier in the republican army while the contending parties wrecked his machinery. But these adventures were only revealed years afterwards. The family continued to receive neither letters nor funds.

Meanwhile, the younger Richard had been taken into the foundry and appears to have been put in charge of the new harbour works, if that is the correct reading of an entry for March the 31st, 1819 "Channel; Paid Rd Trevithick jnr for his attendance from the end of June last to this time, 9 months at £30 [p.a.] £22 10s. 0d.". In due course Francis and the baby, Frederick Henry (who both became distinguished railwaymen) would start their engineering careers at Hayle.

The second son, John Harvey Trevithick, either had no mechanical bent or Henry felt that one of the nephews should be put into the other side of the business which had no heir apparent. It was this — the merchanting side — which Henry had always been more preoccupied with than the

---

[1] Francis Trevithick, *Life*. No nearer date than the year is given.

foundry and the forge, still the province of William West and, to some extent, of Arthur Woolf.

For some boys, the timber-yard, the ropewalk, the grist-mill, the farm and its allied horse transport, the stimulating contact with the ships and their masters, would have been as fascinating as the excitements of the engine works. The choice was perhaps mutual and it turned out well.

Only Jane and the two girls, Anne and Elizabeth, now turned nineteen and seventeen, respectively, were unprovided for. Years passed and nothing further was heard of the missing man. From the few scraps of Jane's correspondence which have survived from those trying times there is no suggestion of a complaint. She remained devoted and loyal and was up in arms at once if anyone offered the least reflection on her thoughtless husband's conduct. We have no clue as to what Henry's feelings were. He was always more practical than sentimental and eventually he devised a plan to make Jane independent and save her from penury with honour — a plan of mutual benefit. It was to build a hotel and place his sister therein as hostess.

Forty years since there were only two dwellings in Carnsew — "Mr. Ellis's House" and the Honeychurch cottage. Now it was a place, the name, Carnsew, being almost forgotten for that of Hayle. But it had no inn, whereas Copperhouse had three — the two already mentioned, Burt's House and Millwood's House and another nearer the copper works. Also, within easy reach of that population was the old inn in Phillack Church Town. Harvey & Co. were now receiving many callers connected with the business, some of whom they or the Wests entertained in their homes. Others had to make do with what accommodation they could find.

That the new inn at Hayle was intended to be something much above the standard of the others is shown by contemporary references to it as a hotel. This word was, as yet, rarely used for country inns. The plan does not appear to have materialised until 1824 as its first mention in the rate-books of St. Erth is not until the following year when the parish clerk, who was not even disposed to call it an inn, writes it down as Foundry Public House. Its sign, the White Hart, is not noted until later.

This is anticipating events out of their time sequence. We return to the early year of 1820. A truly astonishing transformation was pending which must have taken the whole neighbourhood by surprise. The C.C.C. were about to flatter their rivals by imitating hem, though this was not the light in which Henry saw it. In his Memorandum (Appendix IV) he wrote

141

"About the time that H & Co began to build the wharf the C.C.Co began to build a Foundery on a very large scale & to make sure of crushing H & Co and, to make use of an expression used by one of the C.C.Cos agents at the time, lets bleed him, meaning H & Co, in every vein". But most likely, they had found out by now how true was the old dictum quoted by Gilbert (page 47) that copper-smelting in Cornwall could never be made to pay. It had only seemed to be possible while they had no competition on the mine-merchant side of their business and could keep their selling prices and their wharf dues up accordingly.

The new foundry took a year or two to build but the C.C.C. lost no time in taking off their wharf dues. Hitherto, these had been charged to the smelters at eightpence a ton for their ores. As soon as Harvey's quay was ready the charges were reduced to three ha'pence. Henry had no choice but to charge the same. It just covered the payment for the men loading the ship, so that neither party were able to make any profit on their wharfage facilities. The capital invested could only yield returns through what could now be saved on freight charges and the elimination of the old laborious system of transhipment.

It will be remembered that John Harvey had been the very first to start a foundry in Cornwall and had no immediate rival for twelve years, when the Foxes of Falmouth opened theirs at Perran. All the partners in this company were Quakers, as were those of the Coalbrookdale Company, from whom John was getting his pig-iron. And, it will be remembered that, in those early days, Henry wrote a little reproachfully to the latter — fearing the secret combination of a holy alliance — complaining that Foxes were being supplied cheaper by ten shillings a ton than his father was. But the Perran Foundry turned out to be kind and helpful neighbours and such good relations were established between them that they regularly consulted each other on current prices and frequently, then and later, they shared contracts.

The Perran Company could well afford to be generous, and fortunately, unlike the C.C.C., they were disposed to be. A year after they started their Cornish foundry (1792) they acquired the very valuable property in South Wales of the Neath Abbey Iron Works where there were not only blast furnaces for the production of pig-iron but also iron mines, from which the raw material was got. For transport between the two places they had their own ships and all those facilities for loading and discharging them which the Harveys had lacked for so long.

Now, after nearly half a century of struggle, Harvey & Co. had gained an advantage in respect of access to the sea equal to that of the old rival. But each had, after all, only been competing with half his strength — as merchant, not as manufacturer. Now the conflict was to be on all hands — total war! What an irony! As H.H. completes his new wharf, the C.C.C. begins to build a new foundry — and on his own doorstep, or rather, in front of his own front door. A neighbour well tried in un-neighbourliness, he will copy everything that is done on the other side of the Penpol River — make castings and forgings, manufacture machinery for the mines and steam engines. He will not have to scheme and strive after capital, which always appears to be available. How will he get together a team of men of so many special skills? They were still rare in the country at large, and especially in the extreme south-west tip of it. The answer which he found — and had probably counted on in advance — was to buy the local talent which had been so well trained in the school across the river, by offering considerably higher wages than Mr. Harvey paid.

Henry, though he must have thought bitterly about these grim prospects as soon as the volte-face on the part of the Copper Company was known, concentrated on improving his position now that he had the full extent of his quay available and equipped with "cellars" and copper-plots. But in one of the mid-winter gales of 1819-20 the *Elizabeth* was driven on to the rocks at Morwenstow and became a total wreck, though the captain and crew appear to have escaped with their lives[1].

Neither the ship nor her cargo were insured but, although Henry was much encumbered with the cost of the wharf and other expenses, he immediately ordered a new vessel. She was to have almost the same dimensions as the other but rigged as a schooner and not a sloop. This time he went to a shipwright at Neath called Thomas Williams As before, the same strict economies were observed, the builder supplying the hull while rigging and sails were to be forwarded from Hayle. She was to be called *John Adams*, a name which struck me as singular, for I could not discover anyone associated with Harveys, or any local or national notable so called — I ruled out the American President. Not until I was going through the letters of nearly twelve years later did I find what I believe must be the right answer.

At the end of December, 1831, Henry received a letter from one John

[1] Appendix, p.347.

143

Hocken of Bude telling him of a disaster which had befallen a farmer who "rendered some assistance when a vessel of yours was wrecked at Morwenstow some few years ago". The poor fellow's farm had been struck by lightning. All the outbuildings had been destroyed, together with fifteen bullocks, eleven pigs, all his store of grain, and the farm implements. He "has strove hard to bring up 11 children and is now suddenly reduced to want in his old age". His vicar had been making a collection in the parish. Would Mr. Harvey send a small subscription? The man's name was John Adams.

If, indeed, the new ship was named in his honour it must have been as a tribute to a gallant act of rescue at the risk of life and perhaps in face of local prejudice, for wrecks were regarded as gifts of God and to succour survivors was generally held to be unlucky, traditions against which the celebrated Robert Stephen Hawker set himself so vigorously by precept and example when he became incumbent in 1834.[1] At any rate, Henry was not slow to respond to the appeal and John Adams returned thanks "for your very liberal and generous donation. I could not suppose that an act of common justice would have been so long remembered and rewarded with such great generosity".

The order for the *John Adams* was given in February, 1820, and Captain Thomas Row, Junior, was appointed watchdog in the owners' interest. It was part of the bargain that the vessel should not draw more than nine feet of water and that she should be finished by mid-summer. But it was not until October that she arrived at Hayle loaded to capacity with sixty-three tons of anthracite. It was then found that she drew ten, instead of nine feet of water, was down by the head, and that her carrying capacity was not as ample for her register tonnage as had been anticipated. Henry was making the final payment to the shipwright, whose bill of exchange had been received for acceptance a few days before, but now, having inspected the vessel, he wrote to Williams expressing keen disappointment and saying that the faults in draught and capacity would cause losses in the use of the ship — "there certainly must have been some great defect in modeling her". He refused to sign the acceptance until those defects should be cured.

Thomas Williams wrote to say that Captain Row had been made responsible for overseeing the work and had raised no objections.

[1] The best known account of him is *The Vicar of Morwenstow* by S. Baring Gould. More reliable is Piers Brendon, *Hawker of Morwenstow*, 1975.

Row pleaded that he had been called to Hayle for consultations and the under-framing had been laid down while he was away. In the end it was agreed that Williams should have the vessel back and reduce the dead-wood (timbers joining either end of the keel with the stem and stern posts) providing he could guarantee to get this done in the course of one neap tide (a little over a fortnight). This was a tricky business, but it was done in the middle of November and the draught successfully brought down to nine feet, on which the shipwright got his final payment.

What glimpses we get of the doings at Hayle during these years come mainly from the "out" letters copied into the series of large leather-bound folio volumes — there are no "in" letters to match them until 1829. The steadily increasing bulk in the "outs", year by year is, in itself, an indication of the growth of Harvey & Co. Yet, as Henry says in his Memorandum, the Company was not yet in a position to pay its members a dividend though it was now paying him a fixed salary of £200 a year, which was the same as Thomas Ellis had been receiving all along.

It is surprising to find that on the merchanting side, the coal and timber for the mines was apparently not more remunerative. The purser of a mine is told on November the 6th, 1820 —

> The profit on Coal and Timber to the Mines being so trifling we are under the necessity of observing that we cannot possibly give more than 4 months Credit. If you now pay up the amount of our Bills for supplies to Wheal Speedwell to end June, we have no objections to continue to supply, otherwise it will not be convenient to do so.

The import of these things which were essential to the conduct of deep mining ought to have paid well. That they were barely doing so was no doubt due to renewed pressure in price-cutting from the old quarter. Yet these imports occupied at least half the time and space of the shipping and caused much additional work. Every bushel of coal, every hundred of timber had to be checked by a customs official before it could be taken away. And a ship could not be discharged until that official had arrived at Hayle from St. Ives, where the nearest custom house was located. Both coal and timber that were used in the mines were allowed in duty free (debenture), but duty had first of all to be paid in full and the money reclaimed later (drawback) after certificates from the mines had been produced.

On the foundry side, business was so brisk that orders had to be turned away and Henry could not even forecast to a most important customer when they could promise to accept work from him. This must have been exceedingly galling in view of the strenuous efforts the C.C.C. were making to get their copy-cat iron works into commission, to catch promising clients, and at the same time to weaken Harvey's labour force by tempting offers of higher pay.

The important customer was John Taylor, a man who occupied a unique position in the mining world. The son of an eminent Norfolk divine and writer of popular hymns, he was, to Cornishmen, an "outside adventurer" — a foreigner. Such "wise men of the East" as they were slyly called, had frequently dabbled in Cornish ventures and had had their fingers badly burnt. They were mere speculators but Taylor was a man of very different calibre. He was working as a mining engineer whilst still in his teens and his practical knowledge of this science was balanced by a genius for finance. From his office in Clement's Lane, London, his Company, John Taylor & Sons, controlled a large number of mining interests both in Cornwall and elsewhere in Britain and also abroad.

The link between Harveys and Taylor was through Arthur Woolf. One comment on the latter by William Pole[1] has already been quoted. He said, further, that owing to his truculence and rough manners he "could not keep on good terms with the miners". But he admitted that he had made one good friend and that was John Taylor. Early in the century Taylor was working mines in the far west, including the parish of St. Erth. In 1819 his shrewdness coupled with local knowledge was shown by a remarkable coup he made in the eastern mining area by acquiring the leases of a number of mines strung out along one of the principal lodes, and others lying closely parallel to it, in the parish of Gwennap. These mines had been very productive in the past but, for some reason, had fallen into disuse. They were amalgamated by Taylor and re-started under the single name of Consolidated Mines.

Taylor was much attracted by Woolf's mechanical skill and interested in his ideas, though critical of them. He made him engineer of several of his mines. In one of the Consolidated group Woolf erected the largest single cylinder engine which had so far been made in Cornwall, the diameter of the cylinder being 90 inches. The castings were probably made at the Neath Abbey Iron Works and not by Harveys. It had a ten foot stroke and worked at a pressure of 40 pounds to the square inch, so that it was a Cornish engine, based on the Boulton and Watt design with those improvements

---

[1] *Treatise on the Cornish Engine.*

introduced by Richard Trevithick. It eventually did a duty of 67m. (million foot-pounds, see page 100).

In other mines Woolf had installed his own compound engines and patent water-tube boilers. These had achieved quite respectable duties compared with other single-cylinder engines then in being, but Taylor was not convinced of their superiority over the more up-to-date Cornish engine or Trevithick's Cornish boiler. He was one to do things in a big way and, to test his own conclusions, he ordered two new engines for Wheal Alfred, in Phillack parish, one a Woolf compound, steamed by his patent boilers, the other a single-acting Cornish engine steamed by Cornish boilers. They were set to work in 1824. The result of the trial showed that the latter did the higher duty.

After this demonstration Woolf did not attempt to push either of his specialities. He built no more compounds but wisely, if reluctantly, concentrated on making improvements to the engine of his absentee rival. Thomas Lean, in his *Historical Statement* tries to explain the failure of Woolf's compounds by saying, "The greater expense in their erection and the want of simplicity in their construction were objections to their general use". The real reason was something quite different. Woolf had worked on an arbitrary theory of his own about the expansive properties of steam and based the capacity ratios of the two cylinders on that, making the low pressure cylinder four times as large as the high which, in itself, was made too small. Many years went by before the compound engine was re-introduced, by which time the error had been corrected. Its true value, together with its sisters, the triple and quadruple expansion engines, was then established and the shades of Jonathan Hornblower vindicated.[1]

The Foundry was now producing all manner of things from domestic fire-grates to large pumping-engines. The latter were still classed as "on Mr. Watt's plan", but as they were intended to work at pressures well above atmospheric, Mr. Watt would have frowned heavily on them. They were, in fact, *Cornish* engines, though not yet known by that name. Some of the engines in this class were "rotative" beam engines, the beam being pivoted on the wall of the engine-house, its outdoor end turning a plain crank, while momentum over the dead centres was maintained by a heavy fly-wheel. Watt had eschewed the simple crank for fear of infringing a patent

[1] In fact as Mr. R. J. Law has pointed out, although Woolf adhered to his erroneous notion of the law governing the expansion of steam, he adopted more suitable cylinder ratios in all the engines made after his first experiments at Meux's Brewery.

taken out in 1780 by James Pickard which covered it (though it could not be called a good patent and would have been easy to challenge) and substituted his "sun-and-planet" gear. Boulton and Watt stuck to this long after Pickard's patent had expired though it was more expensive to make and absorbed more energy in friction. This part of Mr. Watt's plan was never included in the Harvey engines, though the parallel motion was[1].

Harveys were also making that class of engine which had been Trevithick's first love, which was small, worked at a high pressure, and exhausted into the atmosphere without using a condenser. It had never earned a proper distinguishing name for itself. The inventor called it vaguely a *portable* engine. Harveys were now calling it, still more vaguely, a *pressure* engine. It was in great demand at the mines for whim work — winding up the shaft those large buckets of ore called kibbles. As it was just possible to convey its components on mule-back it had been designed to work pumps in those almost inaccessible mines in Peru, and it was now beginning to be popular in mill-work of various kinds. Among its advantages over its old competitor, the Watt rotative engine, was the fact that it could be reversed instantly. The Watt engine had first to be stopped and then the fly-wheel turned by hand to set it going again the other way.

Watt had complained that John Harvey was as slow in delivering the goods as he was expensive, and the same complaints were levelled at Henry throughout the long period during which he held sway at the works. The faults were good ones, based on his insistence on the use of first class materials and careful and thorough workmanship. A hint of the difficulties which had to be faced in ensuring these is given in a letter to R. R. Hodge of the foundry that had recently been started at St. Austell but was not yet capable of making large castings. It is dated August the 21st, 1821 —

> In reply to yours of the 17th Instant the Cylinder ordered would have been ready ere this, but we have been so unfortunate as to have cast two imperfect ones, the third is this day taken out of the Pit, & to appearance perfect. It will be immediately put into the Mill & if no imperfection should be discovered

[1] In the pre-Watt engine, where power was only applied on the down stroke, the piston-rod was attached to the beam by a massive chain. This gave sufficient flexibility between the beam-end which described the arc of a circle and the piston-rod which had a vertical movement. As the pump-rods pulled the piston up again by their weight, the chain was in tension both ways. But when Watt came to design rotative engines and made his engine double-acting (but still a beam-engine) the chain would have been useless on a powered up-stroke. It was to solve this problem that he invented the parallel motion. It was used on all Cornish engines whether single or double acting.

in boring it, you may rely on its being ready in a few days. However we will shortly let you know the day you may send for it.

The large cylinders for Cornish engines, which would stand as much as twelve feet high, were cast in a pit sunk in the foundry floor. The molten metal run into them from the furnace did not always flow quite evenly, causing that waste of time and material seen in the above letter.

Another sidelight shows that not everyone else was so particular in turning out and passing reliable stuff. It is in a letter addressed to Captain Grenfell of Botallack and Wheal Hermon Mines on the 30th of April, 1823 —

We will make a Boyler for you of the best Shropshire Plates, & best tough rivets for £21 10s. — per Ton delivered here, & we certainly would recommend your having one made of the Shropshire plates more especially after hearing of so many accidents by Boylers being made of inferior Plates.

The mention of many accidents from bursting boilers is an indication of the extent to which "strong steam" was being used at the mines. Although Richard Trevithick was shirking his family responsibilities in a most reprehensible way, his brother-in-law and many others, including Arthur Woolf, were thriving on the rich legacy of ideas he had left behind.

Henry had now closed his small tin smelting-house but was selling block tin produced elsewhere. The chief reason for his starting in that line of business was to collaborate with Wheal Vor mine in which he had large interests. But when the Cornish Copper Company turned over to iron founding the Wheal Vor adventurers arranged to take over their disused smelting plant and had their tin refined there. Harvey then received his quota of block tin to dispose of from that formerly ill-omened quarter — an odd turn of events.

Though the C.C.C. had given up smelting copper for iron they continued to receive copper ores from the mines for transhipment to Wales and Bristol. If there was now little profit in this, having abandoned their old quay dues, it enabled them to keep freight charges on inward cargoes down. As iron-founders, they had dropped their old style and were properly known as Sandys, Carne, & Vivian, but the old name stuck to them for long after in Henry's letters and elsewhere and, for the present, we shall continue to call them the C.C.C. As for the Gurney peace-pact, they seem to have observed it for a matter of three years, after which, they apparently could not contain themselves and, in 1822, they broke out again. On July the 19th Henry writes personally to James Pascoe —

An attempt having been made by Mr. Millett to encroach on Carnsew rights I think it necessary to call the attention to the agents of the Lords of the fee of that tenement to the matter, & to request that they will name an early day for meeting on the Spot & examining the evidence which can be adduced in order that no further disputes may arise touching the boundry between Penpol & Carnsew. I shall by this post write to the agents of the Lords of the other two thirds of Carnsew to the above effect.

As to what the fresh trouble was we may discover by yet another reference to the invaluable Brief —

In the Summer of 1822 Mr Millett sent his Men and Carts with a quantity of Rubbish and deposited it on the Eastern Bank of the River just opposite the Sheds on Messrs Harveys new Wharf, and Mr Harvey sent his Men and removed it into the Penpol right, under where the old cliff stood previous to the alteration in the road. Much altercation took place on this occasion and Mr Millett afterwards served Mr Harvey with a writ for trespass. Mr Harvey appeared, but no declaration was ever filed and Mr Millett was nonprossed for want of proceedings and paid £1 10s. for Costs.

The point seems to be that the rubbish was tipped in order to obliterate the last traces of the old course of the Penpol River which had divided the two parishes of St. Erth and Phillack and the two estates of Penpol and Carnsew. Most of it had been masked by the new quay but not quite all. Harvey still claimed that small strip over the water about which there had been the great ruction of four years earlier. This was "the spot" mentioned in the letter to James Pascoe to which Harvey continued to assert his claim and from which his men shovelled back the rubbish into "the Penpol right".

James Pascoe was the last of all the "lives" on which the tenure of any part of Carnsew depended. When he died, the C.C.C. would lose their only hold over the long contested fee unless they could persuade H. M. Grylls, steward of the St. Aubyn estate to grant them a new lease. Notes in the Brief reveal that they were already pressing Grylls for a firm promise to this effect.

In 1823 Thomas Ellis died. He had been the sole survivor of the old Blewett partnership in which he had managed the office and finances, and it is sufficient testimonial to his ability that he had been retained by Henry in the new Company. If he hadn't actually been born in "Mr. Ellis's House" he had been associated with the varying fortunes of Carnsew as long as anyone else, had seen his own family business extinguished by the rapacity of the C.C.C., and had taken an active part for fourteen years in the affairs of the more successful rival. But we seem to know nothing more about him as a human being than what may be revealed in the drafting of hundreds of signed letters, though these are done in a copperplate hand so immaculate as to mask character. We can only guess that his long experience in this complex business of simultaneous producing and trading — and "finding the money" for both — would be greatly missed — one has constantly to bear in mind that this hard worked staff had no telephones, typewriters, or filing systems. One may also guess that there were personal bonds of friendship which would be mourned.

Thomas Ellis's share in the partnership was reckoned at £2000, which Henry paid out to his executors by instalments over the following four years. He had a son, Hannibal, who had been employed as a clerk in the office for a long while and was now getting a salary of £100 a year. There seems to have been no thought of taking him as a partner in his father's stead, perhaps because it was wished to keep the Company, as it now was, in the hands of the two families of Harvey and West, related by marriage; the third, so allied, would eventually be represented by John Harvey Trevithick. It may be mentioned here that John Harvey's sister, Anne Trevithick was, some years later, married to Hannibal Ellis, so that the faithful Thomas may be said to have had a posthumous link with the founder of Harvey & Co.

Early in the summer of that year Henry and Arthur Woolf departed on an exploratory expedition. The letters show that they returned about the same time at the end of July and that Henry visited Birmingham, Tipton, in Staffordshire, and Neath. It is not quite clear whether they did the whole round together but, later, Henry charged the Company with £50 "for expenses with Mr. Woolf at Birmingham and Wales".

The great John Taylor was now offering work to Harveys again. They still seem to have been over-booked with orders but were prepared to give his requirements priority. In the course of a few months he was calling for engines and equipment to serve mines controlled by him in Cornwall, North Wales, and Mexico. I shall give extracts of the correspondence resulting, as it is illuminating in the matter of the "two good faults" recently referred to and the perennial difficulty the Company suffered from in recovering payment for their work, even from the wealthy.

It has been explained that the Neath Abbey Iron Works, with its foundry, forge, and local iron mines, had been acquired by the Perran Foundry Company in 1792, and that they were good enough neighbours to compare prices for mutual regulation and often to share contracts[1]. On his recent visit to Neath, Henry had called on Joseph Price of the Abbey Works, and on the 18th of the following October he wrote to him—

> Refferring to your letter to E. O. Tregelles of the 1st Ulto and the conversation we had when I saw you at Neath, on the faith of which I have been induced to act, I now beg to inform you that I have, in unison with Mr Woolf, contracted for two 70 inch single cylinder Engines for Wheal Sparnon Mine, the nozzles [valves] and other principal parts to be the same as those you are now making for Wheal Alfred to be delivered here by the end of February next for the sum of Fifteen hundred pounds for each Engine, payment in bill of six months date from delivery, or in bill of 30 d/d on allowing 2½ pr ct, subject to a penalty of two hundred pounds for nonperformance of contract. Not doubting that this will meet with your ready concurrence from what has passed between us. Mr Woolf will forward you the drawings for one of the engines as speedily as possible.

Wheal Sparnon was one of Taylor's mines. Wheal Alfred was another; that engine for it which is mentioned in the letter must have been the one which competed successfully with Woolf's compound, as already told. As Harvey was putting in hand his share of the contract (one engine for Wheal Sparnon) he was completing the first of Taylor's orders which had been finished exactly on time, and he wrote to Taylor on the 25th —

> We have now the pleasure of waiting on you with invoice and bill of lading of the Sixty-six Inch Engine for the Mold Mine. The *Sophia* is still here and will proceed in a few days for her destination.

The *Sophia* had been chartered for this voyage and covered by insurance. The engine was for draining a lead mine near Mold, in Flintshire, managed by Captain Absolom Francis whose brother, William, was Taylor's agent at the Consolidated Mines in Cornwall. The awkward, unwieldy cargo would probably have to be discharged on the open beach at Flint. This bill for £1,225 was settled by return of post (the London Mail now took three days each way).

It was a terrible winter at sea. The *Sophia* reached the estuary of the Dee safely but one of Harvey's own ships was not so lucky. Writing just three weeks later to a merchant at Neath he says, "Our Vessel [the schooner, *John Adams*] left this place for Neath about three weeks ago, but we are very apprehensive that she was lost during the recent tremendous weather,

---

[1] The partners at the time of the take-over were George Croker Fox, Robert Were Fox, Thomas Were Fox, Mary Fox, George Fox, Thomas Fox, Edward Fox, Peter Price, Samuel Tregelles, Thomas Wilson, John Gould, and William Wood. They were all Quakers and nearly all linked by family alliances.

indeed the case is at present hopeless".

Three other engines ordered for Taylor's Cornish mines, Wheal Busy, Pembroke, and Wheal Alfred (Woolf's competitor compound?) were all late and, in replying to a protest received on December the 27th, Harveys wrote "We are sorry you should be under the impression that we have neglected our engagement with you, having used every exertion for the last six months to fulfill them. The principal parts of the Engines for Pembroke and Wheal Bissy are delivered and the whole of the latter (except an article or two which cannot be made till some of the connecting parts are in their places) will be on the mine next week . . . Wheal Alfred too you may be assured will suffer no delay from us, as we shall have the engines ready in time for the other work".

Of those "Engines" for Wheal Alfred (note the plural number), we know that one 70 inch was being made at Neath, to be delivered at Hayle; was the other Woolf's latest (and last) compound, made at Hayle, and, as we know, due to be tested against a new Cornish engine at Wheal Alfred the following year?

In 1824 further orders came from John Taylor, the first indication of which we have in a letter to Joseph Price on September the 3rd —

> An advance on the prices of Castings having taken place on the 1st Instant in this neighbourhood, we beg to annex particulars of the same . . . Having received an order of Mr. Taylor for Sundries for the Mexican Mines, as we understand you have received orders from him for similar articles, may we beg the favor of your informing us per Return the prices you are to be paid for the following Articles. . . Mr S. Davey has kept back £50 out of the amount of the Engine we supplied Wheal Sparnon which we are informed by our attorney he had no right to do and shall not comply with this unreasonable Act but shall claim the full amount as no damages can be proved by the delay occasioned above the time at first stipulated.

The contract for said "Sundries for the Mexican Mines" was again being divided between Hayle and Neath. It comprised six portable steam engines, a large amount of pit-work and other equipment. The mines were those of Real del Monte, about two hundred miles from the nearest port of the coast. The engines therefore had to be of the small puffer type so that, when taken to pieces, no one part would weigh more than 400 pounds, the limit of a single mule burden. That is what Trevithick had aimed at in designing the engines for the Peruvian mines, and no doubt the present manufacturers were guided by that if not actually following Trevithick's drawings which were probably available, though most of the Peruvian work had been done at Bridgnorth.

Harvey was late in performing his part of the bargain which was doubtless partly due to depletion of skilled staff drawn away by the magnet of high wages which the C.C.C. was blatantly offering. To explain the situation, Henry wrote a personal letter to John Taylor on December the 21st. It is typical of him for, while having to apologise for the delay, he does not hesitate to use the occasion for bringing up his grievance against Taylor's manager at Wheal Sparnon —

> I have Mr. Phillips' [of the London office of the Real del Monte mines] favour of the 17 instant in which he expresses your surprize & regret at the intelligence you had received from Mr Hill that the Engines are not in such a forward state as you had reason to expect. When Mr Ward called here a few days ago with Mr Woolf we then intimated to them that the Engines with the pit-work would be ready in about six weeks from that time, & which I have every reason to expect we shall accomplish in the time stated. I beg leave to observe that we have used our utmost exertions in facilitating the completion of this work; nearly all our men have been and will continue day and night about [it] til the whole is completed. Capt*n* Annear has just called here & requested that one of the Engines and about 10 tons of pit-work should be ready for shipment in 10 days. You may rest assured that every effort shall be used on our part to effect it.
>
> I am exceedingly sorry that I should be compell'd to trouble you respecting a balance of £50 which Mr Stephen Davey has thought proper to keep out of the amount of the Engine which we supplied Wheal Sparnon Advrs. I admit it was not completed in the time specified, but when you take into consideration our numerous engagements, particularly for your mines in this neighbourhood, which I assure you have occupied a great part of our attention, & the very low rate at which this Engine was made, you cannot but allow that such a deduction is unreasonable, more especially when I inform you that the Neath Abbey Iron Company have been paid for an Engine supplied the same mine (precicely under the same circumstances) the full amount of their claim, although it was not rend'd on the mine for some considerable time after ours. I trust that this will convince you that our claim for the balance is both just and equitable, and as such I presume you will represent it to Mr S. Davey.

It was signed by Henry, the next, on February the 4th was in the name of the company—

> We . . . now beg leave to observe that one Engine for the Real Del Monte Mines is now ready, another will be completed next week and the other early in the following week. We have also delivered Pit Work to the amount of £1,500 and the Remainder of all the work will be ready in Ten Days or a fortnight. Having some acceptances which will shortly fall Due we shall esteem it a favour if you will remit us £3,000 in Course of a few days on Account of the work above stated.

Ten days later, Harveys wrote to say that they "lose not a moment in informing you that the three Engines are ready" and delivered to Taylor's agent for putting on board ship at Falmouth "with the exception of some work recently ordered for the Boilers, which shall also be ready this Week. The whole of the Pit Work ordered will be ready in a few days, say next Week, & be assured no exertion on our part shall be wanting (having all our Men almost wholly employed, day & night about it) to expedite its completion".

Those long winter night-shifts were worked wholly by candlelight, huge quantities of these illuminants being expended at the works. There is nothing further among the "out" letters for nearly five months. Then, on July the 6th, Harveys wrote to Taylor to say that the amount outstanding on the Real del Monte equipment was about £2,000, and that for the mine near Mold £733 15s. 6d. As they had some expenses to meet they asked for an instalment of £1,500 or £1,000. The balance could be paid later. As this tentative request bore no fruit, an account for the exact figure due for the Real del Monte work was sent on the 21st — £1,011 10s. 6d. — with the bare formula "which be good enough to remit". Having waited in vain for a further fortnight they had to write again, begging for a settlement by return of post "having some heavy Acceptances to meet by the 12th Inst" [of August].

Further applications were made on August the 22nd and September the 22nd. The silence is at last broken by a letter from John Taylor early in October. Its contents can be gathered by the reply which Harveys sent on the 12th of that month. —

We have to acknowledge the receipt of your favor of the 8th Instant. In reply to which we beg to say that we will readily accede to your proposition in referring the question about the Real Del Monte Engines & all other disputed matters (mentioned at foot) to two respectable disinterested persons. Assuring you that we are as desirous as yourself to avoid any disputes When you have nominated your referee we shall be glad to hear from you.
Harvey & Co.

Consolidated Mines: Deductions made from our Bills for Carriage contrary to the award by Mr Brunton	£92 1s. 2d.
Wheal Sparnon: Short paid on Engine supplied.	£50
Polgooth: Deducted from Carriage of Boiler which we understood was to have been delivered here by us & not at the Mine.	£20

I have not been able to trace the award of Mr. Brunton, who was, as already mentioned, a partner in the Eagle Foundry at Birmingham, with whom Nicholas Oliver Harvey had been serving his time as pupil. But it is interesting to note that, in spite of his anxiety to extract some cash out of

John Taylor to ease financial stringency he has not abated one farthing in the matter of Wheal Sparnon. In the present instance, Taylor's nominee as arbitrator was Robert Bennett who was employed in several of his mines as engineer while Henry appears to have nominated William Brunton again. Bennett wrote at once to say that he had only been instructed to arbitrate on the Real del Monte engines and not on the other items. Harveys duly sent a remonstrance to John Taylor, after which silence reigned again unbroken until January the 11th, 1826 when the following was sent from Hayle —

> A considerable time having Elapsed since we agreed to leave the matters in dispute relative to the Real Del Monte Engines &c. to arbitration. We are exceedingly anxious that it should be closed at once. We find Capt*n* Francis [Agent, Consolidated Mines] has informed Mr R. Bennett that Mr Wm Davey jnr. [solicitor, Redruth] has forwarded us nearly a fortnight ago a copy of the Bonds of award for our inspection, which, however *has not yet reached us*. We do not ourselves see any necessity for Bonds of Award in this Case more than in that of the Consolidated Mines which was (of greater magnitude) referred to Mr Brunton. We however do not object to any measure which may be thought necessary so that no impediment be thrown in the way of closing the transaction.

After this we are left to guess what happened, as there is no further reference to the matter in the letter books. There are hints from other sources that Henry did get satisfaction for his claims after having to wait for considerably more than a year for his money, and we know that where he considered his rights were involved he seldom compromised. I have quoted this correspondence at some length as a sample of what Harveys had to contend with in recovering payment for their work. But it is only one of constantly recurring instances of the kind though their debtors had not even the excuse of exercising a penalty for late delivery of goods. Nor is it the only case of resort to arbitration in these years to settle a dispute on payment claims. Not long after the above Henry, himself, was invited to act as referee in a dispute between a Bideford shipwright and a sail-maker. The former, William Brook of Bideford, was a customer of the Hayle rope-walk and it may be that in selecting Henry as the "respectable and disinterested person" to represent him he had hopes that where a patron's cause was involved this arbitrator would not be altogether disinterested. Henry had answered the request with, "We have not certainly been in the habit of settling any party disputes, but to oblige you we will readily render our assistance in the settlement of the business referred to". His treatment of the affair as revealed in the letters is an interesting sidelight on Henry's character.

Brook's complaint was that, having ordered a suit of sails for a vessel in his yard from one Rowe, a sailmaker, they were delivered late, not cut to the right dimensions, and made of inferior canvas. Henry prepared for the meeting with his usual thoroughness by asking Brook to send him copies of all the letters he had sent to Rowe and all those received from him. He asked for reports from other witnesses and, having collected all this evidence he met the other arbitrator without delay, taking with him Matthews, the Penzance sail-maker whom he usually employed, to assess the value of the canvas. Two ships' captains were also called.

The following day Henry announced the award in a letter to Brook with a detailed account of how it had been arrived at. It was that his complaints were not justified and that he should now pay the remainder of the debt due to Rowe. Expenses for the meeting were appended. They were one guinea each for the attendance of Matthews and the two captains and for the entertainment of the party at the new hotel, "Mrs. Trevithick per Bill of exps, Dinners, &c", the whole amounting to £4 17s. 0d., of which Henry had chosen to pay half. The result did not encourage Mr. Brook to send any further orders to the Hayle ropewalk.

Henry's insistence on first class quality in all the materials he used at the Foundry or passed on as merchandise was frequently thwarted through the fault of his suppliers even those with whom he had had long dealings. These let-downs could sometimes be checked on arrival of goods or in process of manufacturing. The most exasperating were those which could not be detected until the finished article had been passed and put into a customer's service, such as the following instance quoted from a letter of July the 1st, 1823 to Messrs. Garry & Curtis of London, tallowchandlers and dealers in hemp, flax, and tar. They had been supplying Harveys for years, and were now being sent payment of their last bill for £468 4s. 6d. —

We are very sorry to inform you again that the Hemp you have purchased for us for a considerable time past has been very foul & particularly weak. Our Roper has just returned from a Mine where he had the mortification to witness a new Capstan Rope (made of topp*d* hemp & supplied by us only a few days before) parted twice, bearing but a small proportion of the weight that a Rope ought to lift, of that size: we may say with propriety not more than one third. We have had similar complaints from several other mines, which operates very considerably against our interest. We use a great many Crane Ropes in our Works which [we] are sorry to observe parted when nearly new & which has been attended with very serious disadvantage & even risque of Men's Lives. We may probably send you a few yards from the Capstan Rope which broke, you will then have an opportunity of seeing its inferior quality.

An interesting glimpse of things at Hayle in 1825 was put on record by a distinguished outsider, Samuel Goodrich, the leading mechanical expert of the Navy Board. He was one of the few professional men who had taken a lively interest in Richard Trevithick's early trials of steam locomotion, had made personal friends with him, and had a high opinion of his inventive genius. In his diary[1] he describes a journey into the West Country. At Camborne he met Arthur Woolf. His account of what followed then runs —
"Mr. Woolf had gone on to Hayle Works about 4 miles further to the Westward whither I was to follow him. I mounted my Rosinante who gaily galloped off, Mr. Woolf's servant on another Horse showing me the way. Mr. Woolf had ordered dinner for us at the Hotel at Hayle kept by Mrs. Trevithick, the Wife of the Engineer, she being the sister of Mr. Harvey of Hayle Works, and I was amused to see written up over the Door Richard Trevithick Junr. It does not appear that Trevithick's family have lately heard from him, he does not correspond with them properly which if he be alive I am sorry to hear. I was excessively thirsty when I arrived from the great perspiration I had undergone in the mine and drank off as the best thing a large tumbler of brandy and water, and then set down to dinner.

"Mr. Harvey came and took a Glass of wine with us after dinner and then shewed me round his works which were formerly Copper Smelting Works [an odd mistake!] and are now converted into an Extensive Iron Foundry and Steam Engine Manufactory; most of the great work for the Cornish engines being now executed here. I was surprised to see the extent of this work and the number of Tools and means for doing work considering what is going on in other parts of the country, and notwithstanding this there is a Rival Foundry and Engine manufactory in the neighbourhood of this. Mr. Woolf employs this work in making his Engines. Mr. Harvey was very civil to me in consequence, he said, of my having been so to him on occasion of his visiting the works at Portsmouth Yard but I did not recollect it till he put me in mind of it.

"Returned late in the evening to Camborne Mr. Woolf taking the lead in his Gig and I close after him on Rosinante whose pace was much mended for fear of being left behind and who being well fed began to be more spirited".

Goodrich's confused idea that Harvey's works (and not those of the C.C.C.) were the conversion of a copper-smelting house were probably due to misheard remarks made in the hammer-and-tongs din of the workshops,

[1] Goodrich Papers, Science Museum, South Kensington.

8. Model of the Hayle-Bristol Packet *Cornubia*

9. Former custom house *and left* Steam Packet Inn

10. The Copperhouse floodgates

159

11. The two White Harts

12. Penpol House

but it would be interesting to know whether his reference to "Cornish engines" was intended in the general or particular sense in which, shortly after, it came to be used; and whether, when he spoke of Woolf's engines being made at Harveys he knew that the engineer had by now abandoned his own compounds and was designing those on the lines of Trevithick.

Nicholas Harvey, now out of his time at Birmingham, was taking part in his uncle's works. In June, 1826, he makes his first appearance as signing an "out" letter. It is to give detailed instructions to one Henry Scobel, an employee of the Company who has been sent to Dartmouth to supervise the erection of an engine. The letter is both lucid and well expressed. It is couched in rather different terms from the regular stream sent out from the office or the more individualistic ones signed by Henry. One gains the impression from it not only that it comes from the pen of a very competent young man but also from a person with a distinct personality.

Nicholas did not stay long at Hayle. He took an appointment abroad with an up-and-coming firm of marine engine manufacturers — a branch of steam engineering very much in its infancy. Perhaps a clash of temperament between himself and Arthur Woolf was one reason for these two departures from the home foundry.

XI

THE JUBILEE YEAR

EARLY IN 1827 JAMES PASCOE DIED AND, WITH HIM, there also expired the long series of sub-tenancies by which the Cornish Copper Company held the last remaining third of Carnsew — the St. Aubyn third — granted originally to James's father, Thomas Pascoe, seventy-four years ago, who was declared bankrupt before he had been able to make the slightest use of his lease. As already said, the C.C.C. had made every effort to forestall this eventuality by trying to extract the promise of a new lease to themselves from the agent of the St. Aubyn estate. But in this they had failed. The present owner of the ground, another Sir John, son of the man for whom John Harvey had made a shoe-buckle out of a silver spoon, had already promised Henry Harvey that he should be the next tenant, and he kept his word.

So now Harvey & Co. held the whole of Carnsew with sole rights on its long contested wastrel and foreshore which lay between the Hayle and Penpol Rivers when the tide was out, a boundary coinciding with that of the parish of St. Erth. So it might be thought that all arguments about territorial rights with the C.C.C. were now at an end. But that was not by any means the case. The Copper Company had lost all their old pretensions. It was now the turn of Harveys to assert theirs and they intended to do so, not by force but the process of law.

It will be remembered that Henry had steadily maintained how, through the action of the C.C.C. in setting up their floodgates in the narrows, whereby the tidal water was penned in the eastern lobe of the lagoon and released through sluices at low tide to scour the channel, the mouth of the Penpol River had been diverted. And how Henry had claimed that small strip of ground lying between the new and the old courses of the river as rightly belonging to the parish of St. Erth and therefore to the foreshore of Carnsew. How he had staked his claim with boundary stones which had

162

been overthrown by the Copper Company, who had then built their quay athwart the site.

The obsequies of James Pascoe can scarcely have been decently over when Henry took action. It is only occasionally that one of his private letters gets copied into the letter-book, so the initial stages of what was now being put in train do not appear, but we are made well aware of it by a letter to Francis Paynter dated the 18th of May —

> After Mr Joseph Edwards's reply to your Letter I should think no time was to be lost in asserting the right of the Lords of Carnsew to the quay. It appears quite clear that the Cornish Copper Company mean to resist; & it becomes the more requisite to commence proceedings from the advanced age of many of the Witnesses as I before intimated to you, & one of the old Witnesses died a day or two ago & similar fate may befall others. I hope therefore that you have ere this received Mr Rodd's instructions to proceed. Sir John St. Aubyn will join with the other Lords. Mr Wm Praed, as I before wrote you, will no doubt have spoken to his Father & will concur. Have the goodness to let me hear from you on the subject, the Term you know is drawing to a close and the next far distant.

From this we gather that Henry had prevailed on his landlords to challenge the right of the C.C.C. in the courts to their occupation of that very small piece of foreshore which he claimed belonged to Carnsew. The action would not be one merely for trespass and damages; the aim was to seek powers to eject the Copper Company from the new quay they had built at considerable expense and take possession of it.

This was really a very remarkable development. That the landlords should have been unanimous in backing Henry up was a mark of the esteem which he had at last earned from them. It was they, and not he, who were to appear as plaintiffs, though he was to pay a fair share of the legal costs of the trial — and these were likely to be heavy. If the suit succeeded, what would be the gain to the winning side? The acquisition of that quay would be of little value to the landlords in terms of real estate; and Henry, with his present large wharfage, could do very well without it. The struggle could not be for a commercial prize but only a symbolic triumph — a standard taken from a long victorious foe. But what if it did not succeed? The trial would then act as a boomerang and strike the prestige of Harveys a blow which might even be fatal to the survival of the business.

The chances of success were not very good. They depended on whether it could be proved that the course of the Penpol River, at its mouth, had, in fact, changed, and that such change was due to the action of the Copper Company in erecting their floodgates and sluices. But that was done forty years ago, and to find reliable witnesses to swear to the course of the stream before that time would not be easy. Henry, himself, was only a boy of twelve at the time. Such traces of the old bed as had been visible in more recent times had been successfully eliminated. In spite of these considerations, preparations for fighting the case went on though little more is heard of their progress for some time.

Meanwhile, the C.C.C. (or Sandys, Carne, & Vivian) who were well aware that a public trial of strength was at last going to take place between the two rivals managed to steal one march on their neighbour. The sorry tale is told in a letter from Harveys to A. H. Kier of Dram, Norway, with whom Henry had been dealing for timber for many years, dated June the 1st, 1827 —

> We are favoured with yours of the 3rd Ulto which came to hand abt a fortnight ago, informing us that you had shipped a Cargo of Dram Timber per the *Two Brothers*, N. Bull, Master, which you had instructed him to offer us; but you will not be a little surprised when we inform you that Cap; Bull is arrived at Falmouth and yesterday sold his Cargo to Messrs Sandys Carne & Vivian of this place without offering it to us or giving us the least intimation of his arrival. We should have been ignorant of the circumstance at this moment but for our Mr Charles Harvey who, yesterday, accidentally saw Capt Bull & an agent of Messrs Sandys, Carne, & Vivian together at Camborne (a town between Falmouth & this place).
>
> When our Mr Charles Harvey told Capt Bull that it was his duty first to offer the Cargo to our house, which he readily admitted, notwithstanding which he immediately sold the Cargo to the party before mentioned. We fully relied on having the Cargo in question, which prevented us looking out for a Market one, and the disappointment is great as we shall now be unable to fulfill our engagements for the supply of Timber to some mines in this Neighbourhood. We regret that the interest of Mrs Bull and the other owners of the *Two Brothers* should be represented by a man who will so deliberately sacrifice his Honor, and whilst Capt Bull continues to be Master of the *Two Brothers* you will not ship another Cargo in that vessel for us.

Henry still had only one ship of his own in commission, the brig, *Fame*. He was anxious to augment his fleet again but did not intend to build this time. Two second-hand vessels lying in the Welsh ports were successively offered to him. He sent over captains he could trust to vet their condition and their stores but turned both offers down. In the autumn he heard that the brig *Rosewarne* was for sale. This was Captain Frank Cundy's own vessel and had long been considered a pattern of her kind in her lines and handling. When Cundy had been sent to supervise the building of the *Fame* at Bideford he had been told "We have no particular plan respecting the Cabin, you will please order it the same as the *Rosewarne's*.

We wish you to get the bilge slabs put on in the same way as the *Rosewarne's*". And one gathers that the owner had that pride in his vessel and affection for her such as Conrad describes Lingard entertaining for his brig, and Henry's first offer was not only rejected but roused the old sailor's indignation. Agreement was reached, however, and the *Rosewarne* changed hands for £900.

Just as this transaction was completed there was other news afoot. It can best be told in the words of Francis Trevithick. "In the early part of October, 1827", he records "the writer, then a boy at Bodmin School, was asked by the master if any particular news had come from home. Scarcely had the curiosity of the boys subsided, when a tall man with a broad-brimmed Leghorn hat entered at the door, and after a quick glance at his whereabouts, marched towards the master's desk at the other end of the room. When about half-way, and opposite the writer's class, he stopped, took his hat off, and asked if his son Francis was there. Mr. Boar, who had watched his approach, rose at the removal of the hat, and replied in the affirmative. For a moment a breathless silence reigned in the school, while all eyes were turned on the gaunt sun-burnt visitor; and the blood, without a defined reason, caused the writer's heart to beat as though the unknown was his father, who eleven years before had carried him on his shoulder to the pier-head steps, and the boat going to the South Sea whaler".

And what sort of reception did the prodigal, who had left his family without assistance or even tidings for so long, get when he reached Hayle. He, himself, supplies the answer in a letter to J. M. Gerard shortly after, directed from Hayle Foundry, "on my return was so fortunate as to join all my family in good health, and also welcomed home by all the neighbourhood by ringing of bells, and entertained at the tables of the county and borough members, and all the first-class gentlemen in the west of Cornwall, with a provision about to be made to me for the past services this county has received from my inventions just before I left for Peru, which they acknowledge to be a saving in the mines since I left of about £500,000, and that the present existence of the deep mines is owing to my inventions. I confess that this reception is gratifying ..."

Davies Gilbert, in a letter to his sister, notes the triumphant return of the hero with some reservation, "I must add that on last Tuesday Capn Richard Trevithick, after an absence of eleven years, during the whole of which he has not held any communication whatever with his Family, arrived suddenly at Hayle". We may be sure that the loyal and devoted Jane received him with open arms and no recriminations, but we may wonder if her brother did not smile a little wryly in view of all the junketing, and what the reactions of Arthur Woolf were.

I have already said that one of the most curious, indeed fascinating, traits of this remarkable man was the way in which he seemed to attract adventure and dramatic situations, though in his manner he was no poseur, and in his speech and letters, though always forceful and individual, he appears to have been perfectly natural. Such fragments of the story of his doings in South America as were later collected from reliable witnesses would seem, even in schoolboy fiction, to be too over-spiced to believe in. I feel that the reader must have just a brief sample of that saga although Richard's association with Harveys continued after his return to be of the same semi-detached nature as before.

The following is an extract from a letter written to Francis Trevithick in 1869 by Captain Liddell, a naval officer, who had been lieutenant in the *Aurora* when she called at Callao in the early 'twenties. "The Pasco-Peruvian mines were those which your father was engaged to superintend before he left England, and he had actually managed, by incredible labour, to transport one or two steam-engines from the coast to the mines, when the war of independence broke out, and the patriots threw most of the machinery down the shafts. This fearful war was a deathblow to your father's sanguine hopes of making a rapid fortune. About a year after this terrible disappointment... the *San Martin*, an old Russian fir frigate, purchased by the Chilean Government, sank at her anchors in Chorillos Bay, ten miles south of Callao, and your father entered into an engagement with the Government in Lima to recover a large number of brass cannon, provided that all the prize tin and copper on board which might be got up should belong to him. This was a very successful speculation, and in a few weeks your father realized about £2,500. I remember visiting the spot with your father whilst the operations were carried on, and being astonished at the rude diving bell by which so much property was recovered from the wreck, and the indomitable energy displayed by him. It was Mr. Hodge [a mines engineer of St. Erth], and not I, who then urged in the strongest manner that at least £2,000 should be immediately remitted to your mother. Instead of this, he embarked in some Utopian scheme for pearl fishing in Panama, and lost all!"

The episode in which Richard was forced into soldiering in the rebel army of Simon Bolivar (founder of Bolivia) seems to have been due to his ruling passion for invention. Hearing that the leader's cavalry were short of fire-arms he designed a new type of carbine which had a short barrel of large bore and a skeleton metal stock. An advantage was that the weapon could be cast in brass all in one piece though the lock had to be a separate fitting. Bolivar then insisted on his enlistment to prove in practice the efficacy of his gun. But, says Francis, "He was never a good shot, nor particularly fond of shooting; and after a long time, Bolivar allowed him to return to his engineering and mining. Scarcely had he got to work again when the Royal Spanish troops, getting the best of it, over-ran the mines, and drove Trevithick away penniless, leaving £5,000 worth of ore behind him ready for sale".

Bolivar eventually sent him on a mission up into the north. On the way he met J. M. Gerard (to whom that letter about his homecoming was addressed), a north countryman, who had been trading on the Pacific coast but, having heard of a rich discovery of gold and silver in Costa Rica, had visited the newly opened mines there. On hearing Gerard's account, Trevithick abandoned the errand he had been sent on and the two men proceeded to Costa Rica where they spent four years together making a survey of the whole mountainous district adjoining the mines and acquiring large concessions from the Costa Rican government.

At the end of that time, with Trevithick's mind bent on access to the mines from the Atlantic coast by *rail and locomotive*, the two men set out to find such a route through hitherto unexplored country. A few native attendants were engaged, whilst a Spanish grandee who wished to have his two boys educated in England, had the extraordinary temerity to entrust them to the party. After hair-raising experiences which lasted for three weeks "through woods, swamps, and over rapids; their food, monkeys and wild fruit; their clothes, at the end of the journey, shreds and scraps, the larger portion having been torn off in the undergrowth", they reached the small port of San Juan del Norte (Greytown) in Nicaragua.

But that was not quite the last thriller in the story. Richard is next heard of several hundred miles to the east, near the mouth of the Magdalena River in Colombia, seated in a canoe with an angry Negro who is said to be seeking revenge for some unspecified slight. This took the form of capsizing the boat, leaving Trevithick to reach the nearest bank as best he could. He appears to have been only an indifferent swimmer and while he was struggling to keep his head above water he was spied by a large alligator. In that then almost non-populated area his cries for help might well have been futile. But it happened that someone, having a days sport among the wild pigs, was within earshot. It happened that he had a loaded gun and was a good shot. He aimed at the advancing alligator and hit him in a vital spot. It also happened that he had a lariat and that he was a dab hand at throwing it. He aimed at the sinking Trevithick and successfully lassoed him. The rescuer was an officer in Bolivar's army, who was an Englishman called Bruce Napier Hall. Like the good Samaritan, he cared for the distressed man, got him mounted, and escorted him to the nearest Inn — at Cartagena, about a hundred miles away. And who, in the whole wide world, should they find lodging here, but Robert Stephenson!

Nearly forty years later, Sir Edward Watkin, first instigator of the Channel Tunnel, and known (like George Hudson) as a Railway King, was fascinated by this chance meeting of the two founders of his dynasty and dwelt on it at a public meeting. This drew from Napier Hall's friend, James Fairbairn, a letter corroborating all those haphazard coincidences with some interesting details about the last. "And thus it was that he fell in with Mr. Stephenson who, like most Englishmen, was reserved, and took no notice of Mr. Trevithick, until the officer said to him, meeting Mr. Stephenson at the door, "I suppose the old proverb of 'two of a trade cannot agree' is true, by the way you keep aloof from your brother chip. It is not thus your father would have treated that worthy man, and it is not creditable to your father's son that he and you should be here day after day like two strange cats in a garret; it would not sound well at home.

" 'Who is it;' said Mr. Stephenson. 'The inventor of the locomotive, your father's friend and fellow-worker; his name is Trevithick, you may have heard it', the officer said; and then Mr. Stephenson went up to Trevithick. That Mr. Trevithick felt the previous neglect was clear. He had sat with Robert on his knee many a night while talking to his father, and it was through him Robert was made an engineer. My informant states that there was not that cordiality between them he would have wished to see at Cartagena. The officer that rescued Mr. Trevithick is now living. I am sure he will confirm what I say if needful".

Napier Hall was, in fact, in England. Watkin wrote to him and received full confirmation, with added emphasis on the point about non-cordiality. Robert Stephenson had had almost as depressing an experience as a mining engineer in South America as Trevithick, and had suffered two severe illnesses as well, and was doubtless not in very good form. He was now hastening home to put matters to rights in the locomotive works which had been established at Newcastle and to help his father, George, in the construction of the Liverpool and Manchester Railway, neither of which ventures would have been in existence but for Trevithick's pioneer work, and he probably suffered from what is now called an inferiority complex. Nevertheless, he gave Trevithick fifty pounds to get himself a passage back to England and it seems uncertain whether one can call this generosity or conscience-money.

Richard would have found no difficulty in getting from Cartagena to Jamaica where he could join the regular mail-packet for Falmouth and the money should have been quite sufficient to see him through, but Francis says, "On reaching England he possessed nothing but the clothes he stood in, a gold watch, a drawing compass, and a pair of silver spurs. His passage-money being unpaid, a chance friend enabled him to leave the ship. In a month from that time he counted on getting a share of the £500,000 saved in the Cornish mines by the improvements he had effected in their steam-engines".

In spite of his long series of past adventures, of present convivialities, and the excitement of future hopes set on the reward just mentioned and the prospect of finding adventurers with capital to enable himself and Gerard to work the large and valuable concessions they had got in Costa Rica, Trevithick seems, for the time being, to have settled down at Hayle to a life very like that which he led before his departure to South America. He lived at the White Hart Hotel, which was managed by his wife, and seems once more to have been *persona grata* at the Foundry, where he was working on some new ideas. On the 23rd of October Harveys wrote to William Brunton in connection with an order for an engine and added incidentally — perhaps in answer to a question from W.B. —

> We annex Mr R*d* Trevithicks remarks which we give you in his own words with a reference to the improvement of duty of Steam Engines in this County. Mr Woolf attributes the improvement in a great degree to the closeness of the clothing of the Steam Vessels.

Unfortunately these comments were sent separately and not copied into the letter-book; Trevithick's might have added something to our scrappy knowledge of him. But the letter, in itself, is of some interest for it seems to show that, for all his sins of omission, Richard was not only tolerated by Henry but deferred to and given a hearing on a vexed question "in his own words". Woolf's answer, so far as it went, was perfectly correct. By "clothing of the Steam Vessels" he means the insulation, by lagging or otherwise, applied to all parts where useful heat might be conserved instead of radiated, from the boilers to the cylinder. This was an improvement initiated by Samuel Grose, Trevithick's old pupil and employee, closely studied since Richard's departure, and sedulously copied by other mines engineers. Woolf evidently abstained from going back beyond the improvement stage to the pioneering work done by Richard at the outset in introducing the Cornish boiler and Cornish engine, both of which he, himself, was now building.

Gerard and the two Spanish boys arrived safely in England only a short time after Trevithick. The latter were placed at a school in Highgate and Gerard was then free to set about looking for capitalists to finance the working of their joint mining claims in Costa Rica. He presently joined Trevithick at Hayle to prepare a public prospectus of the venture.

Now it is an odd fact that Gerard's arrival in England was only a week or two later than that of Richard. He and the boys had travelled with Stephenson and had taken a much longer and more circuitous route. They had first of all been delayed by the wreck of their ship, but eventually reached New York. But Stephenson wanted to see the Falls of Niagara, so the party made a detour into Canada. Trevithick must have loitered somewhere and got rid of that fifty pounds before he joined the Falmouth packet in Jamaica, for we know someone else paid his fare.

In 1828 the older William West retired. This must have been a painful break, for West had been associated with the company from its very beginning and, time was, when he and Henry, as a boy of sixteen, had run the whole business in the absence of the master, though plagued by hostile neighbours and unhelpful landlords. He had made those models and also the vital parts for the first locomotive vehicle and had had a share in its patent. But since those days he remained so modestly in the background that there is scarcely any news of him at all. He was now seventy-seven but his powers were not by any means played out. He went to live at St. Ives, returning with zest to his old love of making small machinery — not models, now, but clocks[1]. His share in the partnership was assessed at £1,349 4s 1¼d, and Henry managed to find the whole sum for his old friend in one payment.

[1] This was not a new employment. As one of the four co-partners of Harvey & Co., he is named in the register of the *John Adams* (1820) as joint owner of the vessel and described as "Watchmaker". See also H. Miles Brown, *Cornish Clocks and Clockmakers* pp26-27.

HENRY'S ATTESTATION

In the same year, soon after West's retirement, Henry wrote that short autobiographical sketch I have called the Memorandum (page 340). I think it was just a private paper intended to place on record the course of events in case the still pending lawsuit should go against him. He is clearly apprehensive of the result, for he says "there are no other partners at present but H. Harvey and [Elizabeth] Harvey who are saddled with a property consisting of Buildings & machinery & mines that is worth very little if the C.C.Co overpowers them".

Eighteen hundred and twenty-nine was the fiftieth year of the Company's existence—the jubilee year. The critical trial had not yet taken place. Henry had urged speed two years ago, lest old age should rob him of his most reliable witnesses. Many law terms had passed since then. Francis Paynter, Steward of the Hearle estate, was also a solicitor of the firm of Paynter and Whitford, St. Columb, and was acting in the case for Henry. The landlord plaintiffs were employing Joseph Roberts, a Helston lawyer. The delay seems to have been caused by difficulties in securing what were thought to be the best counsel. The most sought-after was one Serjeant Thomas Wilde who had distinguished himself in the defence of Queen Caroline, but he was booked first by the C.C.C. The plaintiffs then secured W. W. Follett (who prepared the Brief to which we have made so many references). He was supported by Sir James Scarlett who had just been made Attorney-general (and later became Baron Abinger).

The trial was now due to take place at the summer assizes at Bodmin with Mr. Justice Burroughs on the bench. On July the 29th Roberts wrote gleefully to Henry to say that Serjeant Wilde had had to go specially to plead at Hereford and would not be available to defend the C.C.C. Follett wrote the following week saying the C.C.C. had applied for a special jury and sent the names of "forty-eight men struck this moment" from which the jurymen would be selected, asking for comment. Henry wrote back, taking exception to seven and querying nine.

The hearing was fixed for August the 20th. A little before-hand both parties collected their witnesses for briefing, and refreshments were provided — a point on which each counsel in turn was to seize on avidly. Arthur Woolf, William Brunton, and Richard Trevithick were named as scientific experts. Richard, with his usual ingenuity, had made a model of the Penpol, Copperhouse, and Hayle rivers in three superimposed layers, showing what he believed to be the courses of those streams at three periods and how they had been affected by the flood-gates and sluices erected by

171

the C.C.C. This was shown at the briefing and put in at the trial.

When the great day came, defendants had replaced Serjeant Wilde by Thomas Erskine, son of the famous Lord Chancellor, a friend of Charles Kingsley, and a future judge of the Common Pleas. Acting with him was Serjeant Merryweather. The long dispute with the Copper Company based on the complex question of foreshore rights had never been submitted to a court of law for decision: nor was it to be ruled on at the present trial. It had ceased to exist since Henry had secured the whole of Carnsew and its wastrel, and the present action was brought to assert his full rights there. The issue had become a simple one, namely, whether or not the C.C.C., in building their new wharf, had transgressed the old parish boundary which rested on the Penpol River—as also did that of the Carnsew estate. If the plaintiffs could prove that the river had been diverted from its original channel by the action of the flood-gates they would claim that as much of the Copperhouse quay which stood on the St. Erth side of the old watercourse belonged to the occupier of Carnsew — Harvey & Co. The plea, therefore, was a straightforward one of *ejectment*.

Reading the notes which Follett had prepared for his brief, one gathers that he was not by any means certain of a clear win any more than Henry Harvey. It would depend on the memories of old men who might not have been reliable observers in their youth and whose evidence was certain to be biased by local allegiances to one or other of the two great rival employers of labour.

Shorthand writers from Chancery Lane, London, were in attendance to take down a verbatim report (still preserved), doing the best they could with the broad Cornish of most of the witnesses. Sir James Scarlett, opening the case for the plaintiffs, must have believed that the hearing would be protracted and of so monotonous a character he felt bound to give a warning against somnolence and "to tell you at the outset that a more uninteresting or a more dry discussion was never presented to the attention of a jury". In fact, it proved shorter and more lively than he anticipated.

Sir James then gave a short summary of the intricacies of the tenure of those three "undivided thirds" of Carnsew, their subtenancies, and the parcelling up of these again into other holdings — certainly a dreary beginning and not essential to the immediate question except as giving a background to the story of the development of the two companies, which he now outlined. Mr. Follett then began to call his witnesses.

Some of the old men were not very happy under cross-examination and tried to stave off the probes of counsel by saying they were "thick of hearing". They all swore that the Penpol River had altered its course due to the action of the Copperhouse sluices. Each one recalled how the river used to flow into the main stream opposite the inn called Burt's House, whereas it now emerged nearly two hundred yards to the west, and that part of the Copperhouse quay was built on top of the old course of the river, and beyond, so that nearly half of it stood in the parish of St. Erth. One of the most convincing of these elders was a man who said he had often had occasion to take a rowing-boat down the river after dark when the tide served. He relied for guidance on the light in Burt's House which brought him out directly opposite the junction of the two streams, and he always steered for that. Finally, the three witnesses described as men of science were called — Richard Trevithick with his three part model, William Brunton, and Arthur Woolf. They based their evidence on tests they had made with local sands and muds and observed tendencies of the tides, the gush of the sluices, and the levels they had taken of the river and channel beds, all of which supported the plaintiffs' claim.

There followed a crucial interlude. Counsel recalled that agreement which had been drawn up between Henry Harvey and Joseph Carne in 1818 under the auspices of the Rev. Samuel Gurney who, in his capacity of magistrate, had quelled the riot and induced the parties to agree on a treaty of non-intervention. Mr. Erskine at once objected that the document could not be produced. It had been lost. The Attorney General said he would show a true copy and would call Mr. Gurney to attest it. Happily he was still Vicar of St. Erth and in court.

Mr. Gurney regretted that the agreement was inexplicably missing. He had searched the whole house for it but it could not be found. It then turned out that Charles Anthony Harvey had had the gumption to go to the vicarage immediately after the event and make the copy named by Sir James. Erskine's further objections were overruled by the judge on being told by Gurney that Charles Harvey had copied it in his parlour in his presence.

It will be remembered that at the time the agreement was made the Copperhouse Company still held one third of Carnsew which they expected to retain indefinitely, and therefore wished to insert the clause that they were to be at liberty to build their quay "to the point of the triangular piece of ground . . . without molestation from Messrs. Harvey & Co. but without prejudice to their claim in respect of the undivided part of the tenement of

Carnsew to so much of the said piece of ground as they consider to be of that tenement". But now that tenement belonged to Harveys and here was a clear admission that the "said piece of ground" was part of it. On this crescendo note the evidence for the plaintiffs ended.

Mr. Erskine then rose to say that he would prove that the Penpol River had never altered its course at all, that it never did debouch opposite Burt's House but at a point opposite the site of an old well, now covered in. But first he would show how entirely unreliable were those witnesses who had just been heard. For instance, one man, the former keeper of a toll-bar on the turnpike road had been prosecuted successfully for pocketing money collected at the gate, and dismissed. He had evidence that another had attempted to suborn two of his own witnesses at the inn at Phillack by standing treat there and promising them money if they would give evidence for Mr. Harvey. As for the man who took his boat at night down the river saying that he was guided by a light in the public house called Burt's, Counsel could show that he had good reason to make for that particular destination, and to do so under cover of darkness, for he was a noted smuggler.

Mr. Erskine's destructive speech lasted for some time, and then he began to call his witnesses. Among them were a number of men who announced themselves as ships' masters and pilots; as such, unless their claims were bogus, they must have had better facilities than any landsmen for knowing where and how the channels lay forty-one years ago if their memories served. Yet they all swore that at that time the Penpol River flowed out opposite the site of the old well and certainly not by Burt's House. The landsmen spoke to the same effect. They were still being examined when the court adjourned at the end of the fourth day.

The next day, hearing of the defence witnesses was continued. Several more would be called before counsel made their final speeches when, at mid-morning, there was a sudden suspension of proceedings. The shorthand writers began reporting in narrative style instead of dialogue. They wrote "A negociation was entered into between Counsel & Attornies" after which ensued "a very animated discussion (which was carried on in an undertone) of nearly two hours. Then Counsel on each side signed a paper as basis of the arrangement they had come to".

One then learns with no small surprise that the Copper Company had actually thrown in their hand. They had admitted that Harveys were entitled to the possession of part of their quay — the only question was how much of it? This was a point which obviously could not be decided at the present trial. The "arrangement" agreed to was that a disinterested surveyor, one Mr. Peter (there present) should undertake a minute exploration of the quay (removing its surface and probing to ascertain the original course of the Penpol River) and give a ruling as to what part of the quay should be handed over to Mr. Harvey. Furthermore, that Mr. Harvey should then offer to let his portion to the Copper Company at a reasonable annual rental.

Counsel on both sides then made flattering speeches about the honourable intentions and good sense of their own and their opponents' clients and the jury, without retiring, returned a verdict for the plaintiffs, assessing damages at one shilling, and costs two pounds. Mr. Peter was asked if he would make the proposed survey, to which he assented, and Mr. Justice Burroughs wound up the trial in these perspicacious words. "I certainly, gentlemen, must say that I have a very strong opinion in favour of the Plaintiffs in this cause. I had no doubt, almost from the beginning of it, that it was a mistake on the one side going to the boundaries of the other — for the Defendant's case it clearly was so".

I must confess that, after reading the report closely, it is not so clear to me as it seems to have been to the learned judge how that "negociation" was started and on what grounds in the foregoing so sudden a victory had been achieved. But that this triumph over the old and inveterate enemy should have come in the jubilee year of the Foundry must have seemed like a symbolic portent for the future to Henry Harvey.

XII

ARBITRATION

FTER THE BODMIN TRIAL, WHICH HAD ENDED WITH such an unexpected suddenness and with an outright win for the plaintiffs, nothing appeared to remain to confirm the verdict but the fact-finding survey ("reference") which Mr. Peter, acting as arbitrator, would conduct in order to decide how much of the Copper House wharf should be awarded to Harvey. He got to work in the autumn of the same year and, in order to discover, if possible, the old bed of the Penpol River, he removed paving-stones and some of the walling of the quay. A number of holes were then dug down to the low-tide level.

On January the 7th, 1830, Joseph Roberts, the solicitor, wrote happily to Henry saying "Mr. Peter has awarded every particle of the quay we sought to recover". Surely, one would have thought, that clinched the matter! But the clever Joseph Edwards had evidently foreseen a loophole when the "negociation" was drawn up and signed and had been able to repudiate the award. Details of this development have not been preserved but they can be gathered from a letter to Henry by R. B. Follett. He was a brother of the K.C. and conducted all his business affairs. He wrote on April the 23rd —

> The point on which I understand the defendents will rely is — That the cause having been referred, and they having revoked their submission to arbitration before the arbitrator [Peter] had made his award the whole matter falls to the ground. We, on the other hand, shall contend that nothing but the reference falls to the ground and we have got the right to make use of our verdict as if no reference had taken place.

So the dispute had to drag on again, and the next thing to do was to take the case to the Court of King's Bench and obtain a "rule of law" authorising a new reference to be held by a disinterested barrister acting as arbitrator. That would mean a large undertaking, for this arbitrator would know nothing of the circumstances, affidavits would have to be sworn by both

176

sides as to what was said and done at the trial, and all available witnesses (old and new) would have to be examined again.

The man who knew most about the ins-and-outs of the Carnsew case was Joseph Roberts, the plaintiffs' solicitor and, in order to prepare for the next step he had, just now, left his home at Helston and set out for London with some of the necessary papers to confer with the Folletts. He travelled by the Exeter Mail but, on leaving Wellington, the coach overturned and Roberts was badly injured, one leg being crushed. He was taken to the White Hart Inn in the town and news of his mishap was at once sent to Hayle and London. A good recovery was hoped for after an amputation, but Henry took the view that most likely there would be no recovery. He felt that the key-man was doomed, while the essential documents for getting up the case anew were all in different places — some at Helston, some in London, some with the solicitors, Paynter and Whitford of St. Columb, who were stewards of the Hearle estates, some now lying at Wellington.

It happened by a providential stroke of luck that the man who had been clerk to Roberts until recently had been translated to the Foundry office, from the solicitor's regard for Henry and the young man's betterment. This was Thomas Rawlings. On hearing the news, Henry at once despatched Rawlings to Wellington to find out exactly how things stood and tactfully to sound the mind of his old master. He arrived only a short time before Roberts died, and was back in Hayle within a week, bringing the abandoned dossier. Meanwhile, Henry had sent a messenger to St. Columb with the whole file of the Follett correspondence for the time the Bodmin trial was being prepared, determining that they must now act in the place of Roberts.

There was no thought of resting the traveller, who must, in these and future journeys, have had to use the coaching services which operated by night, doubtless as an outside passenger. Before he arrived back, Henry had already planned his next tour which he detailed in a letter to Follett. "We expect him tomorrow . . . An examination of Mr. Robert's papers will be made on Thursday [at Helston] and we wish him to attend there. On Friday he shall proceed so as to reach Town on Sunday. We will make the necessary pecuniary arrangements for fees to counsel &c. with him. In the mean time you will be visited by one of the Firm of Paynter & Whitford ... They were present at the trial at the Assizes and have frequently been employed by us in our disputes with the Cornish Copper Co.".

Posthumous tributes to Joseph Roberts show that there was real regret at his death which was shared fully by Henry though he was not given to sentimental expression. The letters of the late lawyer are more human and less formal than those of his successors and it is clear that his principal clients were also his friends.

Henry's powers of administration and the management of everything connected with the affairs of his business may be judged by the way in which he handled the emergency just described. A still stronger sidelight is shed on this capacity from the letters which he sent almost daily to Thomas Rawlings as soon as he had arrived in London. He was bent on making the fullest use of the young man's stay in the capital, not only on the mission which took him there but a variety of errands listed in the successive letters. He was to make personal calls on customers who were overdue in their payments and he had instructions about the shade of diplomacy he was to use in making these approaches. Davies Gilbert was on the list, though not as a debtor. Harveys had made him a heating apparatus for his London house for which he had over-paid them twenty-two shillings. This money Rawlings was to deliver and, at the same time to remind him of a petition which Gilbert had promised to place before the Trinity House Brethren two years earlier.

The petition had been framed by Henry on behalf of Mary King, wife of the captain of the *John Adams* which had foundered with all hands in 1823 "praying for a pension as widow of a drowned Master Mariner . . . ask him how the matter stands and if he will again remind the Trinity board thereof. We understand a pension has been granted to a person at St. Ives since Mary King's petition, not perhaps so well entitled as Mary King". With his usual persistence he reinforced this reminder by a personal letter to Gilbert a few days later recalling all the circumstances and saying of Mary "she is a very industrious woman and has earned a scanty maintainence for herself & children by taking in some of our workmen to lodge. She is we think a fit object for the bounty of the Corporation & would be very grateful if you could attain it for her". But one learns eventually that the petition did not succeed.

Then there was the great John Taylor to be looked up whose patronage seems to have been withdrawn after Henry had stood out so firmly for his rights four years earlier. But now Taylor's cashier, a Mr. Williams, had received some help from Harveys in the matter of collecting a debt from a third party and Rawlings was deputed to "take this opportunity of saying to Mr. Williams and also to Mr. Taylor, if in Town, and you can see him, that we have done nothing for a considerable time for his Mines except Wheal Hope; and should be obliged for some favours from the Consolidated Gwennap Mines, or any others where he is interested. Between ourselves 'one good turn deserves another', & if they are really obliged for what we have done respecting Wheal Hope this would be the fittest mode of showing it".

A still more important commission for his *pro tem*, agent in London was to do a deal with the owners of Binner Downs, a mine situated only a few miles south of Hayle which had been heavily in debt to Harveys ever since the dissolution of the Blewett partnership. The manager of this mine was Captain William Gregor and his letters stand out as high spots in the welter of routine communications. They are written and expressed like those of a well educated gentleman blessed with a strong sense of humour. Owing to the longstanding debt of the mine, Gregor, for years, had had to make-do with his machinery, and he would write pathetically about a piece of detached metal doing its so-many miles a day on top of the piston of an engine. As a mining engineer, he was highly thought of and often consulted on the possible productivity of other mines which were about to be acquired or threatened with abandonment.

In spite of the Binner Downs debt, though Henry had written sharp letters to Gregor at different times demanding payment, or supplies would be cut off, they never were; nor had the usual threat of legal proceedings to recover the money ever been uttered. This was probably due to several things. He certainly shared the common respect for Gregor. Apart from that, he was, himself, a shareholder in the mine and, no doubt, believed that its failure to pay was due to lack of capital. It happened that at the time when Rawlings was due to arrive in London, Henry had a letter from the secretary of the mining company which owned Binner Downs and other setts — one Henry Carne (to be distinguished from the wicked Joseph Carne of the C.C.C.). It said that Captain Gregor had written to the directors strongly recommending the erection of an engine on Wheal Treasury sett, estimating the expense at £1,200. "As adventurer in the mine you will be pleased to give your opinion on the subject & it will be taken into consideration on Thursday next".

The letter was answered by Charles Harvey who said "I am of opinion Captain Gregor's recommendation is a sufficient guarantee for the propriety of the step, and if the Committee adopt it I shall fully concur therein". He went on to say that "Mr. Rawlings, clerk to Messrs. Harvey & Co.", was in

London and was being written to by the same post and asked to call about that and another matter, the nature of which he explained. The other matter was something which Henry had doubtless had in mind for a while but had waited for an opening to propose. The Wheal Treasury engine and the chance of making personal contact through his envoy seemed to present the opportune moment. The instructions sent to Rawlings gives a fair idea of Henry's genius in business strategy and I give it *in extenso*.

Hayle Foundry
4th May, 1830

Mr T. Rawlings

Please go to Binner Downs office, 12 Size Lane, on Thursday next and introduce yourself to Mr Carne the Secretary, whom Mr C. A. Harvey has this day apprised of your intended call. Our wish is for you to prevail on the Directors to make the coal contract with us this year without going to tender, and we conceive the advantages which have accrued to the mine from our supplying at such a low rate in the past years entitle us to a preference. The year before the last the C.C.Co. would not supply at 41s. 6d. per wey [=3 tons] last year they would not supply under that. In the coming year if the Directors decide on tenders we shall be under great disadvantage. You well know that the C.C.Co's. stock which is large has much of it, say the greater part, been lying in the wharf nearly two years—the coals we should supply would be all fresh landed, & the C.C.Co. would, perhaps to get rid of their old stock, put a lower price for it than for new coal, and though doubtless we should meet them it would be at a loss to which the Directors should not subject us. If they would direct Capt*n* Gregor to make an arrangement with us for the year's supply they may rely that it shall be done on as good terms as any other mine may be supplied at. if they apply to him, Capt*n* Gregor can point out the advantage of having coals that are fresh from the pits.

We have saved to the mine many hundreds of pounds, and indeed, at one time, but for us (we allude to the large balance £3,000 due for so long a period) she must have stopped. We drop those hints for your guidance without letting them think we *demand* anything on them. Mr Benj*n* Wood & Mr Burton, two of the Directors, you will perhaps find most accessible, & if they are not at the meeting on thursday you had better call at their residences to which Mr Carne will direct you. Give Mr C. A. Harvey's Compl*s* to Mr Colesworth, another of the directors, & say to him an old schoolfellow will gratefully acknowledge his assistance.

We have in contemplation to make a road by which we shall have easier access to these mines, & if the Directors will engage with us, will at once set about it; & we could save Binner Downs, in carriage, from £350 to £400 per year. We would carry the ores for less, & perhaps this may not at first appear to the Directors an advantage, but the fact is altho' the purchasers of the ore pay the carriage in the first instance, it is, as Mr Wood well knows, made part of the returning charges deducted by the purchaser from every ton of ore. A deduction of 1s. per ton on the carriage of the ore would alone save the Adventurers £200 per year. Write immediately after your interview with the Directors for, on the prospect of having Binner Downs supply, ulterior measures may depend.

Harvey & Co.

In spite of the time that must have been absorbed by these numerous errands to addresses all over London Rawlings paid due attention to his main task, the collating and arranging of all the papers bearing on the Carnsew case. The new attack was being developed auspiciously and R. B. Follett wrote to say "I have today seen Mr. Justice Burrough [the judge at the Bodmin trial] and I find that he will state the case to the Judges of the King's Bench strongly in our favour". The motion was heard on May the 24th and F. C. Paynter sent the news that their lordships had confirmed the verdict. An arbitrator, William Selwyn, K. C., had been asked to conduct a new reference to settle the boundary-line on the quay at which both parties would appear again, represented by counsel. The hearing would take place at Hayle after the summer assizes. It was good news, but the expenses were likely to be even heavier than those of the Bodmin trial.

A little earlier Rawlings had written in high spirits, that he had just returned from the mining office where he had heard that the board had approved Henry's proposal and Captain Gregor was being instructed to arrange a contract for next year's supply of coal. This meant that, at least, the connection would prove more profitable, the old debt would be discharged in due course and, given time, the lodes being worked would prove more "kindly" — which, in fact, they did. Harvey and Gregor came to terms a month later. Binner Downs was to give a year's contract (starting on July the 1st) for two thirds of their coal at a flat rate of 44/- per wey, *delivered at the mine.*

The date of the arbitration had been postponed more than once, due to the delaying tactics of the C. C. C. It was eventually held on September the 13th. To give an appearance of fairness to both sides the first sitting would take place at the White Hart Hotel and the remainder at an inn in Copperhouse. William Selwyn had accepted nomination as arbitrator. He had only just taken silk but became sufficiently eminent by his legal writings to gain a notice in the Dictionary of National Biography. The Copper Company had raised an objection to his appointment on the ground that he was related to one of the plaintiffs — William Praed, but this was disproved.

There had been a great skirmish to collect witnesses which had appeared at the trial and select new ones. One of Harvey's most unshakable old men had died. Trevithick's three-piece model had been taken to London and was now coming back by sea, but it would be more difficult to persuade its maker (now also in London) to attend.

A few brief notes on what Richard had been doing since his return to Hayle from Peru should be given. As soon as he arrived he busied himself in the Foundry with working out an invention which had nothing to do with steam. It was a plan to make use of the energy wasted in the naval gun by its recoil on firing. It is fully described and illustrated in the *Life* and no more need be said here except to point out that the idea of making the recoil do useful work was an entirely new one and, when developed in later times by other hands it proved to be revolutionary as the basic principle of the machine-gun. Yet Trevithick's model was duly turned down by the Office of Ordnance as "wholly inapplicable to practical purposes". At the same time, Richard designed and had built at Hayle, an iron hull intended as a man-of-war launch. It was offered to the Admiralty, but also turned down[1]. This cannot be claimed as a new invention, as John Wilkinson had successfully launched an iron barge on the Severn in 1787, but it was an early forerunner of the iron ship which eventually sailed the seas to the exclusion of the wooden vessel.

Meanwhile, J. M. Gerrard had been busy in London trying to raise the wind for financing work on the concessions which the two men had been granted in Costa Rica and, early in 1828, Richard joined him. Francis relates what must have been the most outstanding episode in these negotiations — a story handed down by Michael Williams, son of that John, already mentioned, the other potentate of the eastern mines (vis-a-vis to John Taylor). Michael was interested in the venture and was present at a meeting of prospective shareholders. It seems that their views on the conduct of initial operations differed from those of Trevithick and they thought the safest course would be to buy him out. A cheque for £8,000 appears to have been already made out and this was offered to Richard in return for the "copper mountain". He had had no money of his own since landing in England and no doubt it was thought that such a tempting bait would be snapped up at once. Instead, "Words waxed warm and the proffered money was refused". When Michael asked him the next day "Why did you not pocket the cheque before you quarrelled with them?", he was told "I would rather kick them down stairs!"

---

[1] H. W. Dickinson says of the iron ship "there is evidence that it was actually commenced, but we hear nothing further about it". An account book of Harveys mentions it several years later as being sold second hand.

In July, Trevithick spent ten days in Holland where he looked up Nicholas Harvey at the works in Rotterdam where they were turning out marine engines. He was received very cordially and, on his return to London, wrote a long letter to Gilbert giving his calculations as to what the Dutch could achieve in their water-ridden country by a proper scheme of drainage. He had secured an order for building a large steam pump, rendered mobile by being fitted in a barge. Richard returned to Hayle, where the work was put in hand. Here, he was assisted by his son, Francis, who had left Bodmin school and was now an apprentice at the Foundry and made the drawings for his father out of hours. This task took a very long time. Richard wrote in January, 1829, to say that the floating pump would be ready by the end of February. But another letter to Gilbert, dated July the 27th, shows that the barge was still at Hayle and not quite completed; Francis had been promised the honour of accompanying it to Holland and setting it to work. Directors of the drainage company had already visited the Foundry to see a trial, when it lifted 7200 gallons of water per minute ten feet high with one bushel of coal per hour, but some adjustments were necessary.

In that letter, Trevithick made an interesting comment on the forthcoming trial at Bodmin—

> On the 17th August the trial comes on between the two companies about the quays. They are as desperate as possible on both sides, and castings and every other article are thrown down to 30 per cent below cost price; iron pumps for 6s. 6d. per cwt., and coal sold to the mines for 37s. 3d. per wey, when 47s. on board ship was paid for it. This never can last long.

As we have seen, Richard, aided by his model, gave evidence at the trial and he was asked to stay on at Hayle while Peter made his survey in September. The portable pump must have been finished by then. Francis gives no date for its completion but he says, "The directors having desired the writer to take the engine to Holland and set it to work with the least possible delay, adjourned for refreshment before starting for London. In those few minutes differences arose, resulting in the engine remaining for months in the barge, and then going to the scrap heap".

In January, 1830, Trevithick was still at Hayle making final attempts to collect from mines adventurers royalties on his patent for the plunger-pole steam engine, with only very limited success. These machines were still being manufactured by Harveys and one gathers from certain unspecified payments to Richard that here, at least, his legal dues were being honoured. At the end of February he left Hayle for London and one guesses the manner of his going from the end of a letter written by Henry to Gilbert about his heating apparatus dated April the 13th. Its apologetic opening is an amusing sidelight on the difficulties he was contending with in trying to meet all the demands being made on him for prompt delivery —

> We have been so pressed with some work immediately wanted by the Corporation at Penzance for watering the Town that we were obliged to let them have the pipes intended for your hot water apparatus. We shall, however, have them all ready tomorrow & will forward them immediately by the first Penzance Trader that sails for London ... As you surmise, Trevithick did not leave here in a very satisfactory manner. When I have the pleasure to see you I will explain. However, be assured his own temper, always ungovernable, led to this last.

Heating by hot water instead of open-grate fires was coming into fashion in London, as Gilbert mentions in a letter to Henry, telling him that the Archbishop of Canterbury is having the library at Lambeth Palace heated in this way.

Gilbert's heater had been designed by Trevithick and put in hand before he made his sudden departure from Hayle. He had written to Gilbert about it on March the 1st from an address in Highgate "to apologise for my neglect in not calling on you, but ill-health prevented it". He had been only ten days in Town and "was compelled to leave for this place, having a free good air". The letter gives particulars of a portable heater which he had invented, and later patented, but it is clear from the Harvey letters that the apparatus in question was not a portable, though, according to Francis, Gilbert did acquire one at some time later.

Probably Richard's complaint was what we should now call a "nervous breakdown". He must, by then have learned that there was no longer any prospect of raising capital in London for his and Gerard's concessions in the South American mines. Gerard had gone to France in the hopes of exciting interest there but, we are told, he died in poverty in Paris. Trevithick's state of mind can be judged by the fact that when Gilbert's heating equipment arrived in London he does not appear to have offered to help put it together though he was only a few miles away from his friend's house. Gilbert had to apply to Hayle for instructions as to how the joints in the pipes should be made. In reply, three different methods were described which could be applied according to the degree of skill a local artisan might be capable of.

We are never told what the cause of the psychological explosion was. Most likely it had been generated through the apparent failure of an experiment, as described on page 195. Henry had been decent enough, allowing him to make free use of the resources of the works and standing the expense of labour and material in the various creations which, one after another, had met with no luck. Now, his return was rather urgently required to give evidence again at the second arbitration. Henry abstained from making a personal appeal but he wrote to R. B. Follett on July the 31st, "As your Brother has named the Engineers as necessary Witnesses would you have the goodness to call on Mr. Wm. Brunton . . . We have also to request your calling on Capt. Trevithick who, when our Mr. Rawlings was in Town lodged at Lauderdale House, Highgate, and endeavour to secure his services on the occasion . . . but we much fear you will not succeed in prevailing on him to come down". Evidently the caller found Richard in his most intransigent mood. He not only rejected the plea but threatened to speak up for the enemy. Follett wrote in alarm to Paynter and Whitford, and they passed the letter on to Henry, who merely remarked "We do not fear but what we shall make our case out without him & are of opinion with Mr. Follett that it is better to say no more to him on the subject. His threat of going over to the other side is a mere idle one and has no meaning."

How well Harvey understood his brother-in-law! Nothing more was said and Trevithick duly arrived full of enthusiasm to give evidence for the plaintiffs.

This second reference, conducted by William Selwyn, lasted for sixteen days and was even then not completed as one or two witnesses had not been able to attend and the matter was adjourned for a further meeting in London to hear the absentees. In reading the account of the Hayle reference which, like the Bodmin trial, had also been taken down verbatim by the same shorthand writers, I had hoped to gain a clearer idea of Arthur Woolf's actual connection with the works. But, in his answers, the engineer was true to his reputation of truculence. He admitted being called Superintendent of the Foundry but refused to say how he was remunerated. "We have never differed about the payment yet, and I don't know that my private business has anything to do with this. I don't think it has. I shan't answer any more questions on that."

The first reference had been held in pursuance of the verdict at the Bodmin trial and was solely concerned with deciding how much of the disputed quay should be awarded to Harveys. But as this had "fallen to the ground", the Copper Company had hoped that, as all the evidence was being re-heard at the second reference it could still be shown that the Penpol River had never altered its course and the verdict upset. The number of new witnesses which had been called all swore to that effect with the others. But a very damaging bit of bribery had been discovered. Old men who had been discharged by the C.C.C. some time ago as unfit for work without any thought of compensation had suddenly been granted small retirement pensions. This was the most important new fact disclosed at the Hayle enquiry.

In February, 1831, Follett told Henry that the award would be made on May the 8th. But the C.C.C. submitted that they had important comments to make on the evidence and asked for a postponement. This having been granted, they yet found means of securing two further stays, pleading that their observations were still not complete. On September the 3rd R. B. Follett said that Joseph Edwards had at last delivered his comments and a copy of them had been sent for his brother's perusal — they occupied two hundred pages. But William Follett was away on circuit and he would not have time to study them until the slack time over Christmas.

All the remaining evidence was heard in January, 1832, and, on the last day of February, 1832, Selwyn issued his award. It was almost identical with the finding of Mr. Peter. The verdict of the assize court was to stand. Two thirds of the quay were to be handed over to Harveys but they were to give the Copper Company an option on retaining the use of it at a rental of £200 a year. On April the 10th William Brunton was told, "We have delayed writing you till now that we might give you the termination of this long protracted affair. The C.C.Co. have declined to rent of us & Mr. Harvey was yesterday put in legal possession by virtue of a Writ of possession directed to the Sheriff of Cornwall". That must have been a great moment for Henry!

XIII

THE EARLY THIRTIES

IN THE "PAROCHIAL HISTORY OF CORNWALL" DAVIES Gilbert makes only that one short mention of the Harveys already quoted. He says nothing of the long series of aggressive acts perpetrated by the C.C.C. or the lawsuit which had lasted for just over two-and-a-half years. So one may have thought, as probably Henry and his legal advisers did, that his silence was due to a partiality for members of the Copper Company and its shareholders, several of which, including Sir Christopher Hawkins, were his landed neighbours. Yet we find that, shortly after Selwyn's arbitration, Gilbert took the trouble to pay a personal visit to Henry at Foundry House. Its purport was at once reported to Follett though it had been made to appear incidental "in the course of conversation". Gilbert had mentioned "that he, at one time, had expected to be called on relative to Carnsew, that he distinctly recollects the river running a *great way higher up to the east than it now does*." Such a piece of evidence from the President of the Royal Society would have been worth more than that of all the old men and scientific experts put together. It was too late to be of use then, but it may still serve the purpose of convincing the reader that justice had been done in the courts.

During that prolonged period of uncertainty pending the issue of the lawsuit Henry was in no way distracted from his plans of expansion. His next venture was a development in the merchanting side — the opening of a general store to supply the whole neighbourhood, with its still increasing population about the mines, with everything they might want in grocery, hardware, furnishings, and drapery. By the autumn of 1830 he had engaged one Henry Noell of Helston to act as both manager and buyer, a keen and energetic young man who had exclaimed on receiving the appointment "It may be made one of the best things in the county!"

In September Noell was sent off on a buying tour of South Wales, Bristol, and London. His experience must have been of a very limited nature but he was fortified by letters of introduction to merchants with whom Harveys had had long dealings to act as advisers in local trades and prices. In the course of his travels he laid out just under £500 and had dealt with twelve different firms including one which is still flourishing — Spode and Copeland, the Staffordshire potters.[1] On his return, an assistant (called a "shop-maid") was engaged, licences had been procured for the premises and for selling tea, coffee, pepper, tobacco, and vinegar. The shop was opened early in the year 1831. The Stock Book for March of that year has a score of closely packed pages covering quite an incredible range of household needs, opening with the odd item "ten dozen black chamber-pots @ 2½d. pr. dozen". By the monthly turnover in the Cash Book, the venture appears to have been an immediate success. Small credits were allowed to members of the firm but I cannot find any suggestion that the shop was made an instrument in the truck system.

The Hayle shop must not be confounded with the more notorious one at Gwennap, in whose parish lay the principal eastern mines. This was owned by another Harvey family not related to that of Hayle — the brothers Collan and James Harvey. Their sister married John Williams of Scorrier House who owned so many mines in that area. As merchants, they had a virtual monopoly in supplies for those mines whilst, in their shop, the worst features of the truck system were practised, giving them a stranglehold over all the workers in those mines.

In the foundry, the volume of business was steadily growing and an extraordinary variety of goods were being turned out, both for special orders and also for stock, though, at this time, as we know, Henry was hard pressed for skilled labour, due to the higher wages which the C.C.C. was deliberately offering to draw away his trained men. The range varied from large pumping engines to small items of domestic use. Everyone expected individual attention and prompt delivery. Among customers for the lesser castings was one who appears to have built some new houses which were complete except for weights to work the sash windows which he seems to have found necessary to keep shut till they arrived. He wrote indignantly that "the houses are perishing for want of air".

An interesting item among the special orders was one from an official of the Duchy of Cornwall. The scale-weights used in the various coinage

---

[1] The name Copeland was lost in 1970, following which the company has operated under the name Spode.

halls had become unreliable through wear and Hayle Foundry was chosen to make new sets. They duly passed the required tests for accuracy — a testimony to the reputation which the company had gained for good work. Agricultural implements were also being made, from Cornish shovels to chaff-cutters and threshing machines. And there were several enquiries for machinery powered by other means than steam — water-wheels, windmills, horse-whims, winches, and cranes. Specifications were constantly being sent out in response to all enquiries as well as tenders for large work. In the latter case there was a new competitor ready to offer lowest possible terms in the shape of Sandys, Carne, & Vivian (the late C.C.C.). All this provisional estimating which might or might not end in definite orders was very fully and carefully made out, accompanied by drawings, which must have kept the limited staff very busy and late to bed.

The trade in domestic fire-grates, kitchen ranges, and ships' cabooses, started in John Harvey's time, was flourishing so well that it would presently have a department of its own in the foundry. A customer in South Wales was moved to write, "I have fixed 4 ranges up within the last 3 months but I must say none so compact and really serviceable as yours". And it may be noted that the galley kitchen in Brunel's *Great Western*, which ran the first all-steam race across the Atlantic, was fitted out by Harveys.

A new departure for the Company in 1830 was the making of equipment for lighting towns by gas. Plant for both Penzance and Falmouth were among the earliest orders. In this unaccustomed work Henry took guidance from William Brunton who was a pioneer in that branch of manufacture. At the same time he asked Brunton for a plan to light his own works by gas. It was provided, though the scheme was not carried out for several years.

But the most promising commission of that year came at the very end of it from a quite unexpected quarter and not one that was notable for progressiveness — the Navy Board, a department on whose doors Richard Trevithick had knocked several times in vain. The order seems to have originated with Captain William King, R.N., who represented the Admiralty at Falmouth and was in charge of the Post Office mail-packet station there. The inveterate horror and distrust of "strong" steam, bequeathed by James Watt had largely been overcome on land, where Trevithick's Cornish boiler was steadily replacing those designed for low pressure only. But at sea, the prejudice remained as obdurate as ever, strengthened, as time lapsed, to crystallise it into a superstition.

Now the charm was to be broken! The Government steamer, *Echo*, was to be re-boilered in such a manner as to exert a pressure of 20 pounds or more, to the square inch, and the valve-gear of the engines modified to make them work expansively. The contract was given to Harveys who were to provide three Cornish boilers (the first ever to go to sea), install them in the vessel lying at Devonport, and effect the necessary modifications to the machinery, which appears to have consisted of two Watt-type engines for turning the paddle-wheels. To watch the interests of the Navy Board, a disinterested party had been named to supervise the work, who was Thomas Ward, a Cornish engineer.

Henry recognised the importance of this trial order as well as the strong prejudice against high pressure steam which he would have to parry. He would remember very well the case of the first Cornish boilers at Dolcoath (page 93) which the enginemen at the mine had rendered useless through sheer cussedness until Trevithick got rid of them and put in his own men. He determined to take all possible means to make the experiment a success and was prepared to spare the foreman of his boiler-makers' shop, William Burell, to see the work through under Ward's direction, though his presence at Hayle would be much missed, for other important orders for boilers were in hand. Francis Trevithick, who had lost his chance of showing his capabilities when the floating pump for Holland was countermanded, was to be sent to Devonport as "mechanic in charge".

Ward came to Hayle to discuss details with Henry and Burell, while Francis went to Falmouth for a preliminary talk with Captain King. He recalls the pith of the interview in the *Life*. It was exceedingly pithy. "Mind, young man, what you are about, for if there is a blow up, by God you'll swing at the yard-arm".

By the beginning of April, 1831, the three boilers were ready, but more than a month elapsed before Henry was able to charter a barge with a hold of sufficient capacity to take them. Then the voyage to Devonport was interrupted by contrary winds which compelled the vessel to put into Fowey for several days. Early in July, Ward was again at Hayle putting in a plea to retain Burell for a little longer. Henry was eager to get him back to the foundry but was equally anxious not to risk a failure at Devonport by doing so. It was agreed that Burell must be allowed to make up his own mind, which he did promptly on Ward's return and wrote on July the 11th —

I confess it would be very desirable to return — but whin i look through the whole of this Business and the responsibility attached to it my decided opinion is that it will be for your interest for me to remain until the Whole is completed. The work connected with the Boilers will be completed in a few days so that they may be filled and if I leave Mr Ward do expect you will send some responsible person to take my place as there will be persons sent to examine the Boilers and see that they are all perfect. I consider myself your servant and should be glad to serve you in any way that you think I shall be most useful ... You will write me as soon as possible and leave me know How to proceed. I am awake to all the prejudice of the people against us and am prepared to meet every obstacle.

So he stayed on, and the next news he sent was on the 29th and directed from Falmouth, at 6 p.m. and in haste —

I had not time to write last evening. Arrived here just now. Cap*n*; King and Mr. Ward are in high spirits. We got up the steam and had the Boilers inspected by men from the Dock Yard and they were all perfectly satisfied. There was not one Single leak to be Discovered. All the principle men say they never saw such a fine job. This will do us credit after all the fuss with Mr Ward. I hope to see you on Monday. Some of Maudsley's Boilers have leaked 18 inches depth in water.

Captain King also wrote no less enthusiastically saying they had made a rapid passage from Plymouth (43 sea miles) in only four hours and forty minutes — a speed of nearly nine knots — and that the boilers were in excellent order. The successful voyage had relieved many apprehensions. There had been no "blow-up" nor had there been any attempted sabotage in the engine room. Perhaps it was the returning Hayle men who stoked the fires and not naval ratings.

Early in August the *Echo* was ordered to proceed from Falmouth to Woolwich. On this voyage she was entirely manned by naval officers and men. On her arrival, a complaint was made about the boilers. They were unsatisfactory — unsuitable for work at sea. Ward was sent for to London and Harveys were informed. Henry at once wrote to Ward begging him to call on William Brunton (he had left the Birmingham foundry and was a consulting engineer in London) and ask him to inspect the boilers and machinery on behalf of the Company. He wrote to Brunton by the same post, who replied, saying Ward had been to see him, and that he would go to the ship and try to find out what had happened. Ward sent the following account —

On my arrival at Woolwich yesterday I found everything was done by the Engineers & Firemen to destroy the Boilers, but I trust all is still right and that I shall have justice done although I have strong opposition to contend with. I have this morning seen the Lords of the Admiralty and they have given directions that I am to have all the assistance that can be rendered to me and requested me immediately to send for Cornish Fire Men or what ever I wanted, and to have Engineers of my own choice, and to take my own time to set things right. This you will say is as much as I had reason to expect, in fact they went so far as to say that it was their opinion that what we have done is the thing wanted and they are determined that it shall have a fair trial & their protection.

You will have some idea of the extent the Enginemen went to when I tell you that the Commander was oblig*d* to go down to the Engine room and request that something was done not to burn down the Boiler, for he was quite alarmed to see the steam going off at such tremendous rate. They have run down all the Fire Bars, and I must have some last before we can work again ...

Ward goes on to ask that Henry will let him have a team of workmen sent down from Hayle, by arrangement with Captain King, in time to catch the *Sir Francis Drake*, a steamship which had recently been put on the Falmouth-London packet service. At the same time, King, who had also heard from Ward, despatched a messenger on horseback to Hayle asking for competent men to be sent at once to London. Henry spared two from his precious personnel but not Burell this time. On the 10th of September Brunton wrote again —

I am happy to inform you that the Boilers which you lately put into the *Echo* (and which I inspected yesterday) have sustained no injury whatever from the treatment they received in their voyage round land. The men, whether from design or ignorance, associated with the ordinary share of prejudice against all things new, badly managed the feeding of the Boiler, and one of the valves rose quite out of its seat & got across, through which I imagine all the feed went for some time, & might well account for the disarrangement which occasioned the complaint. . . With respect to the Boilers &c. I think they will do you credit. There has been a very high prejudice raised against them by the parties usually supplying boilers of the ordinary kind [the Maudslays for instance;], but in conversation with several of the commanding and other officers connected with this department of the public service, I could discover these prejudices giving way and a favourable opinion of the Boilers taking place which I, by everything I could say, endeavoured to strengthen. The engines were not at work but the reversing gearing is said to work very well...

At last, after several postponements, the *Echo* ran her official trials, though it seems to have been managed that she should do so without carrying any competent person to represent Harveys. Brunton wrote again on October the 8th, after the vessel had returned to the Thames, giving an account of what he could gather had happened in this final incident — more extraordinary than any of the foregoing. —

I have been informed from Mr Ward of die proceedings with the *Echo*, since

13. The Leeghwater Engine

14. The Cruquius Engine

193

15. Nicholas Oliver Harvey

16. The mis-cast twelve-foot cylinder

194

she came to the London river, the first part of which I stated in mine of the 10th ult., when she was expected to go to the Continent but which was given up, and the 12th was fixed upon to try the vessel down the river, and I was requested by Mr Ward to attend, which I did, but about 2 hours before the time appointed to go, another order was given to take down the Families of some persons of distinction to Ramsgate &: thus the intended trial was put off till the 14th when I could not attend (being otherwise engaged). However, on that or the following day a party, called by themselves and perhaps by the Navy Board a Commission, consisting of Mr Goodrich (late of the Portsmouth dock yd), one of the Maudslays & Mr Field their partner, and a few others, went on board early in the morning and tho' they gave Ward notice of it did not wait his arrival but sailed without him. He had two Cornish men on board who worked the fires for the usual number of hours, and all went on perfectly well and the vessel going faster & with less coal than she did with the old boilers.

After dinner Mr Goodrich, Mr Field, & one of the Maudslays went into the Engine room and ordered the engine man to blow off the boilers, and the cock or cocks were kept open by Mr Goodrich's watch 7½ minutes, which so lowered the water in the middle boiler that it became red hot & as the water again rose in it it poured out at the joints most profusely. The Cornish men hearing the crackling noise run to see what was the matter and they were, I believe, Mr Ward's informants. It is not easy to make one self believe such a deliberate piece of mischief but, from what has followed, I am inclined to think it correct.

On the return of the vessel Ward inspected what had been done and presented a remonstrance to the Admiralty (not the Navy Board which, you must know, are two distinct parties and take very different views of this measure) who demanded a report from the Commander who is decidedly in favour of the new boiler and whose report, together with Ward's remonstrance appears to have determined the Admiralty to prosecute the plan, and they have therefore again put her into Mr Ward's hands and sent her round to Plymouth to be again put into complete order & to go out with the next Mediterranean Mail.

This supreme effort to justify the use of high pressure steam at sea did not produce (as hoped for) a repeat order. But, as usual, Harveys were kept waiting for their money —"The delay is occasioning us much and great inconvenience in our business".

Francis Trevithick's note on the part he took in the work has already been mentioned. He says further — "The writer who had, as mechanic in charge, worked like a slave, though receiving but 1s. 6d. a day and expenses, was not invited to take any part in the experimental trials, nor ever heard of the result except in the ordinary rumours of Admiralty bungling on board the 'Echo'". To the reader of those volumes I would say that I don't think that is quite fairly put. He was given this post of honour when barely nineteen years old and not yet out of his term of apprenticeship and could hardly expect better pay. As to the trials of the *Echo*, he must have known that he was not the only one left out on that occasion and his remarks suggest that his interests were not properly looked after by his uncle. He gives the same impression throughout his book of the relationship between his father and Henry Harvey.

Francis might well have told his reader that there had been some friction between himself and Thomas Ward — perhaps the "fuss" which Burell spoke of. But the Harvey letters show that Henry was ready to stand up for the rights of his nephew if he were in the wrong. Thus, he had written to Burell on June the 18th —

> Mr Harvey wishes you would get from Francis Trevithick an explanation of what has passed between him and Mr Ward and, as by this time you have had an opportunity of observing their bearing towards each other, that you will give your own candid opinion in your next letter about the differences that have arisen. You will also ask Mr Ward (perhaps without seeming to have any motive) what he has against Francis, and if things are so between them that Francis cannot go on with the work satisfactorily and comfortably to both, had he not better return here? But Mr Harvey does not wish his return unless it would mend matters, & would avoid doing anything to hurt his feelings, if he is not in fault. Do your best about this matter and write your unreserved opinion.

Unfortunately the foreman's comment, both before and after the above are missing from the bundle of "in" letters so we do not know what the trouble was about, but it may well be that Francis had been rubbing in that the boilers were his father's invention for which he was getting neither credit nor reward because, although they were one of his most successful contributions to the world of steam power, he had neglected to take out a patent for them.

Something else was happening in 1831. The primitive communications between Hayle and the outside world which existed when John Harvey started his foundry had already received one large improvement, and another was about to be added. In the first instance, the way to Penzance over the dangerous and uncertain crossing of the sands (to facilitate which Henry had built an archway in his long quay) had been replaced by a causeway under the aegis of a turnpike trust, of which Henry was a trustee. This saved the long way round the estuary by the mediaeval bridge at St. Erth. He was now the moving spirit in a plan to establish a regular public service between Hayle and Bristol by sea.

Early in March promoters of the "Steam Navigation Company" had plans sufficiently matured to call for subscriptions. A new ship was to be built and owned in sixty-four shares, of which Henry took fifteen, but as he presided at all the meetings and nothing important was done without his sanction, he appears to have acted as manager. The purser was Francis Harvey who lived at Copperhouse and owned a wharf on the inner side of the Copper Company's floodgates, fronting on their canal which led from thence to Ventonleague. It seems possible that he may have been a cousin of the Foundry family but I have not been able to trace any relationship[1].

In March, Captain John Vivian went to Bristol to make enquiries about building the vessel but wrote to say "No builder here will engage to build a steam vessel in less than 5 months, after which it will take 5 or 6 weeks to put the engines on board". So he said he was off to Greenock. This John Vivian was the sailor who had been at the helm of Trevithick's road-carriage when it tore down the railings of an astonished cottager on that memorable journey already described. He now owned and worked the schooner *Pendarves* which had been constantly chartered by Henry for many years. At Greenock he was more successful than at Bristol and an order to build was given to John Scott & Son. The new ship was launched complete with her machinery on July the 30th and named the *Herald*. There seems to have been no thought of fitting out any part of her at Hayle. They must have been anxious to get the service established before the winter with its stormy seas set in and the home works had all they could do to keep pace with the orders on hand.

On September the 22nd, the *Bristol Gazette* made the following announcement —

For St. Ives and Hayle
With Passengers and Goods
The beautiful new Steam Packet
HERALD
John Vivian, Commander

This superior vessel is just arrived from Greenock where she was built, with engines of 100 horse power, but built purposely for the Trade, and no expense spared in fitting her for the comfort of Passengers and safety of Goods; she will lay at the Quay taking in Goods till Friday Evening and sail from Cumberland Basin on Saturday next.

The service was a weekly one, leaving Hayle every Wednesday on the tide

[1] April 8, 1831. "Hayle Steamer; paid Francis Harvey deposit on 15 shares £15" Cash Book.

197

and returning on Saturday. Single fares were, cabin, £1 5s. 0d. (including steward's fee); deck, 10s. 6d.; children under ten, half-price. The distance was about 150 sea-miles and a fair passage took 22 hours. The agent at Bristol was yet another John Harvey, again of no proved relationship with the Hayle family, though possibly a cousin. He lived at 66 Broad Quay, Bristol, but soon after the service started he moved to the West of England Tavern (No. 60) where he established a regular ticket-office.

The company was now known as the Herald Steam Packet Co. and was managed on the cost-book system as used in the Cornish mines. Several meetings were held in the course of the year (on board the *Herald* at Hayle) when costs and profits were gone into. If the latter were shown, a dividend would be declared, if the former, the shareholders would be asked to make good. Unlike the fortune of the mines, profits for many years seem to have been steady and good.

This new service was a great boon to the neighbourhood as well as to Harveys who were able to get many of their regular supplies without having to use their own vessels or charter others. Passenger traffic seems to have been good from the beginning both for Bristol and beyond — amongst applicants for tickets there is one from the parents of a boy who was going back to school at Rugby.

Steam packet services had already been established elsewhere in the Bristol Channel and also, quite recently, on the south coast. J. E. Blewett, the uncle of Henry's former partner, who was a ship-broker and a prominent townsman of Plymouth, owned or managed one of these vessels called the *Brunswick*. Henry had always been on good terms with him in spite of the quarrel with his nephew and, on October the 12th he wrote to him asking for particulars of pay and personnel in the *Brunswick* as a model for what should be done in the *Herald*. This new kind of trader set fresh problems not covered by established usage at sea. Blewett sent a full reply.

A little incidental news has come down to us from this time in the autobiography of John Brunton[1]. He was the son of William Brunton and had served two years at Hayle Foundry as Henry Harvey's pupil, ending his time in October, 1831. It will be remembered that Nicholas Harvey had previously served the same time in the Eagle Foundry at Birmingham under William Brunton. Out of regard to his father, Henry had taken the boy without a premium and into his own home at Foundry House where

[1] *John Brunton's Book*. Cambridge University Press, 1939.

the household was presided over by his sister, Elizabeth, and their niece, Nanny Harvey. So we have a few glimpses of the family life. "We had to work the same hours as the men from 6 a.m. to 6 p.m. — long hours for a youngster, but kind Miss Harvey used to cut me a large slice of bread overnight and gave me permission to go into her fine dairy every morning and place on my bread a thickness of Cornish cream, which was indeed a luxury — and gave me a grand start in the morning".

But the ladies, who had true Celtic leanings, were firm believers in the virtue of herbs and would have nothing to do with professional doctoring, a bias which nearly cost John the loss of a limb after an accident at the works. He had a close friend, "This was Frank Trevithick who afterwards became Locomotive Superintendent at Crewe — and indeed was the Founder of the enormous establishments now the principle one of the London and North Western Railway".

John describes an incident which may well have been the whole cause of that sudden rupture and hasty departure from Hayle by Frank's father. "I saw a good deal of him [Richard Trevithick] for he had persuaded Mr. Harvey, his brother-in-law, that he had invented a great improvement in Steam Engines — by which the steam having passed through the cylinders was to be pumped back into the Boiler before it condensed. Mr. Harvey consented for him to make a trial of his system in the works and I was appointed to erect the machinery. I soon saw that it was a mistake — but dare not tell Mr. R. Trevithick so — for he was a very violent and passionate man. However, the Boiler and Engine were completed and tested and then it was shown to be a failure founded on wrong principles. Old Richard Trevithick was very angry about this, and it weighed heavily on his mind so as to derange his judgement".

This was apparently the first trial of what H. W. Dickinson calls the "closed cycle steam engine and boiler", about which Trevithick had written to Gilbert "I am quite satisfyde that the tryall allready will warrent success", and in full confidence of that, he went on to take out a patent (granted, 1831). John's reactions must reflect the opinion of those at the Foundry who were present at the trial. A sarcastic comment from Arthur Woolf could have damned the experiment and have raised just such a storm in the inventor who was so far ahead of his times in all his ideas.

John says that he left Hayle with great regret and, in winding up his account, he shows another side to Henry's character that we should not glean from office books and records. "Mr. Harvey not only gave me opportunities of learning matters connected with my profession as an Engineer, but he kept a horse for me and taught me to ride. He encouraged me to learn boating, in the evenings, to practice shooting, and all outdoor manly exercises. While indoors he taught me the art of Carving at table, in which he was a great proficient".

John Brunton rose to considerable eminence in his profession. He constructed and renovated hospitals in Turkey and Asia Minor during the Crimean war, carried out large railway works in India and finally became a consulting engineer. He reached the age of eighty-six and the last year of his century. It must have been in his later days when he wrote this spirited and exciting account of his life — not for the public but his grandchildren — and his memory of early days is not quite reliable. He says that in the dispute over the Copperhouse quay, the Assize was held at Truro (not Bodmin) and that the case was won chiefly through the evidence given by his father "who had made a complete model of the harbour to explain his views", but we know that model was definitely made by Richard Trevithick.

17. Tom Brogden's replica of the 1803 London road carriage

Photograph: Philip Hosken

XIV

LAST DAYS OF RICHARD TREVITHICK

THE THREE YEARS FOLLOWING 1831 COVERED A MOST eventful epoch in the history of the Company and one from which it emerged with greatly augmented strength, ready to meet from its remote corner of Britain the growing challenge of foundries and engineering works of the great industrial centres with all their advantages in reserves of skilled labour and facilities in communication.

On April the 9th, 1832, as already mentioned, Henry Harvey went in person to take over that bitterly contested portion of the Copper-house quay. For him, it must have been a supreme moment of triumph to enter this salient in the enemy's territory, accompanied by the under-sheriff of the county who was to serve the writ of possession on its defeated builders. By an unhappy irony of fate, the man who filled this office at the time was the Rev. Samuel Gurney, vicar of St. Erth, and it cannot have been an agreeable errand. For he it was who, twelve years before, had quelled the impending battle between the two factions, brought the parties together, and persuaded them to sign the non-intervention pact already described. Yet it was a clause in this well-meant agreement which, when produced at the trial and before the arbitrators, proved one of the most effective arguments against the case of the Copper Company. Under the final award, however, the C.C.C. had been given the option of retaining the surrendered portion of their wharf as tenants of Harveys at a rental fixed by the arbitrator at £200 per annum, but this they scornfully rejected.

Thus, Henry now owned wharves on both sides of the Penpol River, but the Copper Company were still able to make themselves a nuisance in another way — and had been doing so ever since they knew that the Bodmin trial was definitely going to take place. This reprisal took the form of discontinuing the daily scouring of the main channel by the regular operation of their sluices. They now only did this when it suited their own purposes, that is, when preparing for the arrival or departure of a deep draught vessel. In the intervals between scouring, the sand accumulated on the bar in St. Ives Bay so that even on spring tides there was little more than ten feet of water there.

Henry took opinion of counsel as to whether the C.C.C. could be compelled to continue the scouring as heretofore in the interests of navigation, but received a negative answer. His case against the rival company had been based on an objection to the installation of those sluices and flood-gates; what would a court have made of a new action designed to enforce the exact opposite? No doubt the Copper Company suffered some inconvenience themselves from this self-imposed restriction but not by any means so much as Harvey. More shipping was now coming to his quays than to those at Copperhouse, and the preponderance was increasing.

The question became even more vexed by a certain rumour. "A hint has been thrown out" wrote Henry to his solicitors "that the C.C.Co. mean to propose that a contract shall be entered into that they shall be paid a tonnage duty on all vessels trading here, and that the contract shall be for 30 years". In return for reaping this profitable harvest the Copper Company would again open their sluices regularly. Henry scouted the idea; "This will never meet with my concurrence or consent". There the matter rested for the time being.

In the mid-summer there were alarms of a very different kind. This was a visitation from the East of the fearful disease of cholera. It first made its appearance in Sunderland in October, 1830, by the following January it had reached London and began making its way towards the Land's End. On August the 27th Henry, in a letter to his solicitors, mentioned "We are sorry to say that several cases of cholera have occurred within the last few days at a short distance from this place in the parish of Phillack. The nuisance adjoining the White Hart still continues we have succeeded in getting the parish authorities to call a Vestry at St. Erth on Wednesday afternoon next to take into consideration the propriety of forming a Board of Health. We have called on Mr. Gurney, the only Magistrate in the parish, and he declines acting or in any way interfering with a Board of Health, but he has sent a person employed by the Waywardens to give notice to several parties to fill up dung pits &c. but this is not what we want. We have also seen the Rev. Mr Hocking, the resident Magistrate in Phillack. He recommends that the St. Erth Board of Health should, in the first place, interfere in regard to Penpol Pool, not liking to do so himself (Mr. Millett being a relative and parishioner) & alleges that from its peculiar situation it affects this parish to a much greater extent than that of Phillack. Will you please be good enough to instruct us by return of post how we are to proceed to get it abated."

Such indifference on the part of local officials in the face of that virulent epidemic, which had all the horrors of a mediaeval plague, will strike the modern sanitation-conscious reader as extraordinary. But Samuel Gurney had no doubt felt deeply injured by the outcome of his well-meant intervention in the hostilities of the two great powers of Hayle and was resolved not to "interfere" again, especially as the Penpol Pool was in Phillack and not St. Erth parish. William Hocken, a noted scholar and antiquary, would not move to save the lives of his parishioners for fear of hurting the feelings of R. O. Millett of Penpol House, whose wife was his sister-in-law, for he had married another of John Curnow's daughters. And no leading member of the Copper Company had the public spirit to come forward and join forces with Harvey at the moment of common danger.

Henry was probably right in believing Penpol Pool was the chief danger-spot in the two parishes but from its "peculiar situation" it had given rise to one of the main causes of the ancient grudge. What that situation was is shown on the map on page 81, and it will be remembered how, in 1795, this same Mr. Millett had suddenly withdrawn the leave he had given John Harvey to make a leat for the outflow of water which turned the wheels of his boring-mill across a small piece of his waste ground, and expedited matters by sending a strong party of men to fill it up with stones. The sketch, based on a map made in 1810, shows the sharp bend in the ancient course of the river which divided the two parishes and the two estates of Trelissick and Penpol. It was within that bend that Penpol Pool came to be formed at some time subsequent to the date of the map and possibly also to the building of the old White Hart Hotel. It is first shown on a map made about 1832 (page 223). It must, at the time in question, have been a stagnant and noisome pond.

On September the 3rd, only a week after the letter just quoted, Robert Oke Millett died. About the same time the sickness must have spread into Hayle, though the visitation seems to have been transitory for, on the 24th of the month Henry writes to William Petherick of the Fowey Consols Mine, "We thank you for your recipe for cholera in your last. Owing to the severity of the disease our works have been much retarded, but we hope it is now assuaged". In the meanwhile, Henry had not wasted any more time on trying to organise a Board of Health but had taken the more radical step of instructing his lawyers to make an offer to the heir of Penpol Manor for the purchase of the pestiferous pool that he might have it duly drained and filled up. But Paynter and Whitford wrote on October the 3rd to say that they had heard that the estate had been entailed and no part of it could be bought.

During the Autumn of the same year the C.C.C. were again putting out feelers about acceptable conditions for operating their floodgates regularly. For this, they had evolved two alternative proposals. The first was revealed when the lawyers of both sides met informally at the Bodmin sessions in October. It is described in a letter of Paynter and Whitford to Harveys as a "veiled suggestion" and was that they would oblige for the consideration of an annual payment of £200. This bait was not taken. The other was an amended version of the plan for a levy of tolls on all ships entering Hayle harbour which Henry had said he would never consent to and, like that scheme, it was put about by rumour.

The new plan was fraught with much more danger than the old one and likely to be more effective in its adverse reaction on Harveys. The idea of a local arrangement was dropped in favour of a parliamentary measure to be introduced by influential friends of the Copper Company with the aim of superseding or at least modifying the claims to dues of the Port of St. Ives. These were authorised by the St. Ives Harbour Act of 1766 which was brought in to reimburse the town for the construction of its stone pier designed by Smeaton — his first experiment in harbour works.

Meanwhile, however, Henry had conceived a plan of his own — a bold idea, offering a complete answer to the present difficulty and an appropriate pay-off of old scores, recalling the folk tale, where the bad fairy who had for long oppressed the hero is bound under a spell to work for his good. The suggestion was to turn that useless and troublesome foreshore, the Carnsew wastrel, to profitable account by creating within its huge expanse a tidal lake for the storage of sufficient water to scour the channel as effectively as the Copperhouse sluices and thus be quite independent of their workings.

But the operation would be a very costly one. Not only would a huge excavation have to be made but the sea, which at present covered the whole foreshore at high tides, would have to be prevented from overflowing it by reclaiming the remainder of the ground. This would require an embankment extending all the way from the Carnsew Quay down to the junction of the main channel with the Hayle River at the point called the Norwayman's Dock, where it would converge with another following the right bank of the river. Within these banks the spoil of the diggings could be protected from tidal action as the level of the ground was raised and a further curb placed round the lake. Then there would be the cost of the floodgates, sluices, and attendant masonry. Furthermore, there would be an incalculable addition. Harvey's foreshore rights were limited to rights of way and the placing of buildings above ground. They did not include making such extensive works as those contemplated. Permission would have to be gained from the three landlords (who would certainly demand more rent) and the old question of the "undivided thirds" would have to be gone into again.

Henry had approached his landlords on the subject even before the result of the Selwyn arbitration was known, for he wrote to his solicitors on January the 30th to say that he had had a talk with William Praed and his eldest son, James, about "the proposed embankment and flood-gates" and that James had written "to his brother in town to see Sir John St. Aubyn & propose to him to send down Mr. Telford or some other engineer to make a report &c". The said Mr. Telford, then seventy-five years old and in declining health, was, at that time, busily engaged on a round of inspection of his roads, bridges, and harbours throughout England and it is unlikely that the great man would submit to being sent on such an errand, but it shows that the Praeds regarded the work as one of greater magnitude than could be compassed by local talent. It seems, too, that Harvey had not fully revealed his plan about independent sluicing and was only representing it as an auxiliary measure, for the Praeds were still talking of an Act of Parliament which would compel one or both parties to operate their gates regularly but authorise tolls on vessels to meet expenses, a course which Henry had said he would never agree to.

The scheme was shelved for the time being, except that an estimate of the probable cost of the work was made out. On September the 28th Harveys reported to Paynter and Whitford "Mr. Wm. Praed called here on tuesday and asked if anything more had transpired touching the working of the Flood-gates. On being answered in the negative he said something might be brought about if we would offer £150 per year. He said the C.C.C. wished to have a sum which could be made to bear by a tonnage, as it would enable them to ascertain the amount to be charged in their accounts with the Vessels. *This is all fudge*".

Now it will be seen that this did not refer to Henry's plan, which was ignored. It was the earlier "veiled suggestion", unveiled, but reduced by £50 — the new terms on which the C.C.C. were prepared to re-commence the regular sluicing of the channel. Their long abstinence had been such a nuisance that Henry had already gone so far as to offer them £100 a year to restore the old service as a much cheaper expedient than carrying out his separate scheme. This had been rejected. In the meantime the Copper Company had somehow managed to get William Praed on their side and gain his advocacy.

The letter goes on, "If we paid them £100 or £150 per year it would be a charge upon the trade and entered into our books accordingly & they would do the same. He said that he did not think the C.C.C. could ever be expected to submit to our having anything to do with the management of working the gates. For his own part he would not consent if so situated."

How odd that on the very day following Praed's visit another of Henry's landlords favoured him with a call! This was Francis Hearle Rodd, the owner of Trelissick manor and one of the Carnsew thirds. Odder still, the purport of his visit was exactly the same as that of his predecessor. He counselled appeasement and "said something about £150 per annum, which he had we suppose from Mr. Praed. Mr. Harvey thinks coming as this did they [the C.C.C.] are now disposed to come round and, if they cannot make better terms, accept our offer of £100 per annum: this, Mr. Harvey told Mr. Rodd, he would rather wish to be evaded if they were disposed to accept it, & that things should remain as they are & [he would] provide smaller Vessels for the trade. Mr. Harvey begged Mr. Rodd not to listen to anything Mr. Praed might say, evidently inclined, as he now is to side with them. Mr. H. does not think Mr. Rodd wishes to press him into their terms, & if they now come to the £100, if you think he can fairly get out of it he would."

There was to be a meeting of the Turnpike Trustees of Hayle causeway in October when those two proprietors of Carnsew and the agent of the third would be present as well as Henry, who was also a trustee, and the solicitors were asked to make a point of attending, when the whole question of flood-gates could be discussed. But in that month William Praed departed this life and was succeeded by his son, James. I find it impossible to guess why William had become a supporter of the interests of Copperhouse against those of Hayle when, together with the other lords of Carnsew, he had so recently been engaged in that hard-fought battle against them. But the large landowners tended to hang together and several of them were financially committed to the welfare of Copperhouse.

James Praed proved to be more co-operative than his father and matters were soon amicably arranged with the other two owners of Carnsew so that by the following spring he was able to set to work on the huge task that would give him freedom from the malicious caprice of his rivals, though he would know that his efforts would result in benefiting them no less. He had provided for extra capital by staking the greater part of his leaseholds on a mortgage to Sir Charles Lemon for a loan of £7,200 at 4% interest.

This same year of 1833 saw the disappearance from the story of two of its erstwhile prominent figures, Richard Trevithick and Arthur Woolf. We last heard of Trevithick at Lauderdale House, Highgate, the home of William Gittings, whither he had gone after his rupture with Henry Harvey. Early in 1832 he was in touch with young John Hall who had started an engineering business at Dartford. In him, Richard seems at last to have found someone with whom he could not only share ideas but bring them to practical fruition; an alliance which might perhaps have ripened into one exactly similar to that of Boulton and Watt.

Very little is known about the nature of this alliance, but, by the summer, experimental work of some kind was in progress at Dartford. A letter from John Hall to Richard dated August the 23 has been preserved[1] saying "We are proceeding as fast as we can with the work for you" and asking him to come down and inspect it. Perhaps this was a try-out of jet-propulsion for ships for which Trevithick took out a patent in September.

Later in the year Richard left Highgate for Dartford where he lodged at the Bull Inn. There, on the morning of April the 22nd, 1833, he died after only a week's illness. The innkeeper, Rowley Potter, wrote immediately to John Tyack of Copperhouse giving the news. He was Trevithick's nephew, the son of John Tyack who had married Elizabeth Trevithick, Richard's sister. It is remarkable that a man who regarded worldly matters so lightly as Richard did, should have made a will and that the document should have been available as soon as he died. But so it was, and in the will, John Tyack was named as sole executor. It was therefore to him and not to the family that Potter's letter was directed.

Tyack replied by return of post — and it speaks well for the efficiency at which the mail-coach service had arrived — that Tyack's letter is dated April the 24th. In it he said that he had broken the news to the family, and

[1] Trevithick Papers: Private Collection noted on page 26.

207

directed that the will should be handed to his solicitor in London. William Gittings of Lauderdale House wrote to Henry Harvey telling him of the death of his brother-in-law on the day after it occurred. The funeral took place on the 26th. No mourners from Hayle were present, though there would just have been time for them to get there. The arrangements were made by Halls and it was said that the employees of the works paid all expenses. The grave which received the remains of that brilliant genius was dug in the paupers' quarter of the upper churchyard at Dartford.

Richard died very heavily in debt and left no assets. In the list of his creditors[1] a considerable sum is shown as due to his executor, John Tyack. Rowley Potter and William Gittings were also owed money for board and lodging. In addition, Gittings had lent money to bolster up one of Trevithick's schemes but had seen none of it back. The list, which is a long one, does not include Henry Harvey, and the omission must have been made with his own assent though there seems no doubt that he could have made out a large claim. Henry can have received little in return for the materials and the labour expended on Trevithick's experiments during the several long periods he had the entree to Hayle Foundry. A hint of how matters stood even in early days is given in a letter written in 1807 when Trevithick had gone to London and was working on the Thames driftway —

> My sister have communicated to me her wish of going to London with the Family to live with her Husband but say she cannot think of leaving Camborn unless what you owe there is settled ... If you can give me good security for the Money you owed in my Father's time (say about Five Hundred Pounds) I have no objection to let her have what money she want or the £500 given her by will.

It is unlikely that Trevithick made any satisfactory response to these proposals. Jane was eager to join her husband in answer to his urgent calls. How far Henry waived his claim and conditions and helped her to go we can't tell but her loyalty must have been rather strained when, after her arrival in that depressing quarter where she and the children had to make their new home, she discovered in a pocket of Richard's jacket her last three letters to him unopened.

Now that the end had come, it seems that even the devoted family had become estranged by the repeated neglect of their feelings shown by their sire. Richard does not appear to have visited Hayle since he went to give

[1] Trevithick Papers: Private Collection noted on page 26.

evidence at the second arbitration in September, 1830 and, during the remainder of his life, I cannot find that he held any communication with his friends or relatives there. He seems to have behaved with the same indifference towards them as he had over the eleven years when he was absent in South America.

At Dartford, a public subscription was started to raise a suitable monument in memory of the renowned engineer who had been laid in their midst, to be made in cast iron, and "sufficiently elevated to be seen by passers by"[1], but it failed for lack of funds. If the family and connections at Hayle were appealed to, it would seem that they did not respond. Nor, on failure of the project, did they make any move to place a headstone at the grave. Francis Trevithick says in his memoir that he went there "a few years after the funeral" and it is hardly surprising that he was received coldly at Hall's foundry — "The writer was refused permission to go through the works to enquire into the character of the experiments that had been tried, but the mechanics were glad to see the son of Trevithick, and their wives and children joined in the welcome as he passed through the small town. Trevithick's grave was among those of the poor buried by the charitable; no stone or mark distinguished it from its neighbours." Although he made no attempt to remedy this he did what was better by laboriously collecting all the information he could about his father from people still living who had worked with him, and publishing it. But for that, the man, his unique gifts, and the important contribution he made to industrial history would probably have been forgotten. It prompted the centenary in 1933, when a commemorative plaque was placed in Dartford parish church, but there could be no pilgrimage to the grave, for its situation is unknown.[2]

In the same year that Richard died his bitter old rival, Arthur Woolf, retired from his somewhat anomalous position as Superintendent of Hayle Foundry. For the past two years he had suffered much from ill health and had also got into financial difficulties (as one gathers from the Harvey letters) and Henry had seen little of him. In his place, Henry appointed his nephew, Nicholas Oliver Harvey, as manager of the iron works.

It was noted earlier that Nicholas had begun his training under William Brunton at the Eagle Foundry, Birmingham. He finished his time there in 1822 and then came home and worked at Hayle under Woolf, whom

[1] *History and Antiquities of Dartford* by Dunkin, 1844.
[2] A blue plaque commemorating Trevithick's death at the Royal Victoria and Bull hotel was unveiled in 2007 by Phil Hosken, Chairman of the Trevithick Society.

LAST DAYS OF RICHARD TREVITHICK

he assisted in the construction of that compound engine which was made to compete against the Cornish engine at Wheal Alfred mine in 1824, a trial which turned out to its disadvantage (page 147). A little later, he was given an introduction to the proprietors of the Fijnord Engineering Works at Rotterdam, who offered him employment, which he accepted. He was there when Richard Trevithick paid his flying visit to Holland in 1828. The firm specialised in making marine engines. He was with them for five years and then left Holland for Prussia to join a ship-building company called Sterkenrade.

John Brunton, in his autobiography[1], recalls his early friendship with Nicholas in the Eagle Foundry days and goes on to say, "He was a very clever fellow and afterwards, turning his attention to marine engineering, became the leading man in establishing the Steam boat navigation on the River Rhine which, under his fostering care, reached very large proportions. He became a man of note".

Nicholas appears to have returned to England at the beginning of 1833. Passing references in letters indicate that he represented Harveys as agent before taking over management of the works. He was then thirty-three years old and married to a German lady.

At Hayle, the change must have been invigorating. Nicholas was not only an experienced engineer by this time with a wide knowledge of what was going on outside England, he was a Harvey and, as is shown in his future career, he had inherited the leading traits of his uncle and great-uncle, insistence on the highest quality in materials and workmanship. But he was less uncompromising than Henry and, having a naturally genial and open temperament, he became very popular with his workpeople and neighbours.

But it should be noted that the term "engineer" was, at that time, interpreted differently in Cornwall from what it was elsewhere. William Pole, in his classic treatise on the Cornish engine noted with approval that in Cornwall a strict distinction was observed between the engineer and the manufacturer, the latter confining himself to the carrying out of engine designs provided by the former who was a man in charge of the mechanical and pit works of one or more of the mines and trained only in those branches of the profession. He sums up a dissertation on the subject, "The advantages arising from the separation of Engineer and

[1] *John Brunton's Book.*

19. Old shipyard drawing office

18. Crimean mortar cast by Harveys

211

20. Old Carnsew limekiln, demolished in 1980

21. Prehistoric fort and Neo-Roman archway,
now a beautifully kept park

Manufacturer are too important to be over-looked". The strong opposition at first shown to the introduction of the Watt engine into Cornwall was probably due in part to the breach made in this convention.

That Harveys were abiding by the rule as late as 1831 is shown by a letter from Henry to a parent who had applied for an apprenticeship at Hayle for his son. "Mr. Harvey will gladly meet your views for your second son, but I fear he has formed an erroneous & too flattering picture of the profession he would enter on here. We are not 'Engineers'; solely 'Manufacturers', and to obtain a correct knowledge of this branch he should be a thorough-bred workman, which can only be by laborious exertion and application. To fix him in our drawing office for four or five years would give him small insight into the art and Mystery of engineering, and all that he would acquire on this head, if he were an apprentice with us, would be what he could gather from his own observations in casual contact with the engineers who frequent our establishment to give their orders". In Nicholas Harvey, however, the works now had a fully qualified engineer who was quite as capable of designing machinery as of constructing it, and the distinction must have been allowed to die out by degrees.

At the foundry, orders were coming in regularly for new engines and boilers, both of the "Cornish" type, as replacements for old ones, or to work in new sinkings, and there was a steady demand for Trevithick's high pressure *puffer*, at the mines for whim winding gear and stamps for crushing ore, and elsewhere, for a variety of purposes, notably milling and work on the sugar plantations. A new outlet had lately been discovered for this little engine. It had found favour with water-millers in the chalk areas. Their supply of natural power tended to fail in the summer months. A few had installed Boulton and Watt engines to tide over that period, but found themselves nearly as badly off as before through lack of water to cool the condensers. So they resorted to the "pressure engine" which was independent of the millpond. Many orders of all sorts came from outside Cornwall, and a connection with the mining companies of Ireland was steadily growing.

At the end of 1833 the increasing importance of the port of Hayle as an outlet for tin produced in the neighbouring mines was recognised by a mark of unusual distinction. It was made a coinage town, a privilege which had not been granted by the Stannary authorities for a hundred and seventy years, when Penzance was added to the four which had been established far back in the Middle Ages — Helston, Truro, Lostwithiel, and Liskeard. Henry's large new work for ensuring the sluicing of the channel was, by now, well under way and may well have helped in the decision. At all events, it was Henry who found room on his premises for the new coinage hall[1] and Hayle Foundry was again entrusted with the making of new sets of weights for this and other coinage towns. It was the Harveys who had originally raised Hayle to the status of coinage town and customs harbour.

22. The Trevithick Society's replica of Richard Trevithick's 1801 Camborne road locomotive, the Puffing Devil.

Photograph: Pete Joseph

---

[1] It is believed to have been situated on the wharf and it is on record that the key was returned with thanks to Henry when the Duchy abandoned the old levy in 1838.

XV

HARVEY'S YOUNG FLEET

FROM THE VERY FIRST, SEA TRANSPORT HAD BEEN basically essential to John Harvey's enterprises. Neither the foundry, to begin with, nor the mines merchant business which followed, could have been sustained by land carriage. It was only by that long struggle to remain on the beach and keep that line of communication open that the firm had survived and, as its trading grew and became many-sided, more and more reliance was placed on shipping. This lifeline had been carefully fostered by Henry and, in the early thirties, some new measures were taken towards its consolidation.

When Charles Harvey gave evidence at the Hayle Reference in 1831 he was questioned about the Company's expenses and profits. Henry was then the owner of four vessels. Charles said that they maintained themselves and were placed on the same footing as those which were chartered. By this he meant that the captains were in each case paid the freight charges whilst they, themselves, victualled the ships and paid their crews. Freight charges were entirely a matter for the captain to fix. Where Henry's vessels were concerned, this would be arranged between him and their masters but where a vessel had to be found to bring a cargo to Hayle the importer was expected to drive as hard a bargain as he could and Henry would have to abide by that decision and pay on delivery. Importers were constantly pleading that they had done their best, often under difficult circumstances, when ships were scarce or captains hoity-toity, only to be told that they ought to have done better. The skippers of chartered vessels nearly always exacted in addition to the freight charge a gratuity of 5% (called *hat-money* by the Scandinavian captains). Harvey's men did not get this extra.

Henry's attitude towards ship-owning at that time is shown in a letter he wrote to Walter Coffin of the Rhondda collieries, dated the 31st of October, 1829.

215

I daresay your object in keeping Vessels of your own is something like ours, more for the sake of our trade than with a view to profit on the Vessels. Yours will probably make two voyages to Hayle whilst they make one to Cork on account of the quick dispatch here, and if your object in keeping vessels is to sell Coals, you dispose of double the quantity with the same capital and risk of Vessels.

By this we may understand that the small Harvey fleet was used solely for doing the Company's work and not available for charter to other concerns. Each ship's name is entered in the Cash Book at the end of every voyage with the number of the voyage, counting from the time when she entered the Company's service, and what was computed to have been the profit she had earned on this last trip or the loss sustained. Judging from those figures the profit margin was very small and nearly offset by the losses. Exactly how these figures were arrived at I must own I have not been able to discover. Apparently the cost of maintenance was not taken into account and, in those stormy seas, it was often considerable. Changes in policy for using the fleet "with a view to profit" and also for steadily increasing its strength were imminent, as will appear. The room for profit would lie in freight charges. When Harvey's vessels carried coal, timber, or other goods entirely in their owner's interests freights were kept down to the minimum of what could be agreed between Henry and his captains. But when these ships were used to carry goods for other parties the reverse applied. It was then up to the captains, who usually made those bargains, to get the highest possible price.

Walter Coffin, to whom the above was addressed, was an important pioneer in the development of the South Wales coal-field. He was the discoverer and chief exploiter of the rich seams of the Rhondda Valley. Some time earlier, he had taken the trouble to pay a personal visit to Hayle Foundry and Henry seems to have appreciated this and to have found in him a kindred spirit, for his letters to Coffin are more voluminous and intimate than those to any other coal-owner. But Coffin was as keen on prices as Henry and the letters between them are as highly seasoned with acerbity as good will.

In April, 1832, Thomas Bolitho, the Penzance banker, writes to Henry to say that a large brig called the *Phoebe* is being put up for sale and he is given first preference at a price of £500. According to the Stock Book, Henry already had one eighth share (out of sixty-four) in this vessel and after the usual exchange in the process of beating down the figure, he secured her for £437 10s. 0d.

The *Phoebe* had been built in Canada nine years earlier for the lumber trade with Britain, then in the initial stages of development but out to compete with the old established ones of Scandinavia and the Baltic. She was very much larger than any vessel previously owned by Harveys, being 200 tons burthen and with a carrying capacity of 220 tons weight. When laden, she drew twelve feet of water which was dangerously near the limit for entering Hayle Harbour, especially under the precarious conditions then prevailing of sluicing the channel and the bar. It is obvious that she was not intended for coastwise work and that her purchase foreshadowed a change in the Company's outlook on shipping. The bargain price at which she was sold was only a small part of the cost, as Henry immediately had her refitted and re-decked, on which he spent about a thousand pounds. This speculation was another of those bold ventures made with an eye to the future, to which attention has already been drawn.

The object of this acquisition was clearly to make the firm less dependent on Norway for their supplies of timber. It was rarely that the Norsemen could be persuaded to bring their vessels into Hayle, although to do so, a higher freight was repeatedly being offered than to land a cargo in Mount's Bay which meant bringing it all in many cartloads across the isthmus. Also it was hoped that equally good timber could be bought cheaper in the New World where the industry was just starting. But the *Phoebe* was not ready for sea until the autumn, when it was too late to make the Canadian passage. To fill in the time profitably Henry tried to get the Phoebe chartered for a Mediterranean voyage and wrote to merchants in Liverpool and Bristol asking them to recommend the vessel to their friends.

It should be mentioned here that the word "charter" has been used loosely (as in contemporary letters) to mean the hiring of a vessel for a short voyage merely by verbal agreement with the captain, no legal document in the shape of a charter-party being involved. It was in the latter sense that the *Phoebe* was being offered. With regard to the verbal agreements it would be more correct to say "hire" rather than "charter".

In spite of some tentative enquiries the *Phoebe* remained unemployed during the winter. Then, early in April, 1833, she sailed for Quebec, when it was hoped that the St. Lawrence River would be open for navigation. Captain Swan's report on the voyage is given on page 350. He certainly had bad luck but he does not appear to have been much in love with his ship or the prospects of the trade. At all events, on the next voyage, Captain William Lewis, one of Harvey's veteran skippers is discovered

217

in command. This time, the *Phoebe* went to Miramichi Bay in New Brunswick and picked a very good homeward cargo of timber. This inlet was to be her usual destination in future. Among the principal lumber-men here were James and John Cunard, brothers of Samuel, the founder of the Cunard Line.

After the purchase of the *Phoebe* it was determined not to be dependent any longer on the products of outside shipyards. Harveys were to add another department to the works and become shipbuilders. By the end of 1832 Henry had engaged his own shipwright, a man called Samuel Warren. One may see from the numerous letters he wrote when away from Hayle what an admirable choice he was. He was highly skilled in his trade and entirely loyal. Often when he went in search for just exactly the timber he wanted he was put to great trouble and personal inconvenience, but he never complained and his patience and pertinacity were inexhaustible.

The rumour of this new departure seems to have spread quickly as far as Padstow for, about the same time that Warren was taken on the strength of the company, a sailmaker of that port applied to be employed at Hayle. But there was much to be done before a dock and slipway at the head of the old Carnsew Channel were ready for the first keel to be laid and another year went by before a printed circular for the enlightenment of old customers was issued stating that "Harvey & Co. have engaged Mr. John Baragwanath, late of Padstow, to conduct the Sail Making Business for them at Hayle Foundry". Dated February 17th, 1834.

A reason for the decision, apart from the prevailing desire to make the Hayle establishment self-sufficient in as many of its branches as possible, was to ensure that ships intended for the coastwise trade were suitably designed for the class of goods they had to carry, notably that the holds were made with sufficiently capacious openings to take in the long Cornish boilers.

The list of ships given on pages 347-49 shows what the Hayle shipyard turned out down to 1844. Among them is one of particular interest — the *Hayle*. She was not intended "for our trade" but to work "for profit" on charter to all and sundry. How she fared in this venture is recorded in an almost complete set of letters from her master, Captain Bosustow, over a period of seven years addressed to Henry from nearly every port at which she touched. The collection is important, historically, as it throws so much light on a phase of maritime activity which, in less than a century, gained for Britain world supremacy in sea transportation. It was mainly achieved by little ships like the *Hayle* which, in the middle and later years of the nineteenth century, were being built all round the coasts of England and Wales — brigs, schooners, topsail schooners, barquentines, and small three-masted barques. These ships would set out with a cargo of saleable home goods for some port across the Atlantic or the Mediterranean (not always bespoken beforehand) and, having discharged it, get chartered from that place to another, and so on, often not returning to their home port for several years. Some of them were purely free-lance adventurers with no home-based office to make forward arrangements. Others, like the *Hayle*, could rely on guidance when needed from the owners, on credit facilities, and frequently on the booking of freights in advance of their arrival. But long distance communication was slow and uncertain and a rendezvous port was generally fixed near the end of the voyage where they would call "for orders".

It is astonishing how those tough old fellows, some of them practically illiterate and navigating with primitive instruments and charts, managed to find their way about the world, often under the most extreme conditions of exposure and hardship. Captain Bosustow was quite a model of his kind, a good seaman, a competent navigator, a considerate commander, and able to express himself lucidly in clear copy-book handwriting. He was of a sanguine and optimistic temperament which no disappointments or falsified hopes were able to damp. He was given a perfectly free hand in making arrangements for chartering his vessel and choosing what voyage he would make and his judgement, if not always correct, was never criticised by Henry. Some specimens of this correspondence will be found following page 351.

Henry's attitude towards all his seamen was consistently courteous and tolerant (in marked contrast to his keen and hard-headed approach to others) and they, in turn, were loyal and long suffering and seldom let him down. The trials of the coastwise voyages were by no means confined to foul weather and the dangers of unlighted rocks and shoals. The port facilities along the South Wales coast were utterly inadequate to cope with the outflow of the rapidly developing mineral resources in their neighbourhood — in at least one case there was only a small quay surmounted by a single ramshackle crane to serve a whole string of vessels. It was not uncommon to have to wait your turn for the tide and then be delayed as much as a fortnight waiting your turn for a berth at the quay. In the Chester Dee large cylinders, cast-iron beams, and boilers had to be landed on the open beach.

The annual toll of accidents to coastwise shipping in those days was very high and it speaks well for the way Harvey's ships were maintained and commanded that they suffered so few disasters. Letters of the Hayle skippers show standards of general education varying from "good" to "poor", the latter not such as would be passed today by the Board of Trade, but their competence as master-mariners was beyond question, so was their natural aptitude in "figuring" where prices, weights, and stowage were concerned. One of the most astute in bargaining for freights was one of the least literary. He opened his letters to the company with "Genten Men" and spelt phonetically throughout. A few of these letters are reproduced. Among them is the vivid account by Captain Veal (page 357) of the wreck of his vessel, the *Providence*, on the dangerous sands in the Towy estuary, and letters from Samuel Warren, Harvey's shipwright, who was dispatched at once to report on the extent of the damage. She was in a deplorable state, but Warren believed that salvage would be just possible. It was decided, however, to try to sell her where she lay. Accordingly she was put up to auction at Carmarthen a few days later. Warren wrote to report that there had been no bids though "two or three of the Pesantry was inclined to Purchase some of the small stores."

Warren never missed an opportunity to "look for suitable timbers" and now made use of his enforced visit to west Wales by going on to Pembrokeshire to take a walk round one or two likely estates. He stopped at Llanstephan again on the way back and worked out with Veal a plan for getting the Providence off the bank and patching her up sufficiently to get her home to Hayle for full repairs. Veal was then left behind to see the work satisfactorily carried out at the least possible expense. When the captain got back to Cornwall a couple of months later it was on board his own ship. We learn from the Cash Book that the *Providence* set sail again in June, 1834, on her seventy-second voyage, out of which she made a profit of £11 11s. 6d.

While things were going forward in the new shipyard, another vessel was being built at Ilfracombe in which Harveys had a particular interest. She was to be called the *Idas* and is not mentioned in the list of ships as she would not be a full member of the fleet though destined for two or three years to act as an auxiliary to it. Her promoter was James Banfield, brother of John who was the husband of Henry's niece, Elizabeth Trevithick. Harveys provided all the cordage for the standing and running rigging from their ropewalk, the sails by the recently established John Baragwanath, the anchors and bell from the foundry and also the knees for fastening the deck-beams to the side timbers. The latter, of iron, were only just beginning to replace wooden ones. Banfield writes that they are "admired by the ship-builders of Barnstaple who say they are by far the best they ever saw".

The *Idas* was built and launched in the course of 1833 and registered at Bristol. She was financed and owned by ten parties in the usual 64 shares[1]. Among them were Henry Harvey, owning eight shares, John Harvey Trevithick and his brother, Richard (sons of the inventor), and Francis Harvey, agent of the *Herald*, owning four each, while Captain Banfield had sixteen — the largest stake. The other six were of Ilfracombe, Bristol, and London. Banfield had worked for Harveys in other ships for a long time and continued to do so for several years as captain of the *Idas*. When the Hayle shipyard had turned out sufficient vessels to do the Company's work he went into the deep sea charter trade like that carried on by the *Hayle*. Captain Bosustow complained that his brig was undersized for the work and said that if she had only been rather bigger the profits would have been out of proportion to the difference. He used to stuff his personal accommodation in the cabin and that of the always-hoped-for passenger with cargo that could not be stowed in any other space below or on deck. The *Idas* was a larger brig, being 156 tons burthen (new measurement).

In 1834, the two first fruits of the boat-building department — the schooner, *John Harvey* (77 tons), and the smack *Nautilus* (52 tons) were completed and launched. The great work of excavating the tidal pen—a huge marine lake of 37 acres and constructing floodgates and sluices was also completed before the end of the year though it was not in working order until December. It was therefore rather premature for someone calling himself "A Cornish Miner" to write a letter which appeared in the *West Briton* on March the 7th. The reader will hardly fail to guess the source of its inspiration.

> In consequence of the disputes between the old Hayle Company [The C.C.C.] and the new Company [Harvey & Co.] at that place the former have for a considerable time ceased to use the Flood Gates they had erected for keeping the Channel clear of sand. The reason assigned expense of keeping up and working these Gates. They have, however, erected Gates and cut a new Channel [meaning they had embanked one side of the old Carnsew Channel]

[1] *Records of Bristol Ships*. Bristol Records Soc. vol XV.

with a view to keeping the harbour clear of sand; but in this object they had failed. Unless therefore some effective interference so as to induce the old company to put their Flood Gates again in operation, the Harbour of Hayle — the only eligible one during the winter, on the north coast of this county — will be effectually closed against the importers of coals and the shippers of copper ore; to the great injury of our Mining Interest and the general business of the whole district in that neighbourhood. Such an interference might be rendered effectual by the Mine Adventurers and the copper companies resolving to discontinue taking supplies from the party who may resist reasonable terms, or shipping ores from their wharfs. This is the only effectual means of averting a great evil to the leading Commercial Interest of Cornwall.

Henry lost no time in taking up the challenge and, in the next issue of the paper the following was published —

With regard to the charge by A Cornish Miner that we refuse to pay the old Company anything towards keeping up and working the Gates we have only to state that for three years and upwards, after the old Company had ceased to work them, no proposition was ever made to us on the subject of our contributing towards the expenses, nor were we, up to that time, told the reason for their not being worked. About a year and a half since we learned that the old Company would not work the gates unless we paid them for so doing; and notwithstanding we felt that the public had already paid a very full value for the expenditure of these Gates we then offered to refer the question as to what we should pay to any two Gentlemen or two Merchants, one to be chosen by each party. This offer, however, was rejected; but still, to see the harbour cleared of sand which was then fast accumulating, we proposed, after consulting some highly respectable and unprejudiced Merchants, to pay the old Company £100 per year. This offer was also rejected . . .

The Quays we have erected have cost us upwards of £10,000 and the benefit resulting from the opening of the trade caused thereby has been widely felt and acknowledged and this, if the writer of the letter above alluded to is what he professes to be, "a Cornish Miner" must perfectly know, and he must have known too that had it not been for our exertions at Hayle many of the mines in the County would have ceased from working several years since.

Previous to the erection of our Quays all copper ores brought to Hayle for shipment paid a charge of 8d. per ton for plottage, which gave the old Company several hundred pounds per annum; but as soon as our Quays were in readiness to receive ores that charge was reduced to 1½d. per ton, being a sum barely sufficient to pay the porters' expenses.

But the most telling shot was the reply to the statement that although the gates had been erected they had failed in their purpose of clearing the sand. Henry could point out that the works were by no means completed and the gates not even made. In fact, it was not until December the 27th that there was a ceremonial first opening of the sluices when the mines adventurers and other customers and friends of the Company were invited to a breakfast and to see for themselves the effect produced on the sand.

Map 4. Hayle Harbour, c 1832

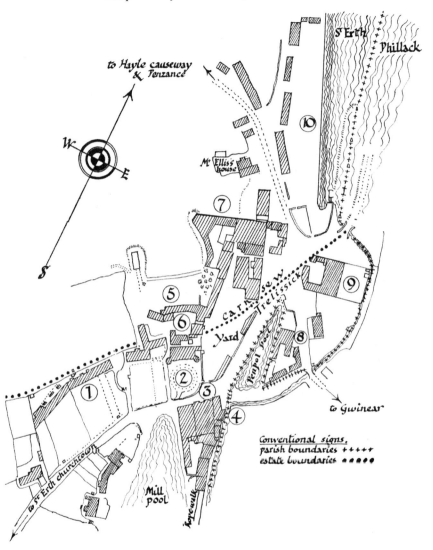

to Hayle causeway & Penzance

St Erth Phillack

Mr Ellis's house

to St Erth churchtown

carnsew Yard

Trelissick

Penpol pool

Copperhouse

to Gwinear

Mill pool

Conventional signs.
parish boundaries + + + + +
estate boundaries ● ● ● ● ●

1	Teamsters' dwelling houses called Drivers' Row	5	Farm buildings and yard
2	Foundry House	6	Stable yard
3	Hammer-mill and **forges**	7	Casting houses
4	Grist Mill	8	Old White Hart Hotel
		9	Tin smelting house
		10	Harvey's Wharf

223

The same occasion was celebrated by a dinner given to the sixty men who had been employed on the work and four of Harvey's captains, for which Jane Trevithick of the *White Hart* "and others" were paid at the rate of 3s. per head for the men and 4s. for the captains. The entry suggests that the feast was spread about in different houses, the little inn could not have contained such a large gathering.

All went off jubilantly. When the expectant crowd saw the pent up waters of the lake rush forth in a foaming cataract to clear the way for the Foundry shipping it must have seemed to some of the watchers a symbolic act of liberation. And here was the triumph of a feat of civil engineering for which it had once been thought necessary to call in Telford! It has proved a work of permanent value for, after a 130 years, the action still goes on at the last of the ebb of every tide.

It will be seen by the list of ships (page 347) that, when another year had gone by, Harvey & Co's fleet numbered sixteen sailing vessels, twelve of which had been built and fitted out in their own boat-yard, and that there had been no more losses at sea. And it will be noticed that the last five were all registered in the name of John Harvey Trevithick. Though these were, ostensibly, personal ventures, they all sailed under the firm's orders and carried whatever cargoes they were directed to. Voyages, now definitely made "for profit" were organised on a different basis from those of earlier days and arranged with a view to the strictest economy, avoiding as far as possible having to sail for any part of their journeys in ballast. They now did rounds of calls rather than direct to-and-from missions, hiring out their services at intermediate stages.

The principal regular imports were coal and pig-iron from Wales. From Bristol came wrought-iron of various kinds — boiler-plates, bar and sheet-iron — and general hardware (for the Hayle shop). Here, until 1827, they had also collected the pig-iron and boiler-plates sent down the Severn from Coalbrookdale. In that year the ship-canal from Sharpness to Gloucester was opened which by-passed the dangerous lower reaches of the river and its ferocious tidal bore. This enabled them to meet the iron at Gloucester and save something in freight charges. Also they loaded salt there which came down by water from Droitwich. Large quantities of salt were needed at St. Ives and Newlyn for pickling Cornish pilchards, to be exported to the Mediterranean in barrels. There seems to have been such an insatiable demand at Naples that the duty was taken off to encourage more ample supplies. For many months after the harvest, oats, barley, and wheat made full cargoes from ports in North Cornwall and Devon, also from places as far apart as Southern Ireland, Anglesey, and Norfolk. Bricks and tiles came chiefly from Bridgwater, slates and paving stones from Tintagel and Boscastle; hemp, tar, and linseed oil (for the ropewalk) from London and Liverpool. Homegrown timber from numerous sources. The wood for their own vessels came nearly all from the New Forest. Their shipwright, Warren, made frequent visits to the creeks in Southampton Water to select just what he wanted.

The hard-worked office staff was continually trying to solve the puzzle of making the tied-to-time exports from Hayle (mainly deliveries of their machinery, copper ore, block tin, and the local moulders sand) fit in most economically with the desired imports, leaving it to their captains to pick up what freights they could between ports where they would otherwise have to go in ballast.[1] But, before any fixed itinerary could be arranged, a barrage of enquiries had to be trained on merchants and dealers to find out where the lowest prices ruled. The quotations thus produced would generally be challenged before terms were agreed and ships given their sailing orders. It must be repeated that when carrying goods for other people, and not the Company, the policy on freights was reversed. It was then for the captains, if not the office to get the highest possible figure.

Wherever grain was concerned — and it formed a large part of the shipments — we may assume that John Harvey Trevithick would be consulted. Since we saw him as a boy, taken by his uncle into what might be called the cereals and agricultural department of the firm, he has remained in the background without a mention. Indeed, in the records, his obscurity is nearly complete. Almost the first sign of any initiative taken by him is when he appears in the register of the *Idas* as proprietor of four shares in her (£120). He is therein described as "baker" — a fact, but very much of an understatement.

In 1833, when the *Idas* was launched, this second son of the distinguished inventor was twenty-seven years old and, by now, holding a responsible post in the Company. From the very few letters I have come across signed by himself (one can only guess where his hand is in the routine "out" correspondence) I gather that he had grown into a man of very decided character, that he had got from his mother much of the Harvey acumen for business but little from his father except a certain sharpness of temper.

[1] See Russell Webber, Journal of the Trevithick Society No. 34 2007 and Old Cornwall vol XII No. 1 1997.

He does not seem to have had any taste for mechanical things. His bent was towards the fundamentals of rural life and his training had fitted him congenially for taking a leading part in that branch of the Company's activities which belonged to these — the grain market, milling, the farm.

The records indicate that Harveys had two mills working at Hayle at this time, named respectively the North and South Mills. It is surmised that they were windmills [1]. The local demand for wheat and barley flour must have greatly exceeded what they could grind, judging from the amount that was regularly imported. An adjunct to the mills was the Company's bakehouse which supplied the public with bread and this, the least of the Harvey establishments, doubtless caused J.H.T. to be classed as "baker".

A good deal of grain was grown on the Foundry Farm, notably oats for the horses for this (as before mentioned) was the road transport depot — the land-link with the mines. There were now fifty-two draught-horses stabled there besides saddle-horses for the principals and messengers. The stock-books give the names of all these animals which have the familiar ring — Daisy, Captain, Beauty &ct. The draught-horses are grouped into teams of four, each team with the name of its driver, responsible for its feeding and management. Among the vehicles was one adapted for carrying the long Cornish boilers. Twelve or more horses would be hooked in to pull that load. It was sometimes borrowed by a mine for transferring its plant to another. There were several yoke of oxen and it would appear that they, and not horses, were used for ploughing.

Betwixt and between the agricultural side and the foundry were the lime kilns. Lime-burning had been done in John Harvey's time and, it will be remembered, that one of his first complaints against the C.C.C. was that they had forcibly unloaded a cargo of limestone from his ship as she lay on the sands and carried it off to burn in their own kilns. It must then have been imported solely for sale to local farmers, who had previously used cartloads of sea sand as a rough and ready fertilizer. But now that Henry had two cupola blast furnaces, a fair amount of limestone must have been used in the foundry as well as what was burnt in the kilns for sale. The stone was brought by sea almost entirely from Plymouth though there is an instance of a merchant at Preston sending samples of limestone from the Lancashire Pennines and offering to supply at cut prices, but the difficulty of getting freights for the outward journey to that port on the Ribble seems to have made the proposal uneconomic.

[1] See opposite page for note on mills.

On the old Carnsew Quay, today, stand two massive circular lime-kilns, tangentially united, which are certainly of a respectable age and may well go back to the time when Messrs. Harris & Ellis acquired the quay from George Blewett in 1780. If so, they must have witnessed all the dramatic events which took place in the port since then and, though idle now, are more deserving than most of their kind of having a place in the Schedule of Ancient Monuments.[1]

How to keep an economic balance in all these departments that revolved like planets round the central sun which was the foundry, and on their seaborne supplies; how to avoid shortages on the one hand and wastefulness on the other; to keep the whole financially solvent, needed the brains, the unremitting vigilance, and the courage of a single person. That all this could be managed with success on a continually expanding basis gives the measure of Henry Harvey's talents for organisation and enterprise. Much credit is also due to the two principal lieutenants he had chosen — his nephews, Nicholas Oliver and J. H. Trevithick.

It has been shown that Henry drew much of his strength from the strong spirit of self-reliance which was innate in him. How much this was respected by his neighbours can be gauged from a letter from that estimable person, already mentioned, Captain William Gregor of Binner Downs Mine, warning him not to be drawn into a compromise agreement with a competitor, dated May the 14th, 1834.

> One thing I must take the liberty of suggesting and as it is only between ourselves I trust you will not be offended with, that is, was I situated as you are I would have nothing to do with Mr P. as to fixing any price for the next year, and I give you as my decided opinion that anything of that sort may considerably weaken the position you have held for many years in the public mind. I do not mean to drop a hint that you should make sacrifices to meet the public feeling, but what you did should be done independently of any reference to any other Party. Stand as you hitherto have done, an independent man and a wonder to all around.

---

[1] Unfortunately these were demolished in 1980.

[2] Trevithick's Mills (from page 222). There were in fact three: North, South and Front Mills as fully described by Mr. John T. W. Higgans in the second of two articles on "The Old Water-Mills of Hayle" in the Spring 1990 issue of *Old Cornwall*. He describes how they were first powered by a pony, then a horse, then in 1832 by steam. In 1879 a 180 h.p. beam engine did the milling and for dressing a 40 h.p. horizontal steam engine which in 1883 was also generating their electric light.

XVI

AUSTEN'S ENGINE

A MONG THE LARGE PUMPING ENGINES BUILT AT THE
Foundry in the early 'thirties was one which not only made fame
for itself but was also the means of considerably furthering the
interests of the Company in a new and profitable field. It was known to
contemporary commentators as "Austen's Engine" and was of the type
which had now come into general use for draining the mines, the prototype
of which, as already described (page 95), was devised by Richard Trevithick
in 1812 for Wheal Prosper Mine — a Cornish engine. In the previous
chapters I have tried to give a general outline of how the Company grew
from small beginnings on a precarious foothold, constantly threatened by
a predatory neighbour, to a position of strength and independence, treating
the account chronologically, year by year, down to 1835. I would now like
to take the story along a single line, following the fortunes of this engine
and those of a replica, made in its exact image shortly after.

In the early 'twenties there was a movement among the younger
generation of mines adventurers to prospect in new country away from the
old-established and heavily worked districts of St. Agnes, Redruth, and the
Land's End peninsula. Successful trials were made on the southern fringe
of the granite mass of Bodmin Moor at St. Blazey and Caradon, above
Liskeard. The former was on land belonging to Joseph Thomas Austen,
an enterprising yet level-headed man who was also blessed with a private
fortune. He had married the heiress of the ancient Treffry family whose
home was the fine old Elizabethan house called Place, in Fowey, which
is still standing. Gilbert gives him a line of unqualified approval as "one
of the most spirited adventurers in mines, and of the most judicious and
enlightened managers that Cornwall has seen for many years. Mr. Austen
has diverted a river for the use of machinery; and he has set the first
example of bringing a canal to the mines, for the purpose of carrying coal

23. Six-ton steam hammer in the forge

24. Beam (or bob) for seventy-inch engine

25. S.S. *Ramleh* (3,800 tons) on the slipway

26. Triple-expansion marine steam engine *(1,000 h.p.)*

and other articles from the sea coast, and of taking down the ores, which are then transported from a harbour of his own construction."

This harbour formed the nucleus of the place now called Par. It is still a busy little port which is, at present, wholly concerned with the export of china clay. The canal still holds water but has no traffic, for the mines it served have long since been closed. They were called Fowey Consols and Lanescot. It was for the former that the Austen engine was made. The diversion of the river was contrived by taking it across the deep ravine of the Luxulyan Valley on a bridge, a hundred feet in height, which carried both the water and a mineral railway. This also remains, spanning that lovely valley — a particular home of the royal osmunda fern — with lofty arches which add a note of elegance rather than discord to the scene. Austen changed his name to that of his wife in 1839 and the bridge bears the coat-of-arms of that house and is still called the Treffry Viaduct.

J. T. Austen held nearly all the shares in the Fowey Consols and Lanescot mines and was therefore virtual proprietor as well as adventurer. But all the business relations with Henry Harvey were conducted through two of his managers, the brothers William and Thomas Petherick. A third brother, John, managed the Knockmahon mines in County Waterford and was one of Harvey's Irish customers. All three write the letters of men of good breeding and education. They were very partial towards the products of Hayle Foundry and were tolerant, when, as frequently happened, there were delays in the execution of their orders beyond times which had been named for delivery, though this sometimes brought forth sharp letters. The only time the name has been mentioned heretofore was when William Petherick sent the recipe for a medicine at the time of the outbreak of the cholera.

In February, 1831, Thomas Petherick sent an introductory note by one W. Pease who was to be given training in Harvey's merchanting department "with a view to qualifying himself to conduct the trade at Par", the harbour which J. T. Austen was then constructing there. In the same letter a mention was made of an 80 inch engine which it was proposed to have made for Fowey Consols mine. Shortly afterwards, Harveys submitted a provisional specification and suggested that the design should be made by James Sims, the engineer of the Carn Brea Mines and son of the partner in Trevithick's plunger-pole engine patent. This was two years before Arthur Woolf retired and it seems odd that he was not mentioned, but he was then in poor health and evidently not very active and Sims had put a good deal of work in Harvey's way. In his reply to the Company Thomas Petherick said "I do not think the engineer named in your last favour would be able to conform to the views which I explained to your Mr. Harvey".

The fact was that a young engineer, in whom they had great confidence, had just been engaged for Fowey Consols Mine. His name was William West. This was also the name of Henry's late brother-in-law and partner and of his nephew, who had acted for some time as the Company's representative at the Neath Abbey Iron Works and was now serving in some capacity at the Foundry. There seems to have been no traceable relationship between these two West families. Where there is any likelihood of confusion the two Williams will be spoken of respectively as "of St. Blazey" (the engineer of Fowey Consols) and "of Hayle". But as the nephew does not take any prominent part in the story the other will be named without qualification.

This William West was by no means unknown to Henry. His obituary notice[1], after stating that he was one of fifteen children born of parents at Camborne, who "received but a scanty education at a dame school", recalls that he was introduced by Henry to Bolitho of Penzance, for whom he erected an engine for his flour mill. It adds, "Mr. Harvey ever afterwards took a deep interest in Mr. West's career". Meanwhile, West had been employed at Great Wheal Towan, a mine in the St. Agnes district, whose engineer was Captain Samuel Grose. Grose, as mentioned earlier, had been a pupil of Richard Trevithick and was already noted for his improvements to the Cornish engine. He appeared regularly in Lean's monthly reports of engine efficiency where the averages of the duty of his engine were outstandingly high. His success was largely due to the measures he took for preventing loss of heat by radiation, lagging every exposed part of boiler and steam pipe with a non-conducting material — chiefly sawdust. West imbibed Grose's ideas to good purpose and proved to be a particularly apt pupil.

There was a long interval before a definite order was given for the new Fowey Consols engine. Meanwhile, Harveys supplied a good deal of material, pit-work, and boiler-work to Austen's undertakings. The contract for the engine was not signed until April, 1833, when William Petherick wrote, accepting the estimate. The price was named at £1,975 to include delivery at the mines. The letter ended with a ringing exhortation; "The

---

[1] Proceedings of the Institution of Civil Engineers 1879.

232

articles to be of the very best quality and the workmanship such as will enable us to vie with any other Engine in the County".

William wrote again on the 25th of May to ask how the work was getting on and when it was expected that the cylinder would be cast. That operation was carried out only a few days later, but the casting was faulted and only fit for scrap. The process was a tricky one and, in spite of long experience, it remained liable to failure. To make one of these large cylinders — the present one had an internal diameter, after boring, of six feet, eight inches, and stood eleven feet, six inches high — the mould and core were prepared in a pit sunk in the ground. Several tons of pig-iron would have to be melted and more than one furnace might be employed to run the molten metal into the mould. Any slight hitch in the continuity of the flow or any miscalculation which caused the supply of metal to run out just short of the complete casting would render it fit for nothing but the scrap-breaker's hammer.

Both the cylinder and the great beam were cast successfully within the next six weeks. The former was sent off by sea but the beam, which was forty feet long, was an out-size for any shipping available and had to go overland on one of the special waggons, drawn by a large team. Petherick wrote to ask how many horses were coming as he was arranging for their feed at ninepence per head.

Austen's engine was not long in getting into the news after it had started working. Its performance so much outstripped any of its neighbours that reports of how many millions of pounds of water it could raise one foot high on a bushel of coal were received, first with surprise, and then incredulity. To allay suspicion it was eventually decided to submit the engine to a trial by impartial expert witnesses so that its actual duty could be ascertained and authenticated. This took place on March the 22nd and 23rd and a detailed account of what transpired is given in *Lean's Historical Statement* (reproduced on page 344).

It would appear that, in order to ensure the validity of the test, the investigators left absolutely nothing undone to arrive at the truth. Their verdict was that the duty exceeded 125m. This figure was not just something rather better than any other pumping engine had ever scored before, it was 30m. better than the nearest runner-up. The triumph of this advance may best be gauged by recalling the jubilant exclamation of James Watt only thirty-seven years earlier, when he had installed one of his latest engines at Herland Mine — "The machine is perfect, and no further improvement can be expected!"[1]. Its duty was 27½ m.[2]

Some months before this notable trial of Austen's engine its owners were already so well satisfied by its performance that Harveys were given an order to build another exactly similar in all respects. This was for one of the mines in East Cornwall, belonging to the same Company between Callington and the Tamar, where they were getting silver-lead. The date given for delivery was December the 22nd, 1834 and William Petherick wrote to say that he hoped there would be no delays such as those which attended the completion of the Fowey Consols engine. But by the middle of March, 1835, though shipments of the principal parts had been made, there were still more to come and on the 18th he wrote to remonstrate. A vessel which had arrived a few days before had brought a further consignment and boiler-plates but no rivets to put them together with, so "the Boiler Builders are idle. This is another vexatious disappointment, but thro' you I am tolerably enured to it". Another letter followed on April the 4th. To expedite matters, a waggon and team had been sent overland to Callington, but the teamster took them to the wrong mine and Petherick was nearly at the end of his patience. "I have never felt such a series of annoyances since I gave the order for the Engine up to the present time. Mr. West informed me of the plug-rod eyes & the false cover not being sent & I now find the bottoms and valves of the Plunger Cataract wanting — & what more I can't say."

Henry, in turn, was inured to complaints about delays. They left him unrattled. He had always believed that it was better to keep people waiting for something well done rather than to scamp work in order to deliver it by a fixed date. Offers of contracts which had penalty clauses attached to them he would turn down. But the protracted piecemeal delivery of the Callington engine had been fraught with elementary sins of omission and misdirection, and for these, no doubt, the new manager of the foundry would be held responsible.

Nicholas Harvey shared his uncle's views entirely about high standards of production, but he had only been in charge of the iron works for a little more than a year and had taken over from a sick man whose visits to Hayle had become rare. In Woolf's latter days Henry had to carry the burden of

[1] *Lean's Historical Statement.*
[2] W. Pole, quoted from Taylor's *Records of Mining.*

the whole business with particularly close attention to those inter-related complexities which kept the foundry fully and economically employed. He had good lieutenants in the foremen of the various departments and his nephew William West (of Hayle), but it was the follow-through which mattered. First there would be the enquiry from some company or person never heard of before. A general answer would be sent by return of post. Next, particulars of price and likely time of delivery would be called for. This meant getting out a specification, costing it, and guessing how the various stages of the work from castings to fittings up could be put through, and by when, in relation to what was already in hand. Whilst this letter was being composed, others would be sent out to persons who might know something about the prospective customer, as to whether or not he was "respectable", that is, financially sound and likely to pay if the deal went through.

If a whole pumping plant were ordered for a new shaft about to be sunk, it would be most desirable that all the etceteras should go through the shops at the same time —boilers, steam-pipes, engine, pit-work (to include the pumps and pump-rods — great balks of timber linking them to the extremity of the engine-beam). If Harveys lent the customer the services of one of his erectors they would expect that their work on the contract should be synchronised at the other end by having the necessary buildings of boiler and engine-houses all ready to receive the machinery when it arrived. The follow-through had clearly failed most exasperatingly where the Austen and Callington engines were concerned except in the eventual completion of those contracts where results showed that both engines turned out to be winners.

One of the greatest difficulties which Nicholas had to face in planning any regular routine in the foundry was the sudden increase in orders which had to be coped with out of proportion to the plant then available to execute them. The "in" letters of 1835 make a bundle nearly twice as large as any of their predecessors. There was no thought of abandoning any of the lines which had been made from the very beginning in order to concentrate and specialise on the more remunerative contracts; nor of cutting out any of the newer ones introduced by industrial progress, notably complete equipment for gas-plants, from retorts to lamp-posts ("pillars", doubtless of faultless classical design); equipment for mineral railways, now multiplying rapidly, from rails and chairs ("saddles") to complete waggons. Miners' picks, Cornish shovels, chaff-cutting machines, weighing machines were also being manufactured. While all these goods were being ordered, customers requiring domestic fittings of all sorts expected to have as much attention paid to them as those who wanted large engines and heavy machinery. The Rev. George Richards, Rector of Ladock, lacked the security of a handrail to his staircase for want of banisters to support it and sent a despairing personal appeal to Henry —

> What can I, what shall I do to obtain the balusters for completing the staircase of the Rectory House, Ladock!
>
> This day month, I received a letter from Mr Nichs Harvey saying "We have about completed the short ones *and I hope next week the long ones will be finished*". I have since sent him repeated letters per omnibus — but I fear they have never reached him. I have once more formed the resolution of again troubling you per mail — and the necessity I am laboring under to get rid of Carpenter, Smith, & Painter will plead my excuse.

There is a note in faint pencil on the letter to say that the goods had been sent off eight days earlier by the public carrier's van. The distance is about thirty miles. Several houses in and about Hayle have ornamental iron banisters which were cast at the Foundry.

The phenomenal performance of the Austen engine at its trial in March drew immediate attention to the capabilities of its designer, William West. Within a month a London firm, Dixon & Bell, acting for the Union Gold Mining Company of Virginia, were asking William Petherick if it could be arranged for the engineer of Fowey Consols to design two 23 inch engines for their clients. This was agreed to and Petherick passed the order on to Harveys. It was to be supplemented with a variety of mining machinery. The contract was priced at £1,270 8s. 10d. and completion of the work was promised for early June.

Henry believed that he could take further advantage of this commission. His new brig, the *Hayle*, was on the stocks in the shipyard, nearing completion. She had been specially built for deep sea trading and, as already mentioned, was to sail under Captain Bosustow "for profit". She ought to be ready for sea when the Union Gold Mining Co's equipment was due to go to America, so here was a ready-made charter for the maiden voyage. Forthwith he quoted his freight charges to Dixon & Bell. But the agents were extremely cautious. They would not trust an untried Hayle-built ship with their goods and said they would charter one from London, themselves. Nor had they the fullest confidence in the manufacturer, but insisted that William West must go to Hayle when the cargo was being loaded and certify that his designs had been properly carried out. He was to be attended by a disinterested expert to check all the machinery before it was put on board, for which they named Thomas Lean of the monthly record. This time Nicholas managed to get everything ready punctually to the day. The *William the Fourth* of London arrived on June the 13th and sailed for Virginia two days later when all conditions had been fulfilled.

Near the end of July there came a letter from Thomas Petherick, addressed to the Company from the London office of the Austen mines saying, "I beg to introduce to your friendly notice Mr. Wicksteed, the Engineer of the E. London Water Works, & should be particularly obliged at any attention you may be pleased to show him on his visit to your place". He added in postscript, "I hope to be with you in the course of a few days".

Behold a harbinger of destiny! But the name has never turned up before in any of the correspondence, "in" or "out", and it is conceivable that neither Henry nor Nicholas knew anything whatever about this Mr. Wicksteed. It is equally possible that the reader may also be in darkness, so a few words of explanation about his business and himself follow.

From the latter part of the sixteenth century down to as recent a date as 1904, supplies of water for London had been provided by a number of private companies; only then were they unified under a single authority — the Metropolitan Water Board — which was given statutory powers to buy out all the existing concerns. Earlier enterprises varied from water-wheels fixed in the arches of old London Bridge which, by tidal action, pumped Thames water, unfiltered, into the city, to the famous New River, engineered by Sir Hugh Middleton, which introduced the purer element from Amwell, near Ware, into a pool at Islington for distribution by wooden pipes.

In 1807, the London Dock Board, which owned two of the older water companies (one of them started in the reign of James II) sold them to a new undertaking called the East London Water Works Company, who established their plant at Old Ford in Bow, by the ancient crossing-place of the River Lea. In 1809, they started operations with two Boulton and Watt engines. In 1829 the situation of engineer became vacant. Out of thirty-two applicants the successful candidate was Thomas Wicksteed, aged twenty-three.

In 1835 one of the engines was suffering from decrepitude and giving results that were so unsatisfactory that it was decided to make an extensive

SECTIONAL ELEVATION OF THE CORNISH ENGINE BUILT FOR THE CALLINGTON MINE AND RE-ERECTED AT THE EAST LONDON WATER WORKS IN 1838

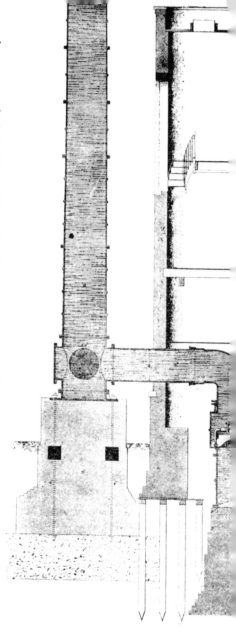

In the full sized drawing all details are lettered for reference but, in this much reduced diagram, I have thought it less confusing to point out principal parts of the machine by a "right to left" reading. In that order are the cylinder (80" diam., 11′ stroke) and its five valves. It is attached to one end of an equal-armed beam, pivotted on top of a solidly built stone wall dividing the engine-house. The other end of the beam is attached to the large plunger-pole pump (diameter of pole 41" working through a water-tight gland in the pole-case). Conversion of the radial movement of the beam to the vertical of piston-rod and pump is made by James Watt's parallel motion. The fluted bulge above the plunger-pole is a case filled with scrap-iron to give that additional weight, normally supplied at a mine by the pump-rods.

Further to the left, outside the building, is the stand-pipe with its high column of water to give pressure to the mains of the town supply. Between it and the pump are seen the two large Harvey and West double-beat valves. Penetrating the dividing wall is the exhaust pipe leading into the surface condenser, and the air-pump, with the hot-well above it, leading into the boiler feed pump. These two pumps are worked by the movement of the beam, a third will be seen, actuated by the plunger-pole. This draws cold water from the main well for circulating in the condenser. On the cylinder side of the dividing wall is seen the longest of the rods worked by the beam. It controls the automatic action of the engine and is called the plug-rod. As it moves it brings slightly projecting chocks up and down, spaced appropriately, into contact with cams which operate the valves. Near the lower part of the rod is seen a small unit (one of two) which acts as the timing gear, controlling the number of strokes to the minute. A piston, working in a small cylinder immersed in water fills and discharges itself through an opening that can be regulated as to aperture — a sort of water clock. It is called the cataract from an earlier and much cruder device in which a box filled itself with water and descended to a point where it upset itself.

The four valves (right to left) are as follows; the governor, steam valve, equilibrium valve-all at the top of the cylinder — and the exhaust valve, near the bottom. All except the governor are of the double-beat type, invented by Jonathan Hornblower and improved by Woolf. The term "governor" must not be confused by what is now generally understood by this name, a device for regulating the speed of the engine which, in the Cornish engine was done by the cataract. It was, in modern usage, the throttle, an ordinary conical valve admitting steam direct from the boilers to the valve-chest. The engine-man set it by hand to whatever opening he required and left it at that, and it was not part of the automatic system operated by the engine, itself, as were the other three valves. When the engine was being started, however, those valves had to be worked in their turn by hand until the machine was fully warmed up, which took half an hour or more. The handles for starting, called "horns" will be easily picked out from their descriptive name.

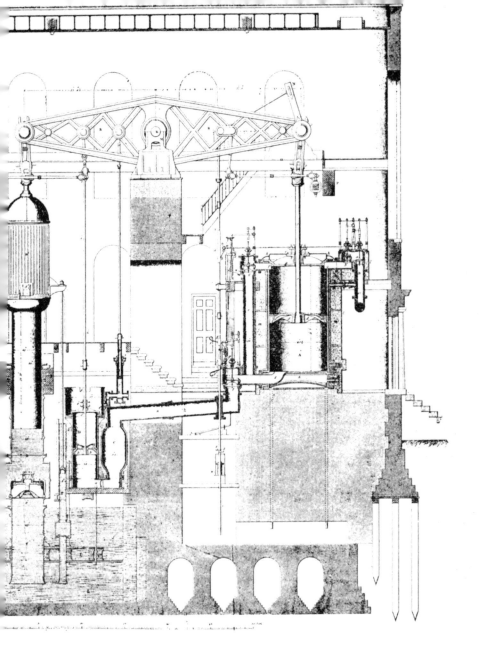

The cycle of the Cornish engine

It was powered only on the down stroke, with steam at boiler pressure above the piston, and vacuum from the condenser below it. Steam was cut off at about one third of the stroke, the remainder of which was worked on its expansion. Thus, reduced to a very low pressure, it was not yet allowed to escape into the condenser, access to which was stopped at the end of the stroke by the closing of the exhaust valve, followed after a brief pause by the opening of the equilibrium valve. This allowed the steam, still confined above the piston, to pass to its underside through the vertical pipe seen in the drawing and distribute its nearly spent force on either face. The following up stroke was made entirely by the force of gravity acting at the other end of the beam. The stroke completed and the piston being in *equilibrio*, the engine paused again. The pauses were important as they gave time for the pump valves to close. The cycle re-commenced with the opening once more of the steam and exhaust valves.

refit of the whole machine. One of the directors, however, a Mr. Grout, advised that it should be scrapped and replaced by a Cornish engine. He told his co-directors that he had been reliably informed that, in their latest development, this class of pumping engine had achieved an extraordinary economy in fuel above those designed by Watt. But no Cornish engine had ever been seen in London and probably never heard of by any other member of the board. The name may have had an outlandish ring about it compared with that of the now entrenched respectability of the Birmingham makers. Young Wicksteed was, however, asked his opinion. Now it happened that John Taylor of the Consolidated Mines, to whom the reader has already been introduced, was a friend of the family and, long before Thomas had joined the Company, he had heard all about the Cornish engine and its virtues, and he came out enthusiastically in support of Mr. Grout. The upshot was that he was sent down to Cornwall to gain information about the engines at work in the mines and make a report. It was most likely Mr. Grout who put him into the hands of Thomas Petherick, who sent him straight to Hayle where he, later, joined him and took him to see the Austen engine.

How many other mines besides Fowey Consols Wicksteed visited does not appear. When he returned to London it was with the conviction that one Cornish engine would answer the needs of his company far better than the two Boulton and Watt machines, even if they were tuned up and rejuvenated, and the saving in fuel consumption would soon repay the expense of the change. But, to use his own words, "although my report was highly in favour of them, the opinions expressed in favour of the *old* system, and against the new, advocated by me, were nevertheless so numerous, and of such high authority," that the plan was cheerfully abandoned.

Nothing further happened for two years. Then, early in 1837, Mr. Grout informed his board that he knew of a good second-hand Cornish engine that was up for sale at a comparatively low price. This was none other than the Callington engine which was being disposed of after only one year's work — not through any fault of its own but the failure of the mine to realise anticipations. Nor was it the only case of an engine being turned idle from the same cause. There had been a flurry of over-speculation and several mines were being forced to close down. Harvey had two sixty-inch engines on his hands which had been countermanded before they could be delivered and only after prolonged legal negotiations conducted by the Follets and his solicitors was he able to recover half the agreed price.

Mr. Wicksteed's visit to Hayle coinciding with the moment when a slump in engine production was being felt must have seemed to Henry to be providential. With his flair for long foresight he could not fail to see the chance of a new outlet for his speciality, the great pumping engine, in a regular service not dependent on the fickle fortunes of a mine. He took his guest over the works where it happened that a large casting, identical with those in the Austen and Callington engines was being machined. Wicksteed was much impressed and wrote to his board "I saw an 80 inch cylinder. 12 feet long, in the boring machine and could not perceive a flaw in it."

The visit was a mutual success; Wicksteed's former opinion was now upheld and the water-company bought the Callington engine; Harveys gained an important contract and, with it, a firm footing in the metropolis. The bargain was that Harveys should dismantle the engine, overhaul it and its three boilers, transfer them to London, and re-erect them at Old Ford. They had also to construct a standpipe alongside the engine-house. The latter, shaped like a factory chimney, but made of metal, was to fulfil the same purpose as a water-tower, to give pressure to the mains supply. The difference is that whereas a water-tower has a large cistern on top (from which the pressure is derived) and is fed by a pipe of comparatively small diameter, in the standpipe the water is pumped in from the bottom and the whole weight of the column is on that inlet valve.

The contract was one of unusual stringency. It bound Harveys under a heavy penalty to effect an average duty during twelve months regular work of the engine, equal to ninety millions of pounds, raised one foot high by the consumption of ninety-four pounds of good Welsh coal[1]. By this time Nicholas Harvey had got the production side of the foundry in all its miscellaneous forms well organised. There were few complaints of delay though in the two previous years they had been almost as numerous as the orders. He was determined that nothing should go wrong with the East London Water Works commission. In August he was in London winding up negotiations. West had been with him and had returned home. On the 28th he wrote from St. Blazey —

Annexed I hand you a drawing for two pumps for the East London Water

[1] This was fixed as the bushel measure for purposes of Lean's tests — by weight instead of capacity, the latter being subject to much variety.

Works which you may immediately set about to cast & on Mr N. Harvey's return you will have the whole order complete, he having closed the Contract with that company for the whole job.

In another part of the same letter one senses even more the urgency that both men felt about this particular contract being put through without a hitch. The *Carnsew* was due back from a rather protracted voyage to Sark and Guernsey, and West asks that "immediately on the vessel's arrival at Hayle you will dispatch her with all possible speed to Cotehele quay in the Tamar, from whence I shall be able to send her to London with two cargoes".

In the course of the next three months the whole of the engine and one boiler had been transferred to the new site without incident, but the last two presented a problem. One of the boilers was found to be too long to stow. As a rule, the Cornish boiler did not exceed twenty-five feet in length, but this one was an out-size and measured twenty-seven feet, ten inches. All Harvey's vessels intended for boiler transport were fitted with specially designed hatchways. Where two boilers were shipped, one was lowered into the hold and the other placed on top with its upper part rising a little above deck level and the hatchway combing. In the smack and schooner it can have left but little clearance for the boom of the mainsail to swing over when the ship tacked. The boilers of Austen's engine were over-size and had been sent by a hired barge. As those of the Callington engine were also made at Hayle and their dimensions, as well as the measurements of the *Carnsew's* hatch were known, why was this elementary mistake allowed to happen.

One of the most remarkable features of this multiple industry was the general intelligence system which its administrative centre had developed, although it had none of the aids to efficiency which are thought essential to a modern office. Somehow they managed to keep up-to date with the constantly fluctuating prices for all the raw and fabricated materials required for their various departments. They could answer an enquiry, often by return of post, as to what kind of an engine would best suit the needs of a new customer, give the pressure of steam it should work at, its horse-power, their price for it, and the probable date of delivery. They would be well up in current freight charges, dues, tolls, and demurrages in home and foreign ports. Yet here was a simple slip at a moment of particular urgency which never seems to have occurred before. Perhaps it was that the foundry had become so self-reliant under the strong government of Nicholas Harvey that the old liaison between it and the office, so long preserved by his vigilant uncle had become temporarily weak.

It was the end of November when the *Carnsew* made her way up the twelve miles of the Tamar's winding reaches to Cotehele Quay, just below Calstock. She had been newly taken over from Philip Andrew by a young Captain Cundy, with the striking Christian names of Henry Harvey. On the 1st of December the following letter was sent off to Hayle addressed to "Mr. Nichs Harvey or Harvey & Co";

> Mr N. Harvey
>> Sir,
>> By request of Capt*n* Cundy who is now buisy with the Carpenter we beg to inform you that we are brought up & can go no further. We want your immediate presence. The Carnsew will not take the Boilers without the main beam & deck coming up. We have got the first Boiler in the angle of the hatchway. The after combing we have [had] taken up by a Ship Carpenter & there is no possibility of getting it down without taking up the main beam, we cannot do any more without further orders. The Boiler is now resting 2 feet abaft the main beam & close up to the fore beam & Mast.
>> You will please come here without delay or if you cannot possible come send orders how to proceed, but much rather that you would come & see how we are situated.
>> We have written Mr West desiring him to come here immediately.
>>> We are
>>>> Sir
>>>>> Yours respectfully
>>>>> A. Tregoning
>>>>> (for) Henry Harvey Cundy

Hayle responded by sending the trusty shipwright, Sam Warren, who must have ridden the seventy odd miles hard, for he arrived at Cotehele at mid-day on the 3rd. West sent a letter. The engineer opted without hesitation for cutting the beam and suggested a means of reinforcement to maintain the rigidity of the hull after that vital member had been severed. Warren, however, being a sea-faring man and not an engineer, rejected this plan at first and said it was the boilers which should be cut. But this would mean that boiler-makers would have to be sent from Hayle to de-rivet the plates and a similar team would have to be found in London to put them together again. But time was now of great importance, and Warren relented so far as to explain his own plan for performing what he regarded as the less desirable and more drastic operation, at the same time giving a warning about the expense entailed. "There must be a Conclusion Immediately ...

If the Beam is Cut it must be Cut near to the Comming on the Both Sides which may be done and a fish Provided and Secured so that the vessell may Continue her intended voyages till she reach Hayle. The Expense of Cutting the Beam with the fish here . . . may be from 5 to 6 Pounds with 20 more to put her in a state or repair again".

The fish-out-of-water referred to was a wooden under-girding designed to fulfil all the functions of the lopped-off beam by transferring them to a lower point of the hull. Warren could not wait to hear the decision which would be made at Hayle as he had another urgent appointment to be at Fowey within the next couple of days. He ended his letter by begging to be informed of the upshot (at Fowey Post Office); "Should the Boilers be Cut there will be no occasion . . . but should the Beam be Cut and Sir you think it Proper for me to return from Fowey to see it secured you will please signify it. . . The Vessel will not have water from the Quay after thursday next . . . but the whole may be done in time for the Rising of the Spring".

Now there was at Tavistock a timber merchant called Richard Marrack who was one of Harvey's principal suppliers, and Sam Warren, who never bought any wood for the ships he was building without selecting it himself, was a frequent visitor. Tavistock was only a few miles from Cotehele Quay, and Warren must have taken the opportunity of looking in on the merchant and telling him about the *Carnsew* dilemma for, on the 7th, Marrack wrote —

> There is a London Barge called the Three Brothers, Capt. Mason, at the Dockyard [Devonport] in want of a freight to London. As her Hatchway is 28 feet long she would take the Boilers at Cotehele without difficulty. I have promised to see the Capt. on Saturday, therefore beg you will write me by return whether you would give up the freight of the Boilers — the cutting of the Boilers or the cutting of the Carnsew are Evils that one would wish to evade.

This was certainly opportune news, but Marrack would most likely feel that, in spite of present difficulties, it would cause Henry a pang to lose the freight on the boilers and have the *Carnsew* return home unprofitably in ballast, but he had a plan to suggest which throws some light on the opportunities as well as the problems of transport in those days before the coming of the railway.

> The Carnsew could go into the Tavy River and load the Oak bought of Burrows of Liskeard. Burrows Oak would bring 2s. per foot at Plymouth in a Moment, so the advantage to you in the Timber would not be trifling. And besides might save Burrows from Ruin. You will not feel at ease in paying

without the Timber, and before you can have the Timber in the ordinary way Burrows Credit will have received such a Shock as may make it doubtful whether it would be worth repairing.

But Henry was not attracted by the proposal or moved by its appeal. As always, he preferred to rely on his own resources and the *Carnsew* was duly "cut". The next news we have of her is in the following January when she is homeward bound, having delivered the boilers safely. Captain Cundy writes from Sheerness, where he has run in, in distress, having ridden out a fearful easterly gale off the Nore with two anchors down. Two of his men are hurt and one is frost-bitten so that he will have to ship three more before proceeding and it is now nine days since he left London — "nothing but fogs, snow, and ice. I have never had such a trying voyage in all my life". But it was a fair test of Warren's surgery and his "fish".[1]

The *Carnsew* appears to have delivered her awkward cargo at Old Ford in the River Lea and set sail on the 17th of January, 1838, so that, by then, the ex-Callington engine and the three boilers were all on the site. It has been noted to what extent of forced pace and sacrifice the contractors had gone to, to achieve this, yet it was only on the 18th that Wicksteed wrote, on behalf of his board, to confirm a fresh contract with Harveys for putting in foundations for the plant. The principal items were two immense blocks of granite on which to bed the engine and the stand-pipe. The engine-house was to be built by the Water Board, and this cannot yet have been started. So it is not surprising to find that the new equipment was not ready for service until the end of the year.

It was the middle of December when steam was raised and the engine started. It must have been a poignant moment for all concerned, for it was the first time that a Cornish engine had been put to this kind of work which, in some ways was the reverse of what it had been designed to do in a mine, and adaptations had had to be made. The engine, being single-acting and steaming only on the downward stroke, relied on the weight of the pump-rods in the shaft to return the piston to the top of the cylinder and, at the same time (where a plunger-pole pump was concerned), to force the plunger down on its delivery stroke. But here, there was no shaft and no weighty pump-rods; the water-level in the well was only a matter of inches below the foot of the pump, while the weight of water which had to be

---

[1] It was after this incident that the *Carnsew* was radically altered, given a further ten feet of length and re-rigged as a ketch.

overcome on the delivery stroke was a head of about a hundred feet in the stand-pipe which had an internal diameter of 43 inches. The very massive pole, twelve feet, ten inches, by forty one inches had a heavy weight fitted to its head to act the part of the missing pump-rods. The great saving in fuel being immediately effected; the pump valves, however, valves for intake and discharge of the water were of the flap or clack type similar to those used in the mines though on a much larger scale.

As to what happened when the steam was turned on in this trial run we have a note by Wickstead. He says that the engine "worked very satisfactorily, a great saving of fuel being immediately effected; the pump valves, however, being of extraordinary dimensions, caused so great a blow upon closing, that the concussion shook the whole of the engine-house". As the engine worked from five to eight strokes a minute, the corresponding number of earthquake shocks must have been extremely disconcerting to both parties in the venture. If this fault could not be remedied, the hopeful future of the Cornish engine in this new and profitable field was in doubt.

Nicholas Harvey returned immediately to Hayle and busied himself with valvular experiments in the foundry. His guiding light was an invention of the far-sighted but unfortunate Jonathan Hornblower — the double-beat steam valve. It had survived the wreck of his fortunes, had been improved on by Woolf, and was embodied in the steam valve-gear of the Callington engine. It was a mushroom valve in two parts, having an inner and outer ring mounted on separate seatings, steam being admitted through ports in the horizontal plane. This had the advantage over the ordinary conical valve of relieving the working parts from direct vertical pressure. Nicholas worked out a clever adaptation of this principle to suit his water-valves. The first trial was made in March. It abated the earthquake but put a strain on the engine. Modifications were made at Hayle and a new set, accompanied by Nicholas went to London at the end of the month. This time the valve was such a complete success that its maker was able to write, "I had a tolerable opinion of it yet it exceeded my utmost expectations; indeed if it continues to work so well, it may truly be said to be a *ne plus ultra*, for in working it is not heard, and it admits such an ample supply of water the Pole does not return ¼ of an inch". Letters patent were immediately taken out in which William West (of St. Blazey) was admitted to a half-share. Thus, the gates of waterworks not only in London but throughout the provinces were thrown open to the Cornish engine and the Harvey and

West double-beat valve was standard practice for many years.

Thomas Wicksteed proceeded at once to devote an intensive study to the comparative merits of the Watt and Cornish engines by a series of exhaustive tests. The result (highly flattering to the latter) was given, with tables and drawings, in a volume published by John Weale, in 1841 under the title *An experimental Inquiry concerning the Relative Power of, and Useful Effect produced by the CORNISH AND BOULTON AND WATT ENGINES, and Cylindrical and Waggon-headed Boilers.*

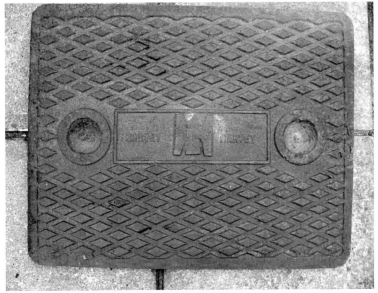

27. Manhole cover marked, but not made, by Harveys. This was recovered from the Foundry Road Industrial Estate in Camborne, the former CompAir factory.

Photograph: Kingsley Rickard

247

XVII

SIGNS OF THE TIMES AT THE INN

W E HAVE BEEN FOLLOWING THE SINGLE THREAD of events which took place after the outstanding success of "Austen's Engine" and led to its counterpart going to London, a move that took the Cornish engine out of the confined sphere of mine drainage into a much wider field of public utility. Meanwhile, several other things had been happening, of which, the most significant was the promotion of a railway between Hayle and Redruth.

Redruth and its neighbouring mines were already linked by two iron roads, one going down to Portreath on the north coast (a primitive plate-way), the other to Devoran harbour in the south. Both were purely mineral lines worked by horses. But the Hayle Railway was conceived in a fully up-to-date spirit and was sanctioned by Parliament in 1834 for steam locomotive traction and to carry passengers.

Both the foundries at Hayle and Copperhouse were closely concerned in the promotion of the scheme and, as two alternative routes had been surveyed, each party tried to secure the adoption of the one most likely to serve its own interests, while the railway company sought to take all possible advantage of both. Accordingly, the route which they laid down in the Bill took the following course. The line to start at Hayle Foundry and follow the Penpol River down to the Copperhouse wharf (Merchant Curnow's quay), then to cross the water near the floodgates by a drawbridge to allow shipping to pass up to the old Copperhouse dock at Ventonleague. Then to proceed along the far bank of the eastern lagoon as far as Angarrack, where there was a steep rise in levels. This to be met by an incline worked by cable-haulage from a stationary engine; another incline negotiated in the same way to be placed at the near approach to Redruth. Such was the plan approved by Parliament, and work on the line began immediately after.

The advantages of the steam locomotive, advocated so ardently by its inventor, Richard Trevithick, long before, had met with no response from the public or their accredited experts. Now, by one of those ironies of fate which so often beset him, within a year of the day when he was laid in an unmarked grave, locomotives were to be used on a line that started at a point scarcely more than a hundred yards from his sometime home at the White Hart Hotel. But the success which followed George Stephenson's Liverpool and Manchester Railway, opened in 1830 for steam locomotion, had amply justified Richard's predictions, though it had not been accomplished without the sustained hostility of George's directors which, in the end, were only overcome by the famous Rainhill trials. Not only was Stephenson's victory in this respect reflected in the plans for the Hayle Railway but his gauge of four foot eight-and-a-half inches was also adopted.

By 1837, the Hayle Railway was nearly complete, except for the short stretch linking Hayle Foundry with the rest, only the drawbridge over the narrow strip of water was still missing. The making of this seems to have baffled the ingenuity of the railway company though the mediaeval castle-builders had found no difficulty with similar construction. Pending its installation, the line could be used from Copperhouse to Redruth as soon as the final section should be ready for operation, and a director of the company called on Henry Harvey to seek his concurrence in the arrangement. This was not forthcoming. Henry at once suspected that his rivals were up to their old tricks. It was clearly laid down in the Act that the line should be completed before opening, and Henry insisted on this provision being observed to the letter. His lawyers supported him and further pointed out that any concession made at this juncture might nullify what the Act had required. If the C.C.C. were allowed to use the line before the drawbridge was made it might well be that, for one excuse or another, its construction could be delayed indefinitely and involve all the expense and trouble of fighting a case in the courts. Henry gained his point and, when the line was officially declared open later in the same year, it started from Hayle Foundry.

It is surprising to find that the order for the first locomotive for the new railway was not given to either of the rival foundries at Hayle but to a firm in Liverpool — perhaps a gesture of tactful neutrality on the part of the railway company — though one of Harvey's vessels was found best fitted for transporting the machine, which the *Carnsew* duly delivered at the

Foundry quay in April.

In 1836, Jane Trevithick, who had managed the White Hart for so many years, wished to retire. In spite of her domestic troubles, during the long absence of her husband, from whom she received neither news nor support and, no less, during the subsequent brief term of residence of the turbulent Richard, she had proved an ideal hostess to every class of guests she had been called on to entertain. Probably her desire to return to a life of her own, such as she had not enjoyed for forty years, was largely due to the fact that her brother was planning a very considerable enlargement of the premises.

Henry had at last succeeded in getting possession of that undesirable sheet of semi-stagnant water which lay immediately adjacent to the hotel, the Penpol Pool, whose existence had seemed to him to have been mainly accountable for infection during the cholera epidemic. He had had it drained and filled up and, on its site, he was building a large new White Hart, connected with the old house by a corridor. On the departure of Jane, he intended to lease out the whole establishment. He found as tenant an enterprising young publican called William Crotch who took Jane's place in December 1837, and carried on the business till the summer of 1838, when the new White Hart was completed and was ready to open its doors under a much more pretentious portico. The illustration (page 160) shows both buildings, their contrasting sizes graphically reflect the scale of expansion in the fortunes of the place over the space of little more than a single decade.

The prosperity of the firm, to which the place owed its origin and growth, was also marked by a less spectacular but more significant event in 1838. This was the repayment of Sir Charles Lemon's loan of £7,200 which had been secured on mortgages involving most of the Company's property. The deliverance from that debt was a great personal triumph for Henry Harvey and a tribute to his conduct of affairs. The son of the village blacksmith of Gwinear could now, like Longfellow's hero of the same trade, "look the whole world in the face". And it was a year of general festivities for, on July the 28th, the young Queen Victoria was driven to her coronation, the Duke of Wellington and Napoleon's Marshall Soult riding together in the procession. The event was celebrated at Hayle Foundry by a feast given to all hands at which a whole ox was roasted on a turnspit in traditional style.

In the Cornish mines, however, things were the reverse of prosperous.

The industry was suffering a depression partly due to over-speculation. Many mines had had to be closed and their engines were being offered second-hand and some were being disposed of through their makers at the Foundry who attended to their transport by sea to the port nearest their destination and sometimes superintended their re-erection. So there was little call for new engines within the Duchy and two contracted for by the de Dunstanville Mines were countermanded and left on Henry's hands, for which he only received a moderate compensation after a long lawsuit.

The success of the East London engine was therefore a timely stroke of fortune, for it was quickly followed by other metropolitan water companies — first the West Middlesex, whose works were at Hammersmith, then the Southwark and Vauxhall, who were building on a new site at Battersea, then the Grand Junction at Paddington, which took its name and drew its supply from the Grand Junction Canal. In fact, Harveys were kept so busy that deliveries began to lag behind time again and the Grand Junction was six months late in completion. As the contract was drawn with a heavy penalty clause the water company felt entitled to demand a fine of £500, though the claim was eventually settled amicably for less. And, in 1840, William West (of St. Blazey) protested "I have received another letter this week from Mr. Hill saying they are much displeased about their Machinery being so long in hand, you will be so good as to make all possible despatch on it ... I must say myself that this job have been too long in hand which was promised in 6 weeks and 6 months are nearly passed by, this is injuring me from getting more orders, by course it must be injuring you. I think you ought to attend to those little jobs as well as the large ones".

Other water companies of a different sort were following the East London lead — the canals. Only the first order need be mentioned. It was from the most remote of all the English undertakings, that connecting Carlisle with Port Carlisle on the Solway Firth but, with Harvey's line of communications it was easy of access by sea.

Old Ford had set the pace for advertising Harvey's pumping equipment and, within a year of its going into service, enquiries began to arrive in a regular stream, coming from as far afield as the Royal Government of Prussia. But the East London engine did not behave itself impeccably. In June, 1841, Wicksteed wrote to say that it had cracked its cylinder-cover (weighing nearly 25 tons) and, at the same time, complaining "from one imperfection or another the engine has been stopped for *two* months out of the last *9* months, a circumstance not very agreeable to me under whose

251

advice this new engine was erected". All the same, as will be noted, the time was soon to come when Harveys made much larger engines which ran for the best part of a century, without anything going wrong.

With the near collapse of the foundry's staple trade in the Cornish mines it was essential to encourage prospective clients and find new ones outside the Duchy, and Nicholas, who believed in the personal touch, spent much time away from Hayle hunting for orders. His genial nature coupled with his expert knowledge made him a successful traveller. Apart from the sales aspect of his missions, he could often tender helpful advice on plant and machinery drawn from experience gained on the Continent as well as at home. At the works he left as his chief assistant William West (of Hayle).

In 1839, Nicholas put in hand further enlargements at the ironworks, of which, the most urgently needed was a new boring-mill. Hitherto, the work of this important department which, with the development of the Cornish engine, had become more and more basic in the foundry's production, was still being carried on in the original premises — the site of early hostilities on the part of the C.C.C. The old mill was now equipped with two horizontal boring-machines of the type invented by John Wilkinson, the Shropshire ironmaster (page 34) and a much larger modern machine, in which the boring-bar revolved on a vertical axis; all of them still worked by water-wheel as in the days of the aggressive John Edwards.

The new mill was more conveniently situated in relation to other departments of the works and was powered by steam. An outstanding feature was the massive new boring-frame calculated to bore a cylinder to the undreamed of dimensions of twelve feet, six inches, internal diameter, and fifteen feet long. The cut was made by a bar no less than thirty-four inches thick. This prodigious machine had been designed and built in the foundry, like so many other of their large tools. To make provision for the possible order of an engine that would use anything like such an out-size of cylinder was typical of the progressive policy of the Company. The mill was finished in 1840.

During the same interval of time (1836-40), six new wooden sailing ships had gone from the shipyard — *Elizabeth* (II), schooner, *Henry* (II), schooner, *Nancy*, schooner, *Trelissick*, smack, *Mellanear*, smack, *Jane*, schooner. These later vessels listed as schooners appear, from their captains' letters to have been of the variety called topsail-schooners which carried a square-rigged topsail above the gaff foresail on the foremast, while the mainmast was wholly fore-and-aft rigged. Tonnage and other details are given in the appendix where, it will be noted, that the four last named ships are registered in the name of J. H. Trevithick and not in those of either Henry or the Company. During Henry's lifetime, however, they served the firm without distinction of ownership and took part in all the varied activities of the rest of the fleet.

During the same interim, common cause had brought the old rivals together on two occasions. In 1836 they both put their names to a petition to the Lords of the Treasury, praying that a custom house should be established at Hayle to save all the time wasted in getting officials to come over from St. Ives to check cargoes before the unloading of ships could begin. In 1837 they combined in mobilising support to get the St. Ives Port Bill repealed. This had been enacted in 1766 to finance the building of Smeaton's stone pier and lighthouse. It authorised a levy of dues on the registered tonnage of all ships entering the port at the rate of 1s. 4d. per ton, and Hayle was included in the port. This happened eleven years before John Harvey set up his small business. St. Ives had been amply repaid for their outlay and the tonnage now entering Hayle was far greater than that going to St. Ives. The custom house plea was rejected, but the other was successful and Hayle harbour gained its independence. Thenceforth the port charges at Hayle were only 2s. 6d. for a vessel (irrespective of tonnage) if she lay at the wharf, or 1s. 6d. at an anchorage.

Apprenticeships at Hayle Foundry were now much sought after. The sons of several of Henry's best customers were serving their time at the works, later to become well known figures in the rapidly expanding world of engineering. Francis Trevithick was already in charge of the locomotive department of the Grand Junction Railway, which had absorbed the Liverpool and Manchester and was to form the connecting link between it and the London and Birmingham. In 1841 he was sending orders to Harveys for equipment for the engine works at Edge Hill on the outskirts of Liverpool. Two years later he moved his establishment (to suit railway strategy) to a spot on the map where no place existed — only one or two farms and a mansion called Crewe Hall. He thus became the founder of the great railway town of Crewe which grew up round his works. In 1846 the Grand Junction was merged in the London and North Western Railway and Francis became its first Locomotive Superintendent. Shortly afterwards he turned out from Crewe Works one of the most celebrated locomotives in railway annals, a single-wheeler with eight-foot-six driving wheels, named after his native land — the *Cornwall*.

In 1839, there arrived at Hayle a candidate for apprenticeship, unheralded by the usual preliminaries of application and apparently at a moment when no vacancy was open. This was a boy of sixteen called William Husband, the son of the Lloyd's Surveyor at Falmouth, destined by his parents for a place in the family business of ship-building. But his heart was set on becoming an engineer and he had left home secretly and trotted off on his pony to Hayle where (it is recorded[1]) "After earnestly soliciting Mr. Henry Harvey, the head of the firm, in his determination to be an engineer, he was received as an apprentice" — notwithstanding. The future was to bring no regrets to either party.

At the foundry there was an increasing demand for two very different types of machines — mechanical blowers for blast furnaces and weigh-bridges. The former was merely an adaptation of the beam engine. Large pairs of bellows worked by water-power had long since been superseded by the steam-driven piston-and-cylinder (of which the modern tyre-inflator is a remote descendant). It was a simple contrivance, one end of the reciprocating beam being actuated by the steam-cylinder whilst the other worked the blowing-cylinder, which was about twice the size (in diameter). Both were-double-acting, and a heavy flywheel kept the pumping action even so that the air was delivered in an almost uninterrupted blast. With his new boring-mill, Nicholas was now able to turn out blowers with diameters of more than a hundred inches. The weigh-bridge was a new departure. Harvey had for some time supplied Cornish market-towns with large scales and steel-yards and now his weigh-bridges were so successful that they followed one another rapidly in adopting them. Many orders also came from outside the Duchy.

There was a steady increase in the manufacture of marine engines and sea-going Cornish boilers. The performance of the latter had fully justified Henry's optimism, and the determined hostility to their use which had so much marred the trials of the *Echo* had been almost entirely overcome, though one or two diehards still pinned their faith to the waggon boiler with external firing. The experience which Nicholas had gained in Holland and on the Rhine before he came to Hayle was of particular value in connection with marine contracts. The Company had requests from time to time to build and fit out complete steam vessels of small tonnage for service as tugs — a type for which there was a growing demand as their usefulness in accelerating the movement of sailing ships in to and out of port became

[1] Obituary notice, *Times*, May 3rd, 1887.

recognised. Nicholas was fully competent and no doubt anxious to take up these orders. But, for some reason, Henry steadily refused to have anything to do with the building of hulls other than those of his own vessels, and those clients were all turned down.

The steamer, *Herald*, still plying regularly between Hayle and Bristol, had become so well patronised, both by passengers and for goods, that before the end of the 'thirties, Henry (as chairman of the Steam Packet Company) was urged to put another vessel into the service, if only to prevent a competitor getting in first. Henry thought the time not ripe and resisted all proposals until near the end of 1841. A new vessel was then ordered and the contract given to Harveys. She was to be a wooden ship and one would have thought that with the combined know-how of Nicholas and Samuel Warren she could quite well have been laid down on the slipway at Hayle. But Henry would only provide the machinery and the hull was designed and built in the yard of James & John White at Cowes and was then towed to Hayle and fitted out there. She was called the *Cornwall* and ran her trials in April 1842. William West (St. B.) wrote "I am glad to hear of such a satisfactory tripp you had in the *Cornwall* on Saturday last and hope that she will beat every other Boat in the North Channel". She was put into service in May.

In spite of the pressure of work on large engines (and the books show long hours of overtime being put in) there was no curtailment of the wide variety of the foundry's productions. The usual small orders for stoves and fire-grates continued to be accepted, customers always demanding immediate delivery and complaining indignantly when kept waiting. A Mr. Phillpotts, who had had an oak table made for his entrance-hall to disguise a heating-apparatus wanted four small panels of open ironwork "nicely finished but not too ornamental" to fit into the framing, expected the busy drawing-office and pattern-shop to devote themselves to the task forthwith.

Amongst the novelties was an order for six hundred tons of cannon-balls (for 12, 18, and 24 pounders) "without hollows, defects, or blisters, perfectly spherical, smooth surface, and of precise weight and dimensions." But the most astonishing thing was a line in drawing-room ornaments and other fancy goods, cast in bronze and iron, the speciality of a Mr. Whitebread, a singularly deft craftsman whom Nicholas had brought with him from Germany and had apparently taken the sensible precaution of Anglicising his name on arrival. They recall the famous "Birmingham toys" which

Matthew Boulton had issued from his Soho works rather more than half a century earlier. A collection of these "Hayle toys" is in the possession of Mr. V. B. Wills.

In 1842, John West, a younger brother of William (of Hayle) joined the Company. He had been engineer at the Great St. George Mine in the St. Agnes area and was a man of natural ability as well as considerable experience. Early in 1843 he was doing a round of the London water-works, attending to small complaints and sending in reports to Hayle.

In the same year employees at the foundry started a Mechanic's Institute in a small room at one of their homes. But the twenty-one members found themselves cramped for space and unable to increase their body. They therefore appealed to Henry to build them a "room, for which we will pay the yearly sum which the capital laid out on the structure demands". The petition contains an ingenuous inducement, "Knowledge (you are well aware, Sir) is the only antidote for disaffected minds, by dispelling that ignorance which is so prevalent among the working classes and which is evidently so inimical to the welfare of the master as his workmen". Henry had already borne the expense of building a room for the first school at Hayle and he seems to have responded as generously to the appeal of the young society. Among the signatories to the petition is that, in a well-formed hand, of the hopeful apprentice, William Husband; there also appear five members of the Bickle family, of which more will be heard later.

We pass on in the next chapter to the year 1843, another most notable one in the annals of the Company.

XVIII

THE LARGEST STEAM ENGINES IN THE WORLD

T HE YEARS 1843-49 WERE OCCUPIED BY AN
undertaking which, of itself, and for the benefit it conferred on
a national economy, must be regarded as the most outstanding
achievement in the Company's history. This was a commission by the
Dutch Government to build the largest steam engine in the world. I propose
once again to follow throughout those seven years the single line of this
story apart from all the other numerous activities of the firm.

For centuries the Hollanders had been engaged in a struggle against
inundations constantly threatened alike from waters salt and fresh. One of
the most persistent sources of trouble was a long depression lying between
Amsterdam and Leiden. A small chain of lakes formed here had, by the
end of the 16th century (partly due to the activities of turf-cutters), grown
into a single large sheet of water, some fourteen miles long by eight broad.
This presented a double danger to the surrounding country, not only due
to an overflow from excess of floodwater, but also to wind-pressure which
strong gales could exert over those flat open spaces. It was called from the
ancient town near its western margin the Haarlemmer Meer.

At the same time that Cornelius Vermuiden was being employed in the
drainage of the East Anglian fens, a distinguished contemporary, Jan
Adriaanz Leeghwater, was propounding a scheme for eliminating the
Haarlem Lake and converting its bed into good agricultural land. His
proposal was to enclose the lake with a strong dyke surrounded by a canal
at sea-level into which the water of the lake could be lifted by a large
number of wind-mills dotted along the perimeter and so pass out through
tidal floodgates into the great gulf of the Zuider Zee. In 1639 Leeghwater
published his plan in book form with a map showing the promised land
of reclamation gridded with small canals in which the spring and surface
waters were now harnessed to a system of irrigation. The book made such

a popular appeal in wishful thinking that it lived on into the 19th century with a thirteenth edition. But the costs of such extensive earthworks and so many windmills put the plan beyond the reach of private enterprise. Palliative measures were taken but they failed to solve the problem.

In 1836, two successive storms of unusual severity caused the lake to overflow to such an extent that it threatened Amsterdam and its waters invaded part of the city of Leiden. This forced the Dutch Government to take action and a Commission was appointed to take immediate measures for the complete drainage of the lake. It sat under the presidency of Gevers van Endegeest. At their first deliberations the question of what power should be applied for the pumping was uppermost. The traditional use of the windmill was strongly urged. Skilled millwrights abounded in the country and a high degree of efficiency had been achieved by them in the method of raising water by means of the wooden-built Archimedian screw. Steam was an innovation of which the Dutch had had little experience and only two members of the Commission spoke for its adoption. They were two eminent engineers, Gerret Simons and Antoine Lipkins, but they would have been over-ruled by the windmillers had it not been for the personal intervention of King William. He had spent some part of his long exile during the Napoleonic wars in England and had no doubts about the superior power of steam. To adopt it would mean importing machinery, men, and coal from abroad, but he strongly backed the two engineers with his authority. A London firm of consulting engineers, Messrs Dean and Gibbs, was asked to advise and, in 1840, the Commissioners sent over a deputation to inspect pumping engines at the English mines.

The party consisted of only two members, the enthusiasts, Simons and Lipkins. They were at once taken by one of their consultants, Arthur Dean, down to Cornwall, where they were joined by Thomas Lean, editor of the *Recorder* (of engine duties) and son of its founder, Joel, who escorted them to that famous show-piece, the Austen engine at Fowey Consols Mine. A view of this engine caused them so much satisfaction that they asked to see its manufacturer and were taken to Hayle. At the Foundry it happened that just then Nicholas Harvey had got his new boring-mill at work on an out-size cylinder which particularly engaged the attention of Arthur Dean.

The Commissioners do not seem to have thought it was worth while extending their tour beyond the Cornish mines and returned to Holland early in September, when Simons put in a glowing report of the visit. As a result of these favourable impressions it must have been expected that the

Haarlemmer Meer project would quickly take practical shape. But King William I, who had for some time been at political logger-heads with his subjects, suddenly decided to abdicate in favour of his son. This he did on October the 7th and the prospects of getting anything done under the new regime faded. It may be assumed that, at Hayle, high hopes had been raised by the visit of the Commissioners followed by a brief exchange of letters between Nicholas and Dean. When nothing further was heard Henry must have recalled Trevithick's abortive deal with the Dutch and the time and money spent on the floating pump which eventually went to the scrap-heap. Nearly two years went by and then, in March, 1842, Nicholas received a letter from Arthur Dean saying —

> I shall be greatly obliged by your informing me whether you can execute work of the following dimensions, viz, cylinders of cast iron 12 or 15 feet long and 130 inches diameter — bored out truly. Pistons for do. turned up. A Cylinder of 84 inches diameter, bored within and turned up truly without, throughout its length or for 12 feet of its length.
>
> When I visited your works in August, 1840, with a commission sent to this country by the Dutch Government you had just completed a Cylinder of, I believe, 120 Inches diameter. I am therefore induced to suppose that you will be able to execute work of the dimensions before stated I will thank you to let me know if you can execute a Cylinder of more than 130 Inches diameter as I am desirous of employing the largest size I can obtain for the machinery connected with the Pumping out of the Lake of Haarlem, of which work myself and Partner have been appointed the Engineers by the Dutch Government.

Nicholas replied at once, quoting prices per hundredweight for both cylinders. For the large one, which only required boring, he asked 30s. per cwt.; for the smaller, which had to be turned on the outside as well as bored, 50s. per cwt. New hopes for getting the contract being thus revived, and the foundry having plenty to do, with fresh orders on hand for the English waterworks at Liverpool, Manchester, Coventry, and Crofton in Yorkshire, Nicholas took an anticipatory step. He sounded the Foxes of Perran Foundry, with whom the Company had so often shared large contracts, as to whether they would take part if the deal came off, and found them quite agreeable to the proposal. But it was December before Dean wrote again, when the arrangement was explained to him as giving a great advantage in the time that could be saved in carrying out the work.

Matters having got so far, Nicholas decided to go to Holland himself and be on the spot whilst decisions were in the making.

He reached Amsterdam on the 24th of January, 1843, and found Arthur Dean already there. There were a few competitors in the field. A firm from

Leeds had put in a tender at a lower price and an Amsterdam ironmaster was demanding to be given at least a large share of the work. Negotiations continued actively into the first week of February when terms were finally concluded. Harveys were to have the contract for the engine, with Perran Foundry as subcontractors, supplying the pumps, Paul van Vlissingen of Amsterdam was to make the boilers and also the beams, and the Dutch Government was to build the engine- and boiler-house. The whole establishment would bear a name, and was to be called appropriately after that prophet whose dream it was to start fulfilling — Leeghwater.

The time allowed for the contract had been eight months, but Nicholas with some difficulty gained an extension of one month and the outside dates now fixed were the first week in February to the first week in November (1843), so that the months were already ticking away when Nicholas got back to Hayle. He had travelled from Holland to London with Dean who must then have handed over the working drawings[1].

In planning the reduction of that seventy square miles of water the consultants had allowed for a trio of engines, each of 350 horsepower, working at three different points of the lake. All were to be of the same design and the Leeghwater engine was to be the pioneer of the group. The Commissioners intended to wait until its performance had been tested before committing themselves to an order for the others.

The design of the Leeghwater engine combined features already well established with others which were new and, until all the very numerous parts had been put together and the steam turned on, its behaviour was bound to remain an open question. It was a compound ("combined engine"), a type which, as already said (page 147), had been twice tried but had fallen into disfavour after the match at Wheal Alfred Mine in 1824, when Woolf's compound had been beaten by a Harvey Cornish engine. But, in recent years, James Sims, the son of Trevithick's partner in the pole-engine patent, had, after several experiments, found a more correct ratio between the two cylinders, and had been more successful. He took out a patent for his engine in 1841. This machine was a tandem compound in which the high pressure cylinder was mounted above the low pressure, with a single piston-rod serving both.

The consultants described their engine as being "on the Sims principle",

[1] These drawings are preserved at the offices of the Haarlemmer Meer Polder catchment area and are signed by Nicholas Harvey, Fox & Co, Arthur Dean, Joseph Gibbs, and Gevers van Endegeest, the President of the Commissioners.

and the design they first prepared was a tandem, differing only from that of Sims by having the high pressure cylinder placed below the other. This plan must have been modified by the time Dean wrote in May, 1842, for, in that letter, he asks that the smaller should not only be bored true but also turned true on its outer face. This must have puzzled the engineers at Hayle if they did not already know that the intention was to place one cylinder inside the other — a new departure, the annular compound. While this form would obviously be more difficult to make and add to the cost of the engine it would be a considerable saving to the Dutch Government in masonry, reducing the height of the engine-house by at least ten feet.

In the final design the large cylinder had an internal diameter of 144 inches, the lesser, 84 inches. Within the latter was an ordinary piston, working a piston-rod 12 inches in diameter. In the low pressure cylinder, which surrounded the other, was the ring-shaped annular piston whose force had to be transmitted by four several piston-rods, spaced at equal distances, each 4½ inches in diameter. All five were fixed to a heavy cross-head of special design which is always mentioned in correspondence as "the great cap". Unlike any other beam-engine yet made, this monster had to rock not one, but eleven beams. The engine-house was a strong circular tower like the shell-keep of Windsor Castle, and the beams radiated from the great cap to the pumps outside and were pivoted in equal spaced openings of the wall.

To compare the action of the Leeghwater and Cornish engines the reader may refer to pages 238-239 and 272-273 where the steaming cycle of each is explained, accompanied by drawings, noting particularly the function of the equilibrium valve and the cataract timing-gear. It was the action of these two which gave the Cornish engine its pre-eminence in pumping, conferring on it a mechanised version of patience and tolerance when dealing with the inelastic fluid — water. It was not only necessary to have perfect control of movement while pumps were working but also that movement should be entirely suspended for an instant to allow pump-valves to close.

The Cornish engine steamed only on the downward stroke, the piston being returned to the top of the cylinder by the weight of the pump-rods or the loaded pole. It was the other way round with the Leeghwater engine. It steamed on the upward stroke and pumped on the return one. The great cap was heavily weighted, much above its structural needs, and rose to the thrust of steam at boiler pressure admitted to the underside of the high pressure piston and cut off for expansion about half way. At the end of the stroke it made that necessary pause for the pump-valves to close and then descended by gravity acting on the heavy great cap, assisted by the remaining energy of the steam above *both* pistons and vacuum from the condenser below them.

The most truly novel feature of the engine was the mechanism which caused it to pause at the top of its stroke. It is always referred to by an unaccompanied adjective and called simply "the *hydraulic*". In the Cornish engine the use of the equilibrium valve was sufficient to suspend its movement by distributing steam to both sides of the piston. The same valve was present in the other engine, but, to keep the weight of the great cap at a dead stop it required reinforcement. This was supplied by the hydraulic.

The device consisted of two hydraulic rams, each connected with a water-tank in the form of a small stand-pipe. Being attached to the great cap they reciprocated with it, but their freedom of movement was intercepted by a valve which, when closed at the necessary instant, locked them in position. It acted in conjunction with the equilibrium valve, both being timed by the same cataract.

This was both the largest and the most complicated steam engine so far projected and who, of all the parties concerned, was actually responsible for the whole design is not clear. Of the consultants it is Dean's name which always appears in connection with the contract, but his partner, Joseph Gibbs was a fertile inventor with twenty-three patents to his name. Yet, what the firm was mainly concerned with was the construction of new railways in England and Wales. The experienced expert in pumping engines was Nicholas Harvey. That his share in the design was no mean one seems to be proved because, early in 1843, there suddenly appeared a claimant for infringement of patent. This was one William Gillman, and it was Harvey & Co. and not Dean & Gibbs who he sued. The series of Paynter and Whitford letters headed "Yourselves and Gillman" goes on for more than a year. Unfortunately the end of the story is missing but it is plain that Gillman's plea did not succeed. The contested point was the principle of the annular compound.

Meanwhile, Arthur Dean took out a Dutch patent for "our system of engine" and on April the 9th, 1843, he wrote to Nicholas offering him a quarter share in the patent for £600 or a half share (conjointly with Fox's of Perran) for £1,100, saying that manufacturers believed that if the

28. Collapse of a crane loading a Cornish boiler

29. Lathe in the new machine shop

31. Thirty-ton derrick crane

30. Marine donkey boiler

264

Haarlem engine were successful there would be a wide demand in Holland for similar engines to drain polders — "The Dutch who are little prone to change and not much given to experimentalising, will stick to that which they see has already answered well". This offer does not appear to have been taken up, nor were those engines, though eminently successful, ever repeated in Holland or elsewhere.

The preparatory work of enclosing the Haarlem Lake with a dyke to isolate it from the surrounding countryside and a canal at a higher level to carry away the water drained from it appear to have been put in hand by the Dutch Government some time before any decision about the pumping equipment was reached. The task was an immense one, for the dyke had to be strong and watertight and the canal on its outer rim was to be made available for sea-going ships from Amsterdam and was 130 feet wide on the west side of the lake and 115 feet on the east, with a broad towing-road between. When the contract for the Leeghwater engine was signed only part of this work had been done. By its terms every part of the engine and pumps were to have been shipped by the first week in November, 1843. But the Commissioners can hardly have expected that the canal would have been ready by that time for drainage to commence. This posed a problem for both parties. Until the canal should be opened all transport from Amsterdam (which was by barge and lighter) had to use the lake and the site which had been chosen for the Leeghwater engine was at its further end, near Leiden.

Building of the boiler-house could be started at once on the piece of firm ground standing above the lake, but the round engine-house immediately adjoining it had to have its foundations laid at a point below the surface of the lake to give sufficient depth for the pumps which were ranged around it to draw from. It was therefore necessary to form a hemi-circular dyke in the lake at that spot when the water, thus cut off, could be drained out.

The foundations for both boiler- and engine-house were laid on a wooden structure supported by several hundred piles. An outer ring of brickwork surrounded the engine-house, pierced with arches below and carrying an inspection parapet above, between which and the house, and sunk several feet, there was a watertight wooden platform in which the pumps (which had open ends) were fixed. The water delivered on this platform (the *collar-launder*), passed to the canal through floodgates, which opened and shut automatically as pressure varied on either side.

The consultants appointed a Dutch engineer, named Verveer, to look after

265

their interests in Holland and act in a liaison capacity. Harveys sent out a very young man to supervise all their work and to pay and attend to the welfare of their workmen. He was twenty years old and only just out of his apprenticeship — the aforementioned William Husband. He wrote in reports at very short intervals and a great many of his letters have been preserved. They reveal how well chosen he was for the great responsibility and trust placed on his young shoulders. The unexpected but constantly recurring difficulties were endless, yet he met all with perfect equanimity. Though his masters were often at fault in delays of shipping machinery and of renewing his financial credit (though always advised by him well beforehand) there was never a murmur of complaint or grievance in any of his letters. With the Dutch —Commissioners, officials, and workmen — he was always on the best of terms and his competence and good nature gained their complete confidence. In his off-times he took lessons in Dutch from the village schoolmaster at Sassenheim and is said to have made such progress within six months as to be able to write and speak the language fluently.[1]

In the month following the return of Nicholas a notice appearing in the local Press shows that work on the Dutch contract was being pushed forward at the Foundry with great expedition. The high pressure cylinder had been cast and its massive piston-rod, nineteen feet long, had been forged. In August, a further account appeared[2], showing that that pièce de résistance of the whole undertaking, the making of the great twelve-foot low pressure cylinder had been tackled. Naming it "the largest cylinder ever cast entire", it declared "The operation was completely successful; more than 25 tons of iron were melted for the occasion, and the whole of that mass of liquid fire ran into the mould in less than six minutes in a manner that afforded the highest satisfaction to a great number of intelligent visitors, who were kindly allowed to be present, without a single casualty having occurred."

If that were so, how was it that this piece of goods did not reach its destination for a further nine months? We may set another account beside the above. It was written by the elder Jebus Bickle who, as a youth, was serving in the foundry at the time. Four years later he was sent out to the works in Holland and, at an advanced age he visited the site again and wrote a detailed description of the engines, in the course of which he says,

---

[1] *Dictionary of National Biography.*
[2] *Penzance Gazette*, 1843.

"The first engine was supplied by Messrs. Harvey & Co., Hayle, Cornwall, and was delivered and erected by this firm at the Leeghwater Pumping Station ready for work. This engine had eleven pumps, each sixty-three inches in diameter and eleven feet stroke, and the large Cylinder shown on the accompanying photo was intended for this Engine. It was twenty-five tons in weight and sufficient iron for same was melted in three large furnaces, but every effort having failed to tap the third furnace in time, there was not therefore enough metal in the other two furnaces to fill the mould and the Cylinder was a 'wastrel' and had to be made over again. This Cylinder is still at Hayle [year, 1900] and will soon be broken up".

The unexpected hitch which caused the failure of what was looked for as the supreme achievement of Hayle Foundry was most unfortunate. It meant not only an indefinite delay in delivering the machinery but a possible undermining of confidence on the part of the Commissioners. They were still divided among themselves on the merits of steam versus wind-power and, although Lipkins and Simons would remain unshaken in their championship of steam, its most powerful backer, King William I, was no longer on the throne. There was every reason for keeping the matter as quiet as possible and the favourable impression of the newspaper reporter and the "intelligent visitors" was allowed to remain uncontradicted.

Harveys had to re-organise some of their plant and make various new tools of a considerable size to cope with other parts of the Dutch order and there appear to have been further hold-ups, undisclosed in the records, so that deliveries had already fallen well behind hand when William Husband wrote from Amsterdam on January the 9th, 1844, reporting the arrival of the *Trelissick* with a fresh instalment of engine-parts. He says there is a sudden change in the weather, "but not happening with the change of the moon it is thought we have nothing to fear from ice". He adds a postscript to say that the temperature in the *Trelissick's* cabin has dropped fifteen degrees in the last twenty-four hours. The next day the vessel was frozen fast in the middle of the dock with no chance of discharging her cargo into the barge for transhipment.

Before the thaw came, Husband wrote, "Last Friday there was a meeting of some of the Commissioners at the Engine-house to see if the work [already] landed there was in good order and according to the bills you have sent. They expressed themselves well satisfied with the work and of course found all the parts as stated by you. They also desired me to write that they were anxious to get the work finished and to say that a forfeit to you of a thousand pounds lay at their discretion, but they appear fully to appreciate the uncertainty of getting such a job finished within a month or two of any stated time".

Not until February did the first two beams arrive from Van Vlissingen's foundry at Amsterdam but, in lifting them from the barge, the ropes snapped and stronger tackle had to be sent for. The masons had suspended work on the engine-house (which was not yet roofed and had no coverings to the windows). Severe weather with heavy snowstorms persisted.

On the 2nd of March, Gevers van Endegecst, the President of the Commission wrote —

> According to Article 3 of the agreement between you and the Commissioners for draining the lake of Haarlem, the work you contracted for was to be put on board ship, within the period of nine months from the date of notice given to you of the approbation of the said agreement. This notice was given in the first days of February, 1843, and therefore the work was to be forwarded in the beginning of November of the same year. Some parts of the work have been delivered in due time, but by far the greatest portion of it we have been expecting since more than four months, without any notice given by you of this enormous delay, which is the more disagreeable to the Commissioners, as the shorter period of time within [which] you promised to finish the work, has been one of the reasons why your offers have been accepted in preference to those of the Dutch manufacturers.
>
> The loss of time, which causes a proportional loss of money, is most injurious to the enterprize, and therefore we are obliged to urge you to complete the work with all possible diligence. In the mean time we wish to be informed by you of the causes of the said delay and the period of time within [which] we may now expect the remaining parts of the engine.

All this was quite true but the President makes no acknowledgment of the fact that the Dutch contingent was also responsible for some of the delays. Only one crane had been provided for moving material from the barges to the engine-house or the shelter which Husband had erected to keep out of the weather such parts as could not yet be moved into the roofless building, and the masons claimed a prior use of it. Within a week after Gevers had got off his ominous reminder, the whole of the Dutch party, masons and dykers, were called away for emergency works elsewhere. Excessive flood water from melting snows in Germany had inundated the province of Guelderland, broken several dykes, and swamped villages.

In April, Perran Foundry writes to Nicholas complaining that "The Dutch Government appear to be very dilatory about the payment for each delivery of the Contract for Machinery. Can anything be done to urge a remittance? We should be extremely glad to receive the needful shortly, which we conceive to be long since due".

In May, Husband is reporting much increased anxiety on the part of the Commissioners who have now got it firmly into their heads that continued delay is due to some mysterious catastrophe having taken place at Hayle Foundry. Their suspicions have apparently been heightened by instructions received from Cornwall to widen the doorway at the engine-house to admit the great low pressure cylinder. Husband asks for the outside diameter of largest flange, "They have no drawing of the cylinder *as it is now made*". This obviously refers to the replacement of the "Wastrel", cast from a new pattern. At the same time, Dean writes to Nicholas from London saying that the Commissioners are getting restive, and then goes down to Hayle; following which, he reassures the Commissioners that "the work presents a good appearance".

On the 4th of June Husband writes enclosing an account from the intermediary, Verveer. It appears that on the arrival of every cargo there have been vexatious delays at the Dutch customs. The account is for services in getting the goods passed. The cost of this accommodation is six hundred guelders and it looks suspiciously like a pretty affair of connivance. The letter ends, "This same Mr. Verveer was sent to prison last week for debt, and if he should not be soon freed which is not very likely, considering that he is debtor to a great amount, I suppose that I may be allowed to arrange for the coming cargo". He then lost no time in making a direct appeal to that well-disposed leading light among the Commissioners, Geret Simons, who intervened vigorously at the Customs and got matters put on a proper footing. Meanwhile, Husband was asked to find accommodation for a party of eight men from Hayle under the charge of John West. Rooms he did succeed in getting at Sassenheim, but no beds could he have authority to buy them?

At last, at the beginning of June, comes the bill-of-lading announcing the sailing of the *Carnsew* with both cylinders on board. Husband wrote on the 14th saying that he had expected she would have arrived by the 11th and went to Amsterdam to meet her, but she was not there, nor was there any news of her having passed through the Sound of Texel into the Zuider Zee. Whatever his reflections were about the spell of ill-luck which seemed to thwart the delivery of the great cylinder at every stage, he merely remarked "Yesterday and today it blew very strong from the S.W., so that it is very probable she has put in somewhere on the English coast if she was in the North Sea. There is now nothing doing at the Engine house".

THE LARGEST STEAM ENGINES IN THE WORLD

But we find another letter, also dated the 14th, from Captain J. H. Clarke, who was now master of the *Carnsew*, headed Niewe Deep, Texel, and saying "We have had a great trouble with our compasses, they being out of the way all the passage and have thrown us many miles out. Also our ship has been very leaky. The pump brake [handle] has hardly been idle since we left Hayle. In fact we have had a troublesome passage. I have no more to say but all is well".

The last fling of the hoodoo having been mocked by the tough Cornish seamen, Husband was able to write on the 28th, "The monster cylinder has already found its way in the newspapers here It is spoken of as a wonderful production of skill and visited by all classes as a great curiosity; the Commissioners were here this morning seeing it, and appeared pleased with its fine appearance".

But the end was by no means yet. Dean was at The Hague in August and wrote —

> I shall be obliged by your informing me as soon as possible when you expect to ship the Great Cap, annular piston, and other work, as we cannot empty the water out of the Basin which surrounds the Engine house at the Kaag, and consequently cannot fix the Pumps until these pieces have been placed on the platform which is round the Engine house.
>
> I must also impress on you the necessity for using every exertion to complete the Engine as quickly as possible for the Commissioners are very much dissatisfied at the delay in its erection beyond the time anticipated, by which they lose one year in the drainage of the Lake and a loss of interest on the capital employed amounting to nearly £30,000. You will therefore perceive it is a matter of grave importance to them that no time should be lost... I am very desirous of having the bottom valves of the Pumps sent with the next cargo that they may be fixed with the Pumps to avoid the heavy expense of draining the Basin again.

John West and his men had duly arrived and Husband reports at the end of the month that "the work still continues to progress very comfortably". The cylinders are fixed in position and secured by their holding-down bolts; joints are being caulked. But there are still many missing parts, including the great cap and (from Perran) the rams for the "hydraulic". By the end of September Husband is making arrangements at Amsterdam for a floating crane to assist with the transfer of the great cap from the *Carnsew* to a barge. The *Carnsew*, however, is already several days overdue. But on October the 2nd Captain Clarke sent word from Texel Sound to say that his ship had been struck by a heavy gale in the North Sea and the cargo had shifted, "in fact none of us ever expected to live to tell our tale. Thank God we are arrived safe to our port with the loss of a few yards of canvas."

And so a second winter came. This time it was a cargo from Perran which was caught out and frozen up in the dock at Amsterdam for eighty days.

On May the 11th there is a long letter from Husband saying that Dean had been to inspect the work, "and the resident Engineer here informed me that Mr. Dean expressed his satisfaction relative to the erection of the Engine to him and he also, when referring to time said 'Considering the circumstances, the miscalculation of time for erecting was not to be wondered at, for they (referring to their Railway work in England) had done scarcely anything for the winter months', — and it is a fact, that no party of men working on a Railway in England, could have been more exposed than the party working on the Leeghwater Engine. The house was without a roof and through openings in the walls, exposed to every wind of Heaven". He mentions the few cases of sickness which had affected the Hayle men and those which had been sent later from Perran. One was down with malaria ("ague"), an affliction very prevalent in Holland at that time, to which Husband, himself finally fell a victim and nearly succumbed. Another was laid up for four weeks with what must have been frost-bite though described as "chillblain".

Some time earlier Verveer had been released from gaol and had returned to his work, an event which seems to have coincided with further difficulties at the Customs. He had put in repeated pleas to Hayle for payment for his account for supposed services in that quarter without result. As a go-between he was primarily responsible to Dean and Gibbs but paid a regular salary by the Dutch Government. On May the 21st Dean gave the surprising news of the sudden death of Verveer saying at the same time that the Commissioners had expressed a wish "that Mr. Husband should be provisionally appointed as our representative in Holland *vice* Verveer. Of course I could not make any arrangement without your consent, and shall therefore be obliged by an early answer. Mr. Husband's new duties will not prevent his attending to your work but he must be considered as acting under our orders. It is very probable that the Commission would appoint him as permanent Manager when the Engines are completed — if you would consent to such an arrangement".

Confirmation of this proposal came from Husband a few days later. The Commissioners were offering him a salary which would substantially increase his present wage, which was not at all liberal. But there was nothing grasping in his nature. He says, "May I be allowed to make an

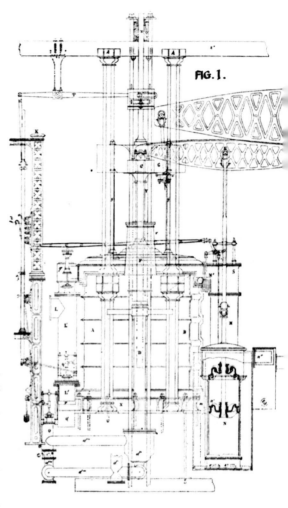

FIG. 1.

THE
CRUQUIUS
ENGINE

Figure I shows an elevation of the engine with driving controls on the left and jet-condenser air-pump on the right. The large beam, which passes through the wall of the building, where it is pivoted, works one of the eight main pumps; the smaller works the air-pump. The open lattice beam, which is uncommon, is used here, as in the East London engine.

Figure 2 is a sectional elevation of one of the main pumps showing the specially designed bucket and clack-valves.

Figure 3 is a simplified version of Figure I, shown at right angles to it and with principal working parts in section. Part of the twelve-foot cylinder is thus exposed to show the arrangement of the pistons. The high pressure cylinder and piston, with its six inch piston-rod is in the middle of the drawing; the annular low pressure piston appears on the left. The two pistons are separated by the wall of the high pressure cylinder. It will be noticed that there is a gap between the top of this and the cover, giving a permanently clear space over the whole area of both pistons. Two of the four rods of the annular piston are indicated; all five are fixed to the massive cross-head — *the great cap.*

The cycle of the Haarlem engines

This is similar to that of the Cornish engine but the reverse of it in action, the engine steaming at full pressure on the upward, or outdoor stroke and returning largely by gravity with assistance from expanding steam, when the actual work of pumping is done. The power is therefore used, as it were, obliquely to raise the cross-head against a weight sufficient for gravity to return the stroke, reinforced by low pressure steam.

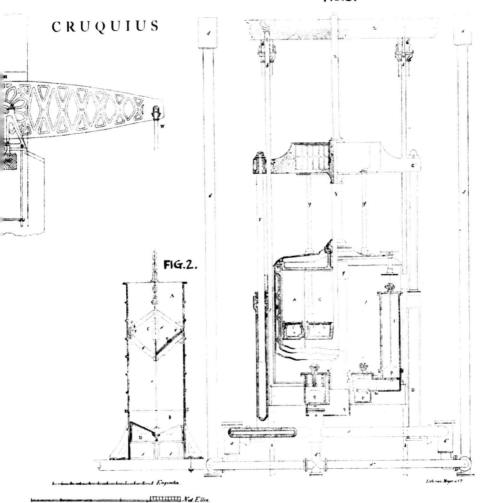

FIG.3.

CRUQUIUS

FIG.2.

Engunta.

Lith von Meyer & Co.

Ned Ellen.

To begin the up stroke, steam at boiler pressure is directed against the underside of the high-pressure piston while vacuum acts above both, the exhaust valve having opened at the end of the down stroke. The underside of the annular piston, however, is continuously in contact with the condenser and therefore in the up-stroke it moves *in vacuo*. Steam is cut off about half way and allowed to work the rest of the stroke on expansion. At the same time the buckets in the pumps sink by gravity through the water held in the pump-barrels and it is necessary for the engine to pause so that the valves can take their time to close. But the steam pressure is not sufficient to hold the great cap in position while this takes place. That is done by what is always called in the letters the "hydraulic."

On either side of Figure 3 will be seen a tall stand-pipe for storing water. They communicate with two rams or plunger-poles fixed to the circumference of the great cap and working in close-fitting cases, as seen in the drawing. That on the left is shown in section. This contrivance enables the machine to be locked against gravity until released by outlet valves which allow the water to return to the stand-pipes. Simultaneously on that happening the equilibrium valve opens and steam, in a further expansion, occupies the whole area above both pistons and the downward or indoor stroke is made which does the actual pumping. The timing for both steam and water is regulated by cataracts.

273

agreement for such a salary? — placing it at your disposal. The work I shall have to attend to will not disqualify me from attending to your business in any way. I should be much obliged if you would write a letter expressing your orders on the above subject". In the next paragraph, as if making a routine announcement, he gives the most important piece of news he had had to convey since arriving on Dutch soil. "On Saturday last, Steam was brought into the cylinders. Everything was tight except a few unimportant leakages on the under flange of casing, caused entirely by uneven expansions ... I think all will be finished this week". Still, it was near the end of July that the great day came and, on the 25th, Husband announced—

> We tried the Engine on tuesday evening last, when everything went oft very well, the engine answered every expectation. On Wednesday we tried her to lift water but the eyes in the pump chains broke [Perran's work!] and the working was again postponed until thursday when we had stronger eyes put in. But owing to the hydraulics not taking their water properly she fell back so from the top of her stroke that we again broke two chain eyes, but we found today on examining the hydraulics that a piece of wood had got under one of the ball valves which had caused the imperfect action. I suppose we shall try her again tomorrow without the pumps in under to insure the proper action of the hydraulics.
>
> The engine, through having lost her load by the breaking of pump chains, has sustained severe trials, and both Mr. Dean & the Commissioner are perfectly satisfied with her. I hope the pumps will answer as well as the engine, in that case perfect success will crown the undertaking.

Henry Harvey had raised no objection to Husband's acceptance of the Commission's offer and he was now acting in the dual capacity of serving both Dutch and English interests with the style of Assistant Resident Engineer. This was fair-minded on Henry's part in view of the fact that he must have made the decision just after receiving formal notice from the Commissioners that they now intended to press their claim for that long threatened fine of a thousand pounds.

The question of whether or not the Dutch Government would order the other two engines as projected by Dean and Gibbs to complete their plan for the drainage of the lake was not yet answered, nor could it be until the Commissioners had carried out their official tests at the Leeghwater station. This they did not attempt to do until the end of the year. In August, however, Dean had written to Hayle saying he was about to return to Holland and asking for a mechanical counter to register the number of strokes per minute made by the engine. He added "The performance of the Engine appears to be of a very superior character". But the pumps were not earning good marks. In September, Husband wrote to say that their buckets were causing immense friction and three of them had broken under the strain.

Early in December, a private letter from Geret Simons to Nicholas reveals a fresh complication. With the traditional Harvey zeal for perfection, Nicholas has been over-spending on modifications and improvements and has apparently made the tactical error of sending in a bill for extras at an unpropitious moment before the official tests of the engine's duty had been carried out. Simons had been the prime mover in everything to do with the scheme and has left a reputation of pre-eminence as a civil engineer; this letter shows that he was also a man of charm and culture. The letter, sent from the Hague, is dated the 2nd of December, 1845.

> All the extras you have been kind enough to make to render the engine more perfect you made them without the approbation of the Commission although you were bound by the terms of your contract not to alter anything [except] as by order of the engineer, specially authorised by the Commission, to make the alterations. Now, to be sure, all you have done is very well; but it is not so easy to convince people of the good and disinterested intentions of manufacturers when these are asking money which was not granted. Some time must be allowed to give them that conviction, which, of course, the Commission has now. But you know, as the money was not granted, we must have the authorization of the Minister first, and then of the King himself. I am quite certain all things will be arranged to your satisfaction, but you must allow us time to get over all the difficulties. I assure you I will do all I can to have things arranged in the shortest possible period of time . . . We have not yet been putting the engine to the test. We will do so when all things are completed and go on more easy. The men you were kind enough to send over [as engine-drivers and firemen] do very well — so have done all your men. Pray remember me to them, specially to Captain West. I hope to see them all again here but, before that time, in their own country.

In the Spring of 1846 Husband returned home and spent a little time at Hayle Foundry. By then, the Commission had proved the efficiency of the Leeghwater engine and decided that they must have the other two, which would complete the plan of drainage as devised by Dean and Gibbs. Husband was back at Sassenheim in June and wrote on the 12th, "Mr. Dean is here and I believe the Commission have come to a conclusion respecting the plan for the other engines; they will still adhere to the old plan of two cylinders and of the same size as the Leeghwater but the beams are to be connected above the cap".

On the 30th of the same month Dean wrote to Nicholas —

> I am now preparing the drawings for the two other Engines for this work (Haarlem Meer). As the Commission are desirous of letting the contract as

soon as possible I have arranged to complete the drawings by the 30th July. The Commission would be glad to see you over in Holland with me so that you could at once give your price and settle the contract. If, therefore you could be in London about the 25th you could see the drawings and make your estimate as the work will not very materially differ from the Leeghwater, except that there will be 8 pumps of 73 in. diameter, instead of 11 of 63 in., to each Engine, and they will be connected by loops over the cap, instead of under by rollers as at present. The Buckets upon the same principle as before.

I propose to use two 40 in. air pump buckets (not plungers), double beat valves and double beat cover valves. Will you oblige me by sending a sketch of what you consider the best form of your double beat valves for this purpose.

The Leeghwater works splendidly now.

I have written to Messrs Fox & Co by this post.

These engines were to be named after two other pioneers connected with early attempts to drain the lake, Nicholaas Samuel Cruquius and Frederik Godard van Lijnden. The site selected for the Cruquius engine was at a point on the bank nearest to Haarlem, that for the van Lijnden was at the middle of the northern shore. A line drawn from there to the Leeghwater roughly bisected the area of the lake and, when dry land should appear, it had already been planned to form a long straight highway between those extremities, covering a distance of about fourteen miles.

It will be seen from Arthur Dean's letter that the only important difference to be made in the new engines was a reduction by three in the number of beams and the manner in which they were connected with the great cap. The increased size of the pumps was calculated to raise the same volume of water per stroke as before. That the beams were now to be placed above the cap instead of below it was partly because the rollers had tended to wear the underside of the cap. But it must also have been due to the fact that in the former position they came down dangerously low. In Holland, it is still remembered that an unwary onlooker met his death by standing under one of the Leeghwater beams when it descended. In the new engines, themselves, nothing was altered except, as mentioned, the valves of the air-pumps in the condenser. Also, in the same unit, there was a slight alteration in the injector to give an alternative of continuous or interrupted flow of the water-jet.

There was no shortage of orders at Hayle Foundry or lack of business in other branches of the Company's industry, and the Dutch were not the only important customers who had had to be kept waiting. Notwithstanding this, and in spite of the penalty recently imposed by the Commissioners and a possibility that history would repeat itself in that respect, Harveys

276

were most anxious to secure the contract for the new engines. This anxiety may not have been wholly prompted by considerations of financial gain or even prestige. There is no doubt that Nicholas took that sort of pride mixed with affection for the creations of Hayle Foundry that a horse-breeder does in his blood-stock. Under his hand there had been reared up the largest and most notable steam engine in the world. That was something to fire the imagination!

Matters were arranged early in September and the new contract agreed. The arrangement differed from the earlier one in that Harveys and Fox and Co. of Perran Foundry were appointed joint contractors. Harveys were to supply both engine and pumps for Cruquius, Perran undertaking the same for van Lijnden. Beams and boilers were again to come from Van Vlissengen of Amsterdam and the Dutch Government to construct the buildings on the same plan as before. The price named by the joint English contractors was £38,250.

Much of the correspondence for 1847 is missing but apparently Captain John West is in direct charge at Cruquius under Husband who is acting in the dual role already explained. Early in 1848, West is replaced by Matthew Loam who makes regular reports of progress. For the past two years Loam had been employed in the erection of Harveys' engines at the waterworks of Liverpool and Coventry. He appears to have been a very competent mechanic but with a temperament entirely opposite to that of Husband. A large series of his letters from Liverpool and Coventry is preserved which show him to have been short tempered, intolerant, and boastful, His style is facetious and his manner of address sometimes astonishingly impertinent.

In spite of high expectations that work on the second contract would have been completed much more rapidly than the first, neither engine was ready to steam before February 1849, a gain in time over the Leeghwater of only one month. Matthew Loam gives the news in a letter dated February the 12th, headed grandiloquently, "Cruquius Machine, de Heemsteed, by Haarlem, Holland".

> I am happy in informing you that the Engine here started on last Wednesday evening; and I believe to the most perfect satisfaction of every one present. We should have worked earlier in the day, but one of the Amsterdam boiler pipe connections broke, and we had to repair it . . . When on Saturday we started in the morning, and continued through the Day, with scarcely a missed stroke, Mr Symons, Mr Dean, they two Co[mmission] Engineers, and several other Gentlemen was here, they one and all expressing perfect

delight and satisfaction, saying they never saw anything like it in Holland; we not having a screw to alter . . . One thing more I have to say at present, i.e. we are Ready before our neighbours at the Van Lyndon, having had this assertion Authenticated by A. Dean Esqr at my Room in presence of Witness on Saturday evening last.

We must suppose that such testimony so solemnly deposed must be true, though it is generally stated that the van Lijnden engine got started first. At any rate, all three engines were soon working at full power and in 1852 the Haarlemmer Meer was officially declared drained.

A plan for the treatment of the bed of the lake had been laid down long before it was exposed to view and was very similar to the one proposed by Leeghwater, whose death took place exactly two centuries before all three pumping-engines began to work in unison. The ground was to be intersected by a rectangular grid of small canals which would be kept at a proper level to irrigate the intervening plots of ground. To control any excess of water due to springs and rainfall pumping was still needed and the three engines were kept intermittently at work until the present century. Then the Leeghwater and Van Lijnden stations were converted to oil power (more recently to diesel-electric). The Cruquius was the last to work by steam and in 1933 it was declared redundant. On the 10th of June in that year, there was a large gathering at the engine-house. Members of the Royal Institution of Engineers (Holland) and many distinguished guests had come to witness the ceremonial demise of the great engine. A contemporary press account records that "the engine received a wreath of flowers for its honestly done duty, year after year, and the engine-man, who had passed many years of his life by that engine, stood by [as the last stroke of the pistons was made] with tears in his eyes and trembling legs, and he said 'Oh! how I have loved that engine' ".

This machine, which, like other lesser members of the steam tribe, could claim the affection of its master by its warmth and life-like action, was not dismantled when its day was done. It has been preserved as a national monument (for its own mechanical sake, and for what it has done for the country) by a society called the Cruquius Foundation.

In the Spring of 1964 I went to Holland to see for myself this unique relic of the Age of Steam and was fortunate in the manner in which the approach to my objective was made. This was in the company not only of one of the engine's most devoted admirers but also the Chairman of the catchment-area, comprising those seventy square miles of rich alluvial land recovered from the menacing watery waste by that trio of Cornish giants, who bore the happy and romantic title of Count of the Haarlemmer Meer Polder.

The Count had a more intimate association with the polder than that given by his official position. He owned a farm within it and his great grandfather had been amongst the first bidders for a stake in the new-made land, which had added 21,288 acres to William II's small kingdom, when it was put up for sale in 1853. We visited his flourishing little estate en route. Here were a huge barn, the size of a large parish church, its red tiled roof covering a span of ninety feet with nave and double side-aisles, and the storehouse for potatoes, with specially contrived floor and wall openings for ventilation to eliminate spontaneous over-heating of the crop which was mainly intended for export to England. This reminded me of a letter from William Husband in which he said he had secured a back cargo for the *Nautilus* of 50 tons of potatoes at 3s. 6d. a hundredweight — "I have boiled some of them on board and there are no diseased so far as we can discover". And now land in the polder is fetching more than £400 an acre (in 1966).

We returned to the higher level of the encircling dyke with its broad canal and towing-road, 60 kilometres in circumference (now a motor-way called the Ring Road), and came to the Cruquius station, monument to a peak achievement of the Industrial Revolution, masked by a feudal decor of battlemented drum-tower, windows of Gothic form and tracery, and surrounding parapet pierced with 14th century quatrefoils.

The boiler-house had been enlarged in more recent years by adding an aisle on either side to bring the number of boilers from six (of Trevithick's Cornish type) up to ten. Their steam was delivered into a long cylindrical vessel placed transversely above their remote ends to act as a single steam-dome. The boilers had been removed after the engine stopped work and their room was occupied by a museum, illustrating by models and pictures a wide range of water-lifting appliances, from windmills to steam and other powered plant.

The Count, having set us down here had to depart for a mayoral reception, it being the Queen's birthday, but we were joined by a learned and very charming member of the Cruquius Foundation. The royal anniversary had kept sightseers in town and we had the place to ourselves for several hours undistracted. In the round engine-room everything is exactly as it was when the last of the Hayle contingent departed except for the resounding noise of those pulsations which had lifted 112 tons of water ten feet high at a single stroke; and the ensuing silence invited timid ghosts to pry about, invisible to the two engineers who expounded on details of the machine but not to my fanciful self who had had a special introduction to them in the days of their

Reproduced by courtesy of the Catchment Authority

toils and frustrations through the letters they had written. And there, above the idle plug-rods, with their handles at the ready for a re-start, was a large enamelled shield bearing the arms of the Duchy of Cornwall above the legend "Harvey & Co, Makers, Hayle Foundry".

To return now to our more properly assigned date in the

33. Demolition of the works (1904)

32. Boiler-plate bending roll

281

34. Model of a seventy-inch Cornish engine

35. The new offices and showrooms, severely damaged by fire in 1969

calendar, there was a final reckoning of costs in 1850. By then, the Commissioners were demanding penalties for delays in construction of £2,666, involving both firms. So, in March, a joint deputation which included Nicholas Harvey and directors of the Foxes of Perran went to Holland to plead for mitigation. There could be no doubt that materials and workmanship of the highest standard had produced machines which had come up to every expectation, both in their power and pumping capacity and their economy in fuel, which was above the most optimistic prediction. The meeting took a friendly turn and it was agreed that the fine should be cut by half.

The year 1850 saw the end of the first half of the century in which steam power had come of age, an event in the history of the whole world to which Hayle Foundry had made no small contribution. When Henry Harvey's days began to be numbered there were no steam engines at the Cornish mines except that primitive and wasteful contrivance of Thomas Newcomen. Now, steam was the ruling power both on land and sea. It was well within Henry's memory that the essentials of the first self-propelled engine had gone from Hayle Foundry and he had lived to hear the unstinted praise which followed the achievement of the Leeghwater engine. By then, his days were fully numbered and he died on the 7th of May, 1850, and was laid with other members of his family in the old churchyard at Gwinear, where his sister, Elizabeth had preceded him only two years before.

XIX

NEW REGIME

THE CONTRACT FOR THE LEEGHWATER ENGINE drawn in 1843 appears to have been the last important document of the kind signed by Henry[1], and it is noticeable after this time that letters relating to business but personally addressed to him become scarce while there is an increase in those addressed to Nicholas, J. H. Trevithick, and William West and, when Trevithick goes travelling, his letters are no longer confined to news of prices and purchases of grain but range over matters relating to coal, iron, and timber. So it becomes clear that Henry is at last taking things easy. He amused himself by tidying up the prehistoric fort which had guarded Hayle Harbour in the much older Iron Age. He made paths in the defensive ditches and planted the breastworks with trees. An inscribed gravestone of some Cornish saint of the Early Christian period, which had been found when making the foundations of the boiler-maker's shop, he had set up in the new revetment beside one of the paths, and he erected a substantial arch in the Roman style prominently inscribed "Anno Domini MDCCCXLIV".

This arch is surely something of more profound significance than a final touch to his essay in landscape gardening. Eighteen forty-four was the year when the *chef d'oeuvre* of the Foundry was being erected in Holland and the monument could well be a triumphal arch set up advisedly by this Imperator of the New Iron Age.

In the late Autumn of 1847, Henry suffered a stroke of paralysis which deprived him of the use of his lower limbs but left his head as clear as ever and in March of the following year he executed a deed of settlement by which he retired altogether from the business and passed it over in trust to all his nephews and nieces, reserving only for himself and his sister, Elizabeth, an income during their lifetime of £350 a year, each.

[1] Preserved in the Record Office of the town of Haarlem.

The trustees of the settlement were Nicholas Oliver Harvey, John Harvey Trevithick, and the solicitor, Thomas Whitford who, although not a member of the Company, was an old and trusted adviser with an inside knowledge of all the many legal predicaments in which the firm had been involved — and still was.

Up to this time, the style "Harvey & Co" has been taken to represent a partnership of Henry and his sister, Elizabeth, but it is clear from the deed of settlement that, legally, everything was in Henry's own hands — freeholds, leases, buildings, all equipment and stores, ships, and book-debts. All this immense and valuable property, excepting only personal belongings at Foundry House was, then and there, "bargained for" by the trustees for ten shillings payable to "the said Henry Harvey".

The beneficiaries under the indenture, set forth on twenty vellum skins measuring two feet by two feet-six, were the three families descended from the founder, the Harveys, the Wests, and the Trevithicks. Each was to have a stake of one-third in the property and profits of the business. There were only two survivors of the Harvey branch, Nicholas Oliver and his younger brother, William, the West beneficiaries extended to nine, for the children of Anna, the wife of J. E. Pool were named and provided for, their mother having died two years earlier. There were six Trevithicks, children of the inventor, all of them married except Richard, the eldest (described as merchant). The latest match had been made by Anne two years earlier, to Hannibal Ellis, whom we met as a clerk at the Foundry office in the earlier chapters.

The ships are mentioned separately. There appears to have been a separate agreement between Henry and J. H. Trevithick (which I have not discovered), bearing on those ships registered in the name of the latter — the *Trelissick, Mellanear, Jane, Joanna, William,* and *Frank* — and two of the older ones registered in Henry's name, the *Park* and *Providence* (II). Trevithick is said to stand "possessed" of these vessels though, at the same time their management and movements are to remain at the disposal of the three trustees (which includes himself), and the fact is now revealed that, although the seven were registered in his name, they were paid for by his uncle, "which vessels. . . were purchased with the proper monies of the said Henry Harvey and are now held respectively by the said J. H. Trevithick in trust for the sole use and benefit of the said Henry Harvey". These purposes must seem obscure, but the clause was to show itself a thing of importance a few years hence, and perhaps this was foreseen by the long-sighted author of the settlement.

But the most striking thing in the lengthy deed is the complete liberty of action accorded to the trustees, guided only by what they should think best to do in prevailing circumstances. This even envisaged selling up the whole or part of the business and premises. If there was a difference of opinion, a two-to-one vote by the three was to be decisive.

In fine, Henry, describing himself as Merchant, Founder, Shipbuilder, Grocer, Draper, Ironmonger, Miller, and Baker, declared that "he hath in himself good right, full power, and absolute authority to assign the said lands and hereditaments . . . and the buildings and erections thereon, and all such part and parts... to the said Nicholas Oliver Harvey, John Harvey Trevithick and Thomas Whitford".

Henry's last years were further clouded by four family bereavements. His unmarried niece, Nanny Harvey, died in 1840. She had spent nearly all her life at Foundry House with him and his sister, Elizabeth, with whom, it will be remembered, she shared a strong preference for herbal remedies which nearly cost John Brunton the loss of an injured foot. Another niece, Anna West, who had married J. E. Pool, died in 1846, leaving five children which were provided for in the deed of settlement. In the following year, Nicholas lost his wife, Clementina, whom he had brought over from Germany. Only three months after Henry had executed the settlement, his sister, Elizabeth, died, leaving him the sole lonely occupier of Foundry House.

But, with his usual care for the realities of time present and future, Henry at once drew up a new will. Part of an old family property in the parish of Stithians[1] which John Harvey had left to Elizabeth she had bequeathed to Nanny. But Nanny had died in her aunt's lifetime and, that will not having been altered, the bequest had lapsed. Henry now left £500 between Nicholas and William Harvey to regain the property "believing it to have been the intention of my said sister" that Nanny's two brothers should have it. Furthermore, he left to Nicholas and John Harvey Trevithick gifts of a thousand pounds each, seven hundred to William Harvey, and three hundred to Richard Trevithick, the inventor's eldest son, of whom we have heard, and continue to hear, so very little. The residue of his personal estate is to be divided among the nephews and nieces in exactly the same proportions as devised in the deed of settlement. In neither of these instruments, however, is there a mention of his only other (and eldest)

[1] It was for this church that John Harvey cast the tenor bell.

sister, Jane Trevithick.

But Jane does not seem to have lacked means, either then or later. Her three younger sons were doing well and could afford to support her, apart from what she may have put aside as hostess of the White Hart. But the omission seems strange and one cannot but wonder at it. Her new home (still standing) was quite a charming moderate sized house with a large garden on the hillside above the town where, from the occasional letters which have survived, she seems to have lived very happily for another twenty years, going abroad occasionally, and taking a lively interest in all the doings of the world which owed so much to the genius of her husband. She reached the age of ninety-six.

There is a single sentence in the will which stands out, as I read it, as something from the depths of Henry's feelings. Unlike all the rest, it is not a command but a hope. Going back over the long past in that lonely house, facing death as squarely and fearlessly as he had faced the issues of life, the testator counted all that had been made good in winning independence — his ruling passion. He would recall his father's early fight for his rights, even for access to the sea; the struggle to maintain the depth of his channel; the crisis over the quays; his remedy for the closing of the Copperhouse flood-gates by making the great basin with its sluices; the success in getting the port liberated from the exactions of St. Ives; the greatly increased shipping at the port which had achieved the distinction for Hayle of being made a coinage town while the Duchy dues were still in force. But yet Hayle was not a completely independent port with a custom house or bonded store of its own though many applications had been made to that end for, although several of the old duties had been rescinded, the distance which the excisemen had to travel continued to cause delays and inconvenience. But all he actually says is, "Whereas considerable sums have been laid out in the improvement of the Harbour of Hayle, now my wish and request is that as soon as sufficient funds can be raised by the persons now entitled to that property that such improvements may be carried out and compleated". And, as if in recognition of his abdication, he signs himself simply "Merchant".

Something must be said about William Harvey who was left £700 in addition to his share in the Company's profits. He has stood in the background up to the present, but he was to play a prominent part in the Company's affairs later on. William was younger by four years than his brother, Nicholas. He had lived a great deal of his life at the old manor-house of Trelissick which, it may be remembered, was part of the property of the extinct Hearle family and came to Francis Hearle Rodd, who never lived there. William rented the manor and farmed its land as far as where it joined the lower portion, which was held by Harvey & Co. The manor-house still looks the part though the older portion has been pulled down, leaving what had been added in the early 18th century, with moulded plaster ceilings, bolection panelling, and mullioned windows, on a pane of which is scratched "William Harvey, 1828" in a neat round hand. Its perpetrator was then aged twenty-three.

In those days, William and John Harvey Trevithick shared the common interest of the land and its produce and were on friendly terms, joining forces in several deals in grain and other merchandise. But, at the time of Henry's death, their good relationship appears to have cooled off considerably. When the dominating spirit and strong hand were finally removed, the many beneficiaries, who seem to have considered that they were rather partners than shareholders under the Trust, began to put forward their views as to what the future policy of the firm should be.

Francis Trevithick, now Locomotive Superintendent of the London & North Western Railway held one of the foremost posts in his profession. His younger brother, Frederick Henry, a civil engineer, who had continued to have a desultory connection with Harveys after serving his apprenticeship at the Foundry was also destined to reach a high place in the American railways, but was still in England. No doubt these two regarded the works at Hayle as being run on old-fashioned lines and out of touch with modern practice. They tendered advice to Nicholas, which was not well received. At the same time, William Harvey who, since the Settlement, had felt himself to have more vital interests in the Company than his farm, was also taking stock of the non-mechanical side of the business which J. H. Trevithick had ruled for so long with little interference from his uncle.

Whatever else these three sons of their brilliant father may have inherited from him, they all had something of his touchy temper, quickly aroused in opposition. Francis and Frederick had something, too, of his generous nature, but this seems to have been lacking in John Harvey Trevithick. If we can judge him at all from his letters, he was a well-trained and thoroughly competent man of business, but of a cold nature and with a narrow outlook. Nicholas and William had their grandfather's temperament. They were genial and kind-hearted, but men of strong purpose.

It was not long before the stability of the Company became increasingly threatened by dissensions, in which family feeling was probably engaged. In 1851 William Harvey and J. H. Trevithick offered to sell out their interests, a course rejected by the trustees but, in the following year, it was recognised that the heritage must be divided. It was agreed that J. H. Trevithick should be allowed to take the buildings where his former activities had chiefly been employed, the grist mill with its stock and stores, and the bakehouse, also the drapery and grocery shops with their stock, and the room occupied by the ironmongery shop but not its stock, and to receive £17,777 for his financial interest in the Settlement. At the same time, proportionate payments were to be made to his brothers and sisters. This resulted in a new company being set up in Hayle under the name of "J. H. Trevithick & Son, Millers."

Everything else remained with the Harveys and Wests — the foundry, the harbour, the rope-walk, and the merchanting trades of iron, coal, timber, and lime. Trevithick retained the ships which had been registered in his name, although they had been paid for by Henry. But he was to pay the nominal rent of £5 a year for permission to land goods on Harveys quays and restricted to landing only those goods which were for his own trade.

The crucial meeting took place on the 19th of March, 1852, and a copy of some notes then made are among the Harvey papers. One of the items is worth quoting, "The foregoing arrangements are entered into with an understanding that a good and friendly feeling shall exist between all the parties and that they shall continue to render future assistance to each other". A further change in the government of Harvey & Co. was imminent and, in August of the same year it was decided that the partly dismembered firm ought to return to a form of constitution which had been abandoned thirty years before — a fully legal partnership. This was to run for fourteen years, and the parties named were Nicholas and William Harvey with William and John West. The deed was signed on August the 15th, 1852.

A month before this new departure was made, a further memorandum was added to the double sheet of notes just referred to, dated July the 13th, 1852. It is signed by Thomas Whitford and another.

"We think that under the circumstances, and considering the misunderstanding which has taken place on the subject, that Messrs. Harvey & Co. should supply Mr. J. H. Trevithick's dwelling house with gas lights at 3s. 6d. per 1000 cubic feet so long as Messrs. Harvey & Co. continue to manufacture gas."

It has been noted that in quite early days Henry began making equipment for gas-works and erected complete plants for the neighbouring towns. They were good long-term investments because at the same time he secured their contracts to keep them supplied with coal. Yet, oddly enough, he did not attempt to give his own foundry, where much work was done after dark in the winter, this superior form of lighting until 1843. Then, and for some time onwards, only a few privileged people outside the Company's premises were laid on. Trevithick, however, apparently thought that he ought to have been supplied for nothing, as he presumably was while still a member of the firm, and the matter of this small gas-bill was an endless source of annoyance to him. It was just one of many trivial complaints that he went on writing about to the Company (whose office was only a few paces away from his) for years. Those which have been preserved relating to the gas go on to 1865. One sample will suffice to show the tone of the "misunderstanding" and to what extent the "friendly feeling" was being maintained.

Messrs. Harvey & Co.   Hayle; 9 Nov. 1863
Dear Sirs,
    In reply to your letter of the 7th instant, I cannot but feel that your having discontinued the lighting of the gas opposite my garden gate is, on your part, a Breach of honourable dealing, but I will defer replying to your proposal of my paying you two guineas per annum until I have taken the opinion of friends on the matter.
    To the other portions of your Mr Rawlings' letter, I will only remark that I do not admit their accuracy.
                        Dear Sirs
                            Yours truly
                                J. H. Trevithick

Harveys replied —

We beg to acknowledge the receipt of your letter of yesterday's date in which you are pleased to charge us with a breach of honourable dealing and to characterize our general statements as inaccurate. We indignantly deny your charges as unworthy, particularly as coming from you who must be well aware that they are unfounded. What are the facts; *1st,* on your asking Northy why he had omitted to light the Lamp opposite your house, he informed you that we were short of gas, and he had acted according to orders, but he added that you could have the light by paying for it.
    2nd. We have often, during winter, gratuitously lighted our lamp opposite your house from which you have derived benefit, and we now feel that you claim as a *right* that which we allowed you to enjoy as a privilege. We have denied the right and shall withdraw the privilege as your letter shows an utter want of appreciation of our past conduct. You do not thank us for having maintained a light opposite your house, but deprecate in unworthy language the exercise of our right to extinguish the same. You say you shall consult

your friends on the subject: better you had done so prior to accusing us of dishonourable dealing. We are satisfied that a *friend* will advise you to retract such charges, provided you state facts without reservation. There is ample ground for recrimination on our part, but motives have nothing to do with a simple question of business.

   Your insinuations respecting Mr Rawlings are unworthy and we are sorry to add show a disposition to reap advantage by attempting to engender mistrust. We can arrive at no other conclusion although anxiously disposed to interpret your letter in a more favourable light.

That was by no means the end of the stinging-match. But Francis Trevithick was more reasonable. He remained on friendly terms and continued to send occasional orders to the Foundry, though it is clear from certain innuendos and notable omissions in the *Life* he wrote of his father that he couldn't forgive Henry for taking up Arthur Woolf in preference to the far more talented Richard, and that he regarded Henry's treatment of his father in general as cold, if not shabby.

A fresh deed of partnership was executed in 1854 to admit a fifth partner, William John Rawlings (mentioned in the letters just quoted). He had been for some time in the service of the Company, but no relationship has been traced between him and Thomas Rawlings (introduced to the reader in chapter thirteen), though it may well have existed. Both came from Camborne.

An important step, which led to a large increase in business had just been taken, by the establishment of an office in London. The manager appointed to run it was William Husband. As already said, he remained in Holland in the employment of the Dutch Government and, in 1848, was elected a member of the koninkijle institut van ingenieurs (Royal Institution of Engineers). Whilst in their employment the D.N.B. says that he "planned and erected the Half-weg engine". There is a tender among the papers in the handwriting of Nicholas, and signed by him, for a rotary horizontal engine, with a cylinder 48 inches in diameter and a thirty foot flywheel, together with three Cornish boilers, addressed to the Commissioner, W. Simons, and dated "Haarlem, 13th March, 1849." It was to be erected near Half-weg, and the "complete outfit" is priced at £5,790. I think this must be the same machine. If so, its design must he largely credited to the young ex-apprentice. An acute attack of malaria ("ague") forced him to return to England in 1849.

Besides being a good mechanic, Husband was also a fertile inventor and, in the course of his life, he took out nearly a score of English patents which show a wide range of versatility. Before leaving Holland he had devised a new method of drying and warehousing grain. In 1851 we find him planning a powder-magazine for Merseyside, after which he was called to the new works going on at the Bristol Docks and designed a bridge for the Cumberland Basin. With these qualifications and his natural gift of tact Harveys were lucky to get him back to start their London office. He remained in the fold for the rest of his life, becoming Managing Partner in 1863.

There had been another development. It had its beginning within Harvey's lifetime. Henry had for some reason, been consistently opposed to the building of a steam vessel, complete with hull as well as machinery, in his shipyard. But in 1846 Nicholas, persuaded his uncle to let him accept the order for a steam tug from a towing company at Ruhrort on the Rhine. The commission was no doubt due to his close associations with Germany and his early connection with the navigation of the Rhine.

The tug, to be called the *Prussian Eagle*, was to have an iron hull, and no iron ship had been built at Hayle since Richard Trevithick made his experimental one intended for a naval pinnace but rejected by the Navy Board. It was at that time generally believed that, as iron could not float, a ship made of it would certainly go straight to the bottom, though John Wilkinson had proved the contrary when he launched an iron barge on the Severn in 1787. But, by 1846, the iron hull was accepted as the coming thing. The plating and rivetting was work for the boiler-maker rather than the shipwright, skilled only in wooden construction. At Hayle, slipway, boiler-makers, and the experienced shipwright, Samuel Warren were all available, whereas the innumerable little fishing ports round the coast that were now building ships — ranging right up to three-masted barques — had to stick to traditional all-wooden construction.

Precedent being thus broken, Harveys became ship-builders in the fullest sense and that side of the business was regularly enlarged till eventually an iron steamship of 3,800 tons register left the ways. Not long after the keel of the *Prussian Eagle* had been laid down an enquiry for a similar vessel came from another towing company on the Rhine, this time located at Dordrecht in Holland. It initiated a long and quite entertaining correspondence, continued over the next six years. The letters are signed by T. B. Hooft and F. C. Deking Dura, written by the former in faultless English and expressed in the most courteous manner, in spite of the differences which arose between the parties.

The first exchange of letters, beginning at the end of December, 1846, was followed in April of the next year by a personal visit of Messrs. Hooft and Dura to Hayle Foundry, where they inspected the German tug which was under construction and signed the contract for their own. They also visited Wheal Alfred mine and asked Nicholas to procure shares for them in it. In August they were asking "When do you intend to come over with the Ruhrort boat and how are you getting on with ours?" In September they were beginning to get nervous and a familiar note is sounded. The Company has had a meeting and "we were requested to address you once more and recommend most earnestly that no time should be lost in her construction as a later delivery than the stipulated time would be the cause of very severe loss to the Company, very much exceeding the penalty for non-performance. The later delivery of the Boat you are building for Ruhrort makes us uneasy and you will oblige us by informing us what is the cause of her not having arrived here".

To expedite matters, but under the cover of offering advice and help, it was suggested that the future commander of the vessel, Captain Koch, should be sent to Hayle. The idea was not very warmly received but agreed on after an argument as to who should pay for his board and lodging. It was August, 1848, before the captain was able to ring up his engines and set off for Holland with a single passenger in the shape of Nicholas Harvey. The tug had been named the Dordrecht and the arms of the city were painted on either paddle-box.

The lesson of the *Echo*, when an engine-room crew, hostile to modern innovations had nearly succeeded in wrecking the machinery, was well remembered, and Nicholas had made it part of the bargain that only Cornishmen should be employed in firing and driving until after the trials, and next, Dutchmen of whom he should approve. The voyage was made successfully in good time but the vessel appears to have done some rolling on the way and, what with this and the pounding of the engines, the working of the iron hull had pressed out all the caulking of the deck.

Jebus Bickle was already in Holland and was to remain with the *Dordrecht* until after her trials. He had approached by a different route, going to Amsterdam in a sailing vessel from Perran Foundry, laden with parts for the van Lijnden engine, together with a heavy four-oared gig provided by William Husband's father for delivery at the Leeghwater station. William met him then, each manning a pair of oars, they proceeded to make the thirty mile journey along the new canal, breaking off to spend the night with John West and his Cornish contingent.

The *Dordrecht* was expected to tow four or more large laden barges up stream on the Rhine and it was found that another boiler was necessary to maintain steam at a pressure to cope with this. Jebus returned to Hayle on October the 16th with this order. Then came the usual rub about the long delay in delivery and the fine was (as in the case of the first of the Haarlem engines) assessed at £1,000. But a settlement was soon arrived at whereby the penalty was cut by half.

In 1849 Messrs. Hooft and Durer called for a tender for a sister ship, though the first vessel had scored some black marks for breakdowns, chiefly in the steering-gear. During 1850, politics in Germany were in a state of critical ferment and the Dutchmen wrote to say that things were too unsettled to give an order, but "your last quotation of £10,000 is still £1,000 higher than by another first rate manufactory. We should, however, wish to give you the preference". By March, 1851, the contract was signed and the keel of *Dordrecht II* was immediately laid.

Harveys appear to have been determined not to be late this time and the new tug was launched before the end of October. Nicholas was as keen on first class workmanship as his uncle had been. No rude letters or threats of penalty would ever hustle Henry in putting speed before quality. In this second Dordrecht the Foundry does seem to have yielded to that temptation. Jebus Bickle was again sent out to put the new tug through her paces before the official trials were run. This is what he reported —

> We left Dordt on Monday the 3rd [of November] inst. with four wood vessels containing about 800 tons and got along tolerably well until within a few miles of Ruhrort when several stays in the fore-boiler suddenly gave way, some in consequence of the eyes which confined the stays to the top of the boiler not having been properly rivetted. Others gave way in the cotters, and some broke in the middle. The steam at the time was at about 20 lbs per inch which would not have injured the boiler had the stays been properly adjusted but some had too much strain, others none at all — in fact, a very slovenly job,
>
> We were now under the necessity of dropping the four vessels and proceeding to Ruhrort with one boiler in order to repair the other. During the voyage from Dordt here the air bucket valves again gave trouble by frequently becoming trigged [stuck] and obliging us to stop . . . The connecting rods and drag-link having got considerably out of truth. On our arrival here we were under the necessity of having two new crank-pins and also new brasses for the drag-link.

This news, when it reached Hayle, reinforced by a letter from the owners, must have struck a double blow. It arrived when internal dissensions and criticism of the policy of the Company were at the climax which was to end in partition. It was also a threat to the hopeful future of the shipyard in its new enterprise of iron steamer construction. Nicholas appears to have been abroad on the trail of further commissions, but the Foundry sent an immediate reply with a further letter the next day.

(November 18, '51) We are in receipt of yours of the 14th acquainting us of the accident with the *Dordrecht* No. 2, & prior to it we received the particulars from our Mr Bickle. No parties can regret this more than ourselves, it being an accident against which we could not calculate and we are of course bound to repair the damage. We do not know if you understand the cause of this misfortune, but it was in consequence of the Air Pump bucket Valve not shutting as it ought to have done, thereby the injection water accumulated and got under the Piston, and this whilst the Piston was going at a great Velocity, as the boat was not at the time towing. Consequently something must give way & it is rather extraordinary that the cross-heads or beams did not.

From what we are told, there is but little doubt but what the Paddle Shafts must be taken out. We have instructed that this be immediately attended to [of] which indeed the intimation has been sent to us. The parties at Ruhrort will do everything that is necessary and will do every exertion to put everything in order. When this is accomplished and, judging from what has already been done, we have no doubt but that the boat will be one of the best.

(November 19th '51) After writing you yesterday we have received intelligence from our Friends at Ruhrort respecting the Boat *Dordrecht* No. 2. We cannot express our surprise stronger than they have on Mr Schottman's insisting that the Boat should be taken to Dordt. We are quite at a loss to imagine the reason for his so doing. We can do nothing to repair the accident there, nor can the extent of the repairs be determined before the Shafts are taken out if whether they can be strengthened or if there must be new ends. When the Boat is at Ruhrort & these parts taken out then, if necessary, one of our firm shall be there to see the completion. At such times many persons have as many opinions, but we are under no alarm as to the principle or quality of the whole job. We believe that when the accidental defects are remedied you will have no reason to complain and we do not flinch in fulfilling our part . . . Nothing further can be required of us, but do not delay in sending the boat to Ruhrort, if not already there, this delay is a wanton loss of time.

The style of these compositions is that of John West. But there is a notable omission. He says nothing about the breakdown in the boiler whose workmanship was so frankly stigmatised by Jebus. A month later, Nicholas writes from Sterkrade, near Ruhrort, saying he is trying to intercept a government official who is on his way to England to seek tenders for two "post boats". He ends by saying that work on the tug is going well and both paddle-shafts have been forged. He hopes to try her out soon, but "I do not wish to see the Dordrecht people before this is all right... I think we may get over the difficulties without lawyers."

But Messrs. Hooft and Dura, still using the most courteous language, refused to pay the final instalment of the price, treating the time lost over the accident before the vessel had run her official trials as a delay in delivery. Nicholas employed a Dutch lawyer to sue in the Netherland courts for default of payment and won his case.

By the end of 1853 the partnership was settling down to its post-partition routine, with Nicholas in the role he had always had as a roving Chief Engineer and acknowledged head of the establishment, William and John West in charge of the foundry, and William Harvey looking after the merchanting of coal, timber, and lime. The hard-worked clerks must have felt relief at the lightening of their former burden in correspondence, with the grain and milling side lifted from their shoulders and the London office taking some of the strain. There were a great many orders on hand and in course of execution both for large pumping engines and all kinds of mining equipment. With the latter a connection had been formed in Australia in 1848, three years before the great gold-rush began. In 1852, a pumping engine designed by William West (St. B.) was sent there. Transport facilities were rapidly increasing. The West Cornwall Railway had absorbed the Hayle Railway. They had eliminated the two awkward cable-hauled gradients at Angarrack and Redruth. The line approached Hayle on the higher ground and crossed the Penpol Valley by the present viaduct. An obstruction directly in its path was that venerable landmark of former days, John Ellis's House. Those who set so much store by inspecting the merest fragment of an ancient monument may still find part of a wall and a small window standing by one of the piers under the bridge.

XX

THE SEVERN TUNNEL CONTRACT

THE SECOND PHASE OF THE COMPANY'S DEVELOPMENT (1852-1904) nearly coincided with the latter half of the 19th century. In this final chapter of the long story it can only be outlined, with principal events briefly noted, while dwelling more fully on one of the more outstanding achievements — the permanent elimination of the Great Spring in the Severn Tunnel.

In 1855, William Husband was called from the London office to the works at Hayle where he remained for thirty years before returning. The Company had just acquired the harbour of Porthleven, where he was engaged on the construction works of an inner basin with similar flood-gates and sluices as those at Hayle to keep the outer harbour scoured.

In 1858, the shipyard was busy on a new steamer for the Hayle to Bristol service, the *Cornubia*. She was larger than her predecessors, being 411 tons register. Her propulsion was by a pair of oscillating cylinders, having that simple type of valve-gear which still survives in small toy steam engines. The lessons learnt from the *Dordrecht II* must have been taken well to heart as she seems to have given little trouble and is said to have had a fair turn of speed. Three years later, she was bought by the Confederates in the American Civil War and led a more adventurous life until overhauled by the enemy. A model of her, shown on page 159, was preserved until lost in the showroom fire in 1969.

In 1861, the Company received an unlooked for blow in the death of Nicholas Oliver Harvey at the age of fifty-eight; after twenty-eight years as a dynamic member of the firm and eleven as its leader. He had been married again to another German lady and, by her, he left five children, four of them, boys. The eldest, named Henry Nicholas, was only five years old but, as he grew up, it was seen that he had inherited his father's inclination and talent and, later, was to bring these strongly to bear in promoting a forward policy of the firm. So as not to be confounded with his distinguished namesake, he was known as Harry Harvey.

The writer of an obituary notice[1] has this to say of Nicholas Oliver —

> All the work undertaken by him was finished regardless of cost, money-making being a secondary consideration. He was a man of great practical experience, both in designing and manufacturing engines, and was very ready in invention. He was much beloved by those connected with him, and respected for his uprightness, hospitality, and truly genial nature.

The vacant place in the Partnership was taken, not unworthily, by William Husband.

After the Crystal Palace had been moved from Hyde Park to Sydenham, a second Great International Exhibition was held there in 1862. Harveys had a stand in it and showed the working model of another pumping engine which they had made for the East London Waterworks seven years before. It had a cylinder with internal diameter of 100 inches, the largest made for any British waterworks up to that time. At full load, it pumped 9,000 gallons of water per minute against a head of 140 feet in the stand-pipe. For the model, the firm was awarded the prize medal of the exhibition "For excellence and practical success of engines". Later, it found a home in the Science Museum at South Kensington.

In the same year, there came the (presumed) fulfilment of Henry's last wish. Hayle Harbour was made "compleat" by the establishment of a custom house. But this was the beginning of a decade during which a sharp decline in the Cornish mining industry set in, from which it never recovered. Our policy of free trade, then prevailing, the rich metalliferous deposits, recently discovered in the Americas, Australia, and elsewhere, came in unhampered by tariff barriers. Mines began to close down all over the Duchy and their employees were forced to starve or emigrate to where the going and the pay were good. In the middle of the decade there was a false spurt fostered by outside speculators, but, after 1866, the market for new mining equipment was negligible. The future for manufacturers in this class of machinery lay abroad.

It was now, under these stresses, that the testing time came for the two foundries on the Hayle lagoon which had for so long and, formerly, so ruthlessly, competed for supremacy. The old Cornish Copper Company, re-named Sandys, Carne, & Vivian, had sedulously followed the Harvey lead at nearly every juncture, with intent to overtake, yet never gaining the

[1] Trans. Inst. Civ. Eng., vol XXI.

initiative. They had, however, achieved a high reputation for the manufacture of the Cornish engine, and one of the most curious and intriguing exhibits of monumental machinery of the 19th century is fortunately preserved by the Metropolitan Water Board in the old waterworks at Kew Bridge. Here, under the same roof, though separated by a party-wall, stand two Cornish giants, complete in lith and limb though deprived of the breath of steam. The elder (1846) is by Sandys, Carne & Vivian, with a 90 inch cylinder, the younger (1871), by Harveys, with a 100 inch cylinder.

As the 'sixties advanced, S.C. & V. were beginning to show signs of distress. How much of this was due to the changed outlook in the Cornish mining industry and how much to the fact that the Company was now being managed by trustees who lacked the fire and ability of the earlier chiefs, it is hard to say. But, in 1867, the trustees concluded that they should realise on part of their property that was likely to fetch the best price and for which there was a likely purchaser. This was the waterside premises — just those properties which were the very bones of the old contention. They comprised Merchant Curnow's Quays on either side of the narrows, the floodgates and sluices, the canal thence onwards to the Copperhouse dock at Ventonleague. Immediately after this decision, the trustees were in treaty with Harveys and a sale to them was concluded on the 10th of December in the same year.

The reaction of the Foundry to this acquisition is piquantly reflected in a Cash Book entry for March the 23rd, 1868. It is noted that the captain of the *Henry Harvey*, a new sailing ship which left the yard the previous year, was paid five shillings "on being the first of our Vessels to go to Copperhouse and fly colours there". But the transaction did more than to silence the ancient grudge, it ended the dual control of Hayle Harbour and made Harveys sole owners of the port, with authority to levy dues for wharfage and anchorage in both lobes of the lagoon and to appoint their own harbourmaster, which they presently did. Thus the haven became even more "compleat" than perhaps Henry had dared to anticipate, and it was a nice touch that his namesake vessel should have been sent to signalise this triumph.

It was a sad thing that, only a little later in the same year, John West should die. To no one can the full meaning of the event have meant more than to him. Those outstanding incidents of the former struggle — the great battle on the sands, the verdict at Bodmin assizes, the final decision of the long drawn-out arbitration tribunal at Hayle, were all well within his memory. His place in the partnership was taken by his son, Nicholas James, a young man of twenty-nine.

In 1869, the connection of the Company with Porthleven harbour was reinforced by a new Act of Parliament (the fourth since 1811). Hitherto, they had been in the position of mortgagees but, under the Act, they gained full possession of the land and buildings. They were to trade as the Porthleven Harbour and Dock Company and "William Harvey, William West, William John Rawlings, William Husband, and Nicholas James West shall be the first directors of the Company".

It had been the intention of the fishermen to oppose the Bill. They argued that the dues previously charged could not be legally enforced, as the Company were only mortgagees and not rightful owners, and had been refusing to pay. They also complained that their traditional rights had been infringed in the matters of where they could draw up their boats for repair and painting and where they could dry and bark their nets. But, before the measure was laid before Parliament, they wisely got together and came to an agreement which was embodied in the Act, as were fixed tariffs for harbour dues and "Rates and Duties for Goods imported or exported to or from the Harbour", which comprised a rare assortment of items such as —

	£ s d
For every sedan chair	0 1 0
For every mahogany or other chair	0 0 1
For every fox	0 0 6
For every tombstone	0 3 0
For every tombstone (marble)	0 6 0
For every corpse	0 1 0

Porthleven had the advantage of being near several important mines with which Harveys had had long connections, among them, Binner Downs and Wheal Vor, which saved long hauls by road. The trade of the port was good while the mines flourished. It was in the parish of Breage that William Cookworthy discovered the presence of china clay in 1756 and went on to manufacture his Plymouth ware — the first true porcelain to be made in England. At a much later time, pits were worked on that site and a good deal of china clay shipped from Porthleven.

Although the trade had shrunk to almost nothing, Harveys did not give up Porthleven until 1961. They had created nearly all of what can be seen there now both in marine and domestic buildings. What is left is good matter for the artist and romancer — a typical Cornish haven in a cleft of

36. The 50-inch Harvey-built Goonvean engine, now dismantled and destined for Hayle, photographed at work in the 1950s by the author.

37. Clock made by William West in the early 19th century, following his retirement from Harvey's Foundry.

The clock face reads:

Wm West
St Ives

38. Harvey employees, late 19th century.

Photograph courtesy of the Morrab Library.

39. Foundry Square, probably in the early 20th century. On the left is Lloyd's Bank, centre are the two White Harts and on the right the Cornubia Biscuit Factory. The latter, dating from 1895, is on the site of the old Harvey offices and Emporium.

Photograph courtesy of the Morrab Library.

302

the rocks, dotted on either hand with colourwashed cottages, facing a sea which can be as wild as any in the world when westerly gales set in from the open Atlantic.

During the sixties, the Trade Union movement had begun to make itself felt. The seamier side of the Industrial Revolution had shown itself plainly in the Midlands and, more especially, in the North of England. Conditions were far happier in Cornwall, except at the mines, where there was no improvement. The Foundry was hard at work but short-handed. Several of their skilled men, having heard of much higher wages being paid in America, had left, and a good deal of overtime was required. From the north came repeated tales of firms submitting to a limitation of working hours — a nine-hour day. The Unions had gained many successes in pressing for it. The idea was in the air.

There had never been anything like a strike at Hayle Foundry, even during the Chartist disturbances. Harveys remained a patriarchal establishment. Now, however, wishful thinking about the nine-hour day was beginning to preoccupy many minds at the works. It found voice in the new year of 1872, when the following was circulated —

NOTICE

There will be a meeting held at the Copperhouse Public Hall this evening (Jan 10) to take into consideration the best means of obtaining the 9 hour system. All mechanics who are interested are earnestly invited to attend. Business to commence at 7.30

The upshot of deliberations was that five men were deputed to form a committee and two to wait on the management of Harveys with a petition, there and then prescribed, asking that the adoption of a nine-hour working day should be favourably considered. The next morning, an account of the meeting appeared in the daily Press and before the petitioners had time to act, they each received a notice of dismissal. When this news was given to their fellows, all the men in the foundry stopped work. In the eyes of the Partners the offence was aggravated by the men's choice of rendezvous "at Copperhouse of all places!". But Husband, always humane as well as realistic, counselled a soft answer, and prevailed. It was returned with extraordinary dispatch. The memorandum recording it is timed 12¼ p.m. Jan. 11. It runs —

It is agreed by the firm that if the many departments in the factory will depute four men from each shop to represent their respective views concerning any subject which [it] may be thought advisable to consider, the members of the firm will be quite ready to discuss the whole subject in an amicable manner at a meeting this evening at seven o'clock in the pattern shop — it being desirable that every man deputed shall firstly represent the position of the artizans & shall have been employed here for ten years or more — also that such person in the respective department will sign a paper stating the names of the men deputed and agree to abide by such conditions as the delegates & Messrs Harveys may jointly agree upon.

This reasonable proposition must have been delivered to the men by "12½ P.M.". They had drifted from their idle lathes and benches into the square opposite the White Hart, their minds, doubtless full of misgivings as to what to say or do, and whether it would now be an act of trespass to go to the accustomed places to heat up their Cornish pasties and spend their dinner-hour.

That evening, at the appointed hour, representatives from the hammer-mill, boiler-making and fitting shops, pattern-shop, shipyard, and saw-mill assembled in the pattern-shop with documents signed by themselves and their men (or their marks), agreeing to abide by whatever decision their leaders should arrive at. It was thought specially venial that two apprentices still serving their time should have been among the rebels. They begged to state that "we acted unadvisedly on this question of the nine hours movement, and would feel much obliged to Messrs. Harvey & Co. if they would look it over and reinstate us as before in their employ". The two expelled men signed a similar apology.

To the gathering, it was William Husband who came to represent the employers, whose case he put before them fairly and listened attentively to theirs. Harveys paid higher wages than other firms in the county, but he was ready to offer a new concession — that work should stop at mid-day on Saturday and count, for wages, as a full day's work. To this proposal there was unanimous agreement, followed by a spontaneous vote of thanks to the employers, which set a happy ending to the first strike at Hayle Foundry, ninety-six years after its inception. The dismissed men were reinstated and the apprentices absolved.

It appears that the Copperhouse meeting had been obliquely inspired by the Amalgamated Society of Engineers, Metallurgists, Smiths, and Pattern-makers, founded in 1851. Harveys had already been approached several times by a counter-organisation, promoted to protect the interests of employers, though, so far, resisting their appeal. But the incident so nicely tided over was a portent which could not be neglected. The day of independent patriarchal rule was passing. Husband wrote to the secretary of the new guild on the 19th applying for membership. Looked back on

Map 5. Hayle Foundry, c 1885

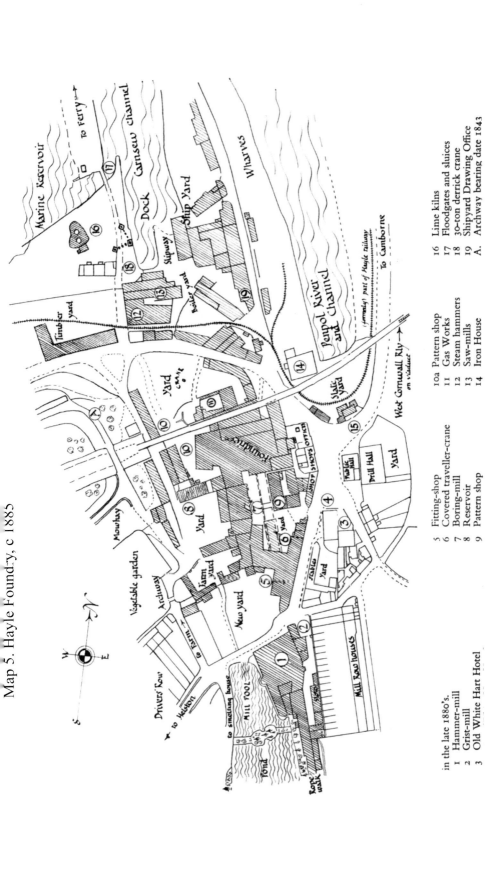

in the late 1880's.
1 Hammer-mill
2 Grist-mill
3 Old White Hart Hotel

5 Fitting-shop
6 Covered traveller-crane
7 Boring-mill
8 Reservoir
9 Pattern shop

10a Pattern shop
11 Gas Works
12 Steam hammers
13 Saw-mills
14 Iron House

16 Lime kilns
17 Floodgates and sluices
18 30-ton derrick crane
19 Shipyard Drawing Office
A. Archway bearing date 1843

after nearly a full century, his words read like those of a prophet — "It is obvious to all who consider the subject that the organisation of the artizans must necessarily defeat any single firm, *provided* the Centre of the organisation can, from the collective *capacity* of the unions funds, supply those artizans who may strike with money . . . No isolated single firm or group of firms in one locality could withstand a combination backed up by all the artizans in England". During the following year the nine-hour day was officially adopted at the Foundry.

Though the Harvey empire had, since 1868, been extended to the old dock of the C.C.C. which lay adjacent to Copperhouse Foundry, that citadel, though no longer garrisoned, had not yet fallen. But, in February, '75, it was billed for sale, to be held on the 16th at the Cornubia Hotel, Copperhouse. On that day it was knocked down (like the walls of Jericho) to Messrs. Harvey & Co. — surely the most dramatic moment in all their history!

In 1883, there was a change in the firm's articles of association, the partnership was re-constituted and became a private limited company with an authorised capital of £300,000. The partners, thus transformed into directors, took the appropriate styles of Chairman, William Harvey, Secretary, W. J. Rawlings, Manager of the foundry, William Husband, William and N. J. West his assistant managers, Commercial Manager, Francis Harvey (son of William Harvey but always called Frank to distinguish him from his cousin, Francis Haniel, son of Nicholas Oliver who was nineteen years his junior).

A few years earlier, Harveys had supplied pumping engines to the Great Western Railway Company who were making a tunnel under the River Severn, a major operation entailing nearly five miles of underground excavation. It had been started in 1873 as a purely railway undertaking though the consulting engineer, Sir John Hawkshaw, was retained to advise. The work went so slowly that, in 1877 the Company decided to let the contract. Three tenders were put in, one of them by T. A. Walker, which Hawkshaw recommended to the directors. Walker was probably the ablest and most experienced of the great contractors who had survived the aftermath of the Railway Mania. The London Underground, from Edgeware Road to the Mansion House had been constructed by three subcontractors under his management, and he had worked under Sir John in the building of the East London Railway. The Great Western Directors, however, complained that he had allowed himself too big a margin for unforeseen contingencies, and turned him down. Except for letting two Small local contracts for sinking shafts they continued the work with an increased labour force of their own.

The initial process was to drive a narrow heading, or passage all the way along the line of the tunnel which, at a later stage, would be enlarged to full width and lined with brickwork. The trains were to follow almost exactly the same path under water as the course which had for so long been taken on the surface by the New Ferry boats which, since 1785, had carried the royal mail from London to Milford Haven. At that point the river is about two miles wide, with a shelving beach on the English side which, at low water springs, dries out to more than half way across, where it drops suddenly into a deep channel which lies steep-to under the Welsh shore, called the Shoots, and it was just there, where the water lay several fathoms deep, that both laymen and experts believed would be the critical danger-spot for the tunnellers. By 1879, however, a heading had been driven from the English side under, and past, the Shoots, to the protection of solid ground in Wales and a shaft sunk from the surface without undue incident. But, when a little further progress had been made inland, an immense volume of fresh water suddenly burst into the workings and the men barely escaped with their lives up a side-shaft which was fortunately near. This happened on the very day that the chairman of the Great Western, Sir Daniel Gooch, and party, were due to pay a state visit to the workings, now being rapidly flooded throughout, till the water stood in the shafts up to the level of the river. The scale of this "unforeseen contingency" impressed the chairman and his board so much that they at once asked Sir John Hawkshaw to take complete charge of the works as Chief Engineer, a post which he accepted only on condition of being allowed to name his contractor. Walker was called on once more and presented the same tender as before, which was accepted. He took over at the end of the same year.

Additional pumping engines had been ordered, but their houses had to be built. It was six months before they could be erected and ready for work, and a full year before the Great Spring could be isolated by heavy headwalls built on either side of it and the remainder of the workings at last drained. Readers, unfamiliar with the story of the tunnel and the other extraordinary mishaps which occurred in its construction, including a storm of exceptional violence which drove a tidal wave over the river dykes and filled up every shaft and headway, will find it well told in the contractor's own words[1].

We are here only concerned with two other incidents. Near the end of 1883, the greater part of the tunnel had been completed, headings having given place to the full-sized arch and invert, lined with a triple ring of brickwork: the only section quite untouched was that small one between the headwalls imprisoning the Great Spring. It was now attempted to make a bypass diversion and seal it off in another manner. In doing so, however, it burst up through the floor, sweeping the gang and all their gear down into the main tunnel where they managed to clamber up on to a staging. The mishap was observed at ground level and the contractor was fetched. He sent for a rowing-boat which was lowered down the shaft, with a crew and torches. But cross-baulks of timber held them up, and they had to call for a cross-cut saw. When received, the operator had to work it with one hand, under water, and he dropped it. Meanwhile, the water was rising and moments were precious. Another saw was lowered, and all the party were finally rescued before the tunnel was choked. The ganger said that the spring had "rolled up all at once like a great horse", and it was estimated more precisely that its force was that of 27,000 gallons per minute.

It then became obvious that whatever they might succeed in doing to eliminate the spring, they must have more pumping engines. The only question was how to get them quickly enough. A sheaf of telegrams was despatched to possible suppliers. Harveys rose to the occasion. At the depleted mines there were several engines lying idle, delivery of three second-hand was promised immediately — two seventy-inch and one sixty-inch Cornish engines. Another sixty-inch engine (which had to be made) was ordered from Hayle Foundry.

By the Autumn of 1885 the Great Spring had been more effectually sealed off —bottled up, like one of those genii in the Arabian Nights, though made to do a little light work by supplying water for the boilers. The brickwork throughout the tunnel had been completed a little earlier, and the double track of broad gauge lines laid through it. On the 5th of September, Sir Daniel and Lady Gooch with a party of friends arrived in a special train and made a to-and-from journey under the river.

Two days afterwards, Walker departed to seek a little rest and peace in a sea voyage to South America, before taking up another commission awaiting him there. He arrived at Buenos Aires on the 6th of October. On

[1] The Severn Tunnel, T. A. Walker, Bentley, 1888.

the 30th, he had a telegram — "Sir John Hawkshaw says you must come home on the 1st". Hurrying back, he found that the genii was no longer dormant; the Great Spring was exerting such pressure on the tunnel wall that the bricks were beginning to break, "pieces of them flying off with reports like pistol shots, and the water shooting through the broken bricks quite across the tunnel".

The only solution left, Hawkshaw declared, was the most radical. The Great Spring must be removed entirely *as it flowed*. There must be no more tinkering. A large new shaft must be sunk, into the bottom of which the spring could pour, and a battery of large Cornish engines must work day and night for as long as the tunnel lasted, to lift it up and cast it bodily into the Severn. At the end of December, an order for six 70 inch engines, with pumps and boilers, and two 65, and two 41 inch engines (for other shafts) was sent to Harveys with the usual request to give the order priority over all other work and deliver on time.

This large commission came at a moment when work at the Foundry was running down alarmingly. The collapse of the Cornish mining industry had been followed by a general depression in trade and although the ruthless rival at Copperhouse was defunct and the friendly iron-works at Perran had had to close — the Foxes retaining only the timber-merchanting branch of their business — the removal of those competitors made little difference. While orders were scarce, prices were rising and wages had had to be cut by 10%; there had even been a resort to half-time working.

In the hope of stimulating the flow of established patronage and of discovering fresh customers it was agreed that, in 1885, William Husband should go once more to take charge of the London establishment. The office had been moved from Adelphi to Broad Street, with the appropriate telegraphic address of "Carnsew". At the same time, Harry Harvey, the eldest son of Nicholas, who had been acting as London agent, went back to Hayle where his cousin, Nicholas James West, replaced Husband as manager of the foundry. Harry was a keen and clever engineer. Unlike his father and great uncle, he was singularly slight in build, though he was fully imbued with the family predilection for demanding the best in materials and workmanship. He was inventive and enterprising but somewhat hot tempered, not suffering fools gladly.

It might well be that Husband's timely presence in London had given him the opportunity of exercising his customary diplomatic skill and clinching the deal for the ten new engines. By the early Spring of 1886 work was well under way at the Sudbrook pumping station on the Welsh shore of the Severn estuary. By the beginning of April the large new shaft, into the bottom of which the Great Spring was to be decoyed, had been sunk, the brickwork lining being completed two months later; two of the six 70 inch engines to work in that shaft were in a forward state of construction by July.

Harveys' engineer in charge was Francis Haniel Harvey, Harry's youngest brother. His letters to Hayle, giving constant reports of progress, are reminiscent of the series sent from Holland by William Husband. And, as in the case of the Haarlem engines, responsibility in matters of construction was divided among various parties. Harveys supplied the engines and the workmen for their erection; also the pumps and pit-work for the shaft, though all work on the latter was to be done by the contractor under his resident engineer, Arthur George Luke. The large engine-house was to be built by the contractor's men. Although the principal part of the undertaking was the erection of the engines, F. H. Harvey did not find it easy to work in amicable co-operation with Walker and Luke who were apt to treat him as a subordinate.

Unlike Husband's experience in Holland, however, there was no difficulty in finding accommodation for the Hayle contingent, for Walker had built a complete village at Sudbrook with infirmary, isolation hospital, and other amenities except a public house, for he was a strict member of the Plymouth Brethren. Many of his buildings are still there, including the principal edifice, a large cruciform mission-hall, in which he, himself, appears to have conducted services and preached. Incidentally, the village and the lining of the tunnel were built largely out of material from the excavation, for that resourceful fellow had discovered in the varied strata which he had to penetrate shale for making blue vitrified bricks, and had installed a large brickyard on the premises which made him independent of the somewhat erratic supplies from elsewhere. Of the seventy-six million bricks used for lining the tunnel, nearly half were home-made.

The machinery was delivered by three several routes. Parts came direct by sea from Hayle; others were sent by sea to Cardiff and thence by rail to Sudbrook; others came all the way by rail via Gloucester and Chepstow. The marine route was the most certain, entailing no intermediate transhipments, but there was often a hitch in the other two, when the Great Western Railway was usually the defaulter. It seems, however, that Harveys were not yet cured of that old inherent weakness for delays and sending consignments that were incomplete or misfits. Their young representative had to bear the blame for all mishaps, whether due to his own firm or to the Railway. The local powers were, at times, trying enough but, towering above them was Sir John Hawkshaw who acted directly for the Great Western, a domineering personality who made occasional descents from London on the tunnel works, usually dragging with him the now ageing William Husband. Sir John was bent on getting the tunnel ready for passenger traffic and a ceremonial opening before Christmas. Down to the middle of July, the Harvey gang had been working a long day shift. In the first week of that month Sir John arrived on the scene and determined that things must be speeded up if his dead-line date for the opening of the tunnel were to be realised. Having spent one night at Sudbrook, he chose to send this short, but quite surprising letter to Hayle —

> I wired you this morning to the following effect, "You must instruct Rowe to work night and day immediately". And I now write to confirm this, and you must attend to it immediately.

There is no suggestion that the engineer in charge of the work had been consulted —Rowe was merely his foreman. To by-pass and utterly disregard F. H. Harvey was a piece of intolerable impertinence. F. H. H. was entirely competent and must, in addition, have been a generous soul, for he showed no sign of resentment when writing his report three days later, merely saying, "I now have a gang on day and night".

Far from being discouraged, all hands worked with a will at what seems to have been the self-imposed task of getting the first two of the 70 inch engines in steam by the end of the month. This race against time ran into exceptional hazards in the last lap.

> July 24 (Saturday) We are getting on well with the work & all the men are working hard. I am afraid we shall have to work tomorrow but I do not quite know how Walker will like it, as last Sunday he said he should not allow us to do so again, but I presume we are working for the G.W.R. and not Mr Walker. July 25 (Sunday). Mr Walker came out just now in a terrible rage & stopped our working, & threatened if we did not stop to turn us out by force. I hear he left the pulpit in order to stop us. We are in rather a peculiar position here, as we have in a way to work for the G.W.R. & at the same time to depend on him for any little tiling in the way of stores we may require, also to use his forge; so that we are obliged to put up with a lot of nonsense. But at the same time I thing he ought to know that he has no right to interfere with us in any way. I have written to Mr Husband to ask him to sec Sir John Hawkshaw about this matter.

A consignment had arrived just before the week-end, but two important items had been left out. One was the final section of sixteen inch steam-pipe connecting the boilers with the engines. Without this they could not receive their breath of life. The other omission was the matching pieces for the pumps, and the engines, although receiving steam, could not be started without the necessary load supplied by the pumps. F. H. H. had immediately telegraphed the news to Hayle. To add to his annoyance, the fitting of those essentials was not within his province but that of the contractor. On Tuesday, the 27th, he wired again and also wrote.

> I have just wired you as follows, "Waiting for steam pipe. Has it been sent on Engines must work on Saturday." I have just seen Sir John Hawkshaw & have told him that we should be ready to start the two Engines by Saturday, as far as we are concerned, but Walker's men cannot fix the steam pipes until we receive the one you have in hand; they are also waiting for the matching pieces for pumps. As Walker's party are only too anxious to throw any blame on us, should the work not be ready by Saturday, I trust you will do the utmost to forward the things you have on hand for the two engines, & have them sent by quickest route.

In trying to account for the delays and aberrations at Hayle, one has to remember the recent changes in management at the Foundry. William Husband, after a long innings in control, had gone to London, changing places with N. J. West, who had returned with Harry Harvey as his second-in-command — both of them tolerably strange to the departmental intricacies of foundry routine. But, during that critical speed-up evoked by Sir John Hawkshaw, West was away in the Highlands of Scotland on what appears to have been a happy holiday combined with a look-out for new business and seems to have been kept in the dark about present urgencies. He writes on the 12th of July from Oban in quite a care-free mood commenting on the weather and the grandeur of the scenery and saying "I am working my way up through Scotland and am thoroughly enjoying the trip . . . There is very little news I can communicate as to business, everything and everybody seem to tend towards pleasure, lots of folk on the move doing the lakes and mountain scenery". He is running out of cash and asks for £50 *per return*", and ends "I shall be glad to hear everything is going on right at home".

It may also be said that Harry had a number of distractions to attend to at Hayle. Besides the orders on hand, other than the Severn Tunnel engines, there seems to have been much repair work going on in the shipyard. Among contemporary letters are sundry telegrams from Lloyd's signal station at the Lizard reporting steamers with a broken propeller-shaft or

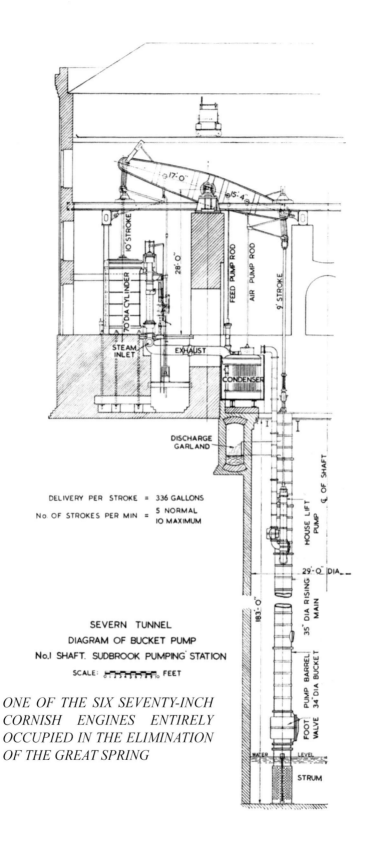

17'·0"

15'·4"

10' STROKE

28'·0"

70" DIA CYLINDER

FEED PUMP ROD

AIR PUMP ROD

9' STROKE

STEAM
INLET

EXHAUST

CONDENSER

DISCHARGE
GARLAND

DELIVERY PER STROKE = 336 GALLONS

No. OF STROKES PER MIN = 5 NORMAL
10 MAXIMUM

HOUSE LIFT PUMP

₵ OF SHAFT

29'·0" DIA

35" DIA RISING MAIN

183'·0"

PUMP BARREL

34" DIA BUCKET

FOOT VALVE

WATER LEVEL

STRUM

SEVERN TUNNEL
DIAGRAM OF BUCKET PUMP
No.1 SHAFT. SUDBROOK PUMPING STATION

SCALE: FEET

*ONE OF THE SIX SEVENTY-INCH
CORNISH ENGINES ENTIRELY
OCCUPIED IN THE ELIMINATION
OF THE GREAT SPRING*

other disability passing by in tow. Again, after the slack period, much new labour had been taken on to cope with the Great Western commission, and extra supervision was needed.

By Wednesday the 29th, the missing links had still not arrived at Sudbrook. It was now Walker who telegraphed a peremptory hastener directing that the parts were to be sent via Bristol to Pilning station "and save a day". This was a short-cut route which does not appear to have been used before, probably because it was only open to the contractor to operate it. Pilning station was on the English side of the Severn, at the other end of the tunnel which, although closed to public traffic, was available for the locomotive and train of waggons allocated to the contractor, the Great Spring having been temporarily side-tracked, its pressure on the lining removed, and the damaged brickwork repaired. Uncertain whether the telegram would arrive before the goods had been sent off on the longer route, F. H. Harvey determined to make doubly sure by going off to Exeter to intercept them at the parting of the ways. He met every train from Cornwall and on the last, arriving at midnight, the matching-pieces were discovered. It turned out that the steam pipe had already gone through via Swindon and Gloucester; it was at Sudbrook when Haniel returned on Thursday afternoon.

Harvey's men had both engines ready to steam by Saturday morning, as promised, but only No. 1 was started, as the other gang (working under A. G. Luke), the contractor's engineer, had not finished their part on the pump connections of No. 2. It was, however, set to work on the following Tuesday. No. 3 was then erected and was started on September the 20th. No. 4 was ready by the end of October. Though the remaining two engines were still incomplete they were intended as auxiliaries and there was now sufficient power to deal with the Great Spring which had been gradually diverted into the sump at the bottom of the new shaft whence, with its daily quota of 23 to 30 million gallons, it was lifted, as it flowed, through a hundred and sixty-five feet and cast into the river. Work was simultaneously progressing on the four other engines in the older shafts which drained lesser leaks into the tunnel.

The Great Spring having been mastered for all time, goods and coal trains were allowed to use the tunnel regularly. It was visited by the Board of Trade Inspector on November the 17th who gave it full marks for safety and, on the first of December, it was opened for passenger traffic.

T. A. Walker's book on the construction of the Severn Tunnel has already been noted. It ends with a chapter devoted to personalities concerned in the work — "The men by whom the work was done". Throughout the main text there is only a passing notice of Harveys, as makers of the numerous engines employed, and no mention at all either there or in the bouquet of eulogies at the end, of their long-suffering engineer-in-charge. This is not a little surprising, as everything depended on keeping the works dry, which had been successfully achieved by that third party who had supplied all the machinery for the purpose, starting from those early days even before the Great Western had put the contract out. The explanation must surely lie in that moment of wrath when the preacher was haled from the pulpit to admonish the Sabbath-breakers — an incident that remained an unforgiven sin. Yet, apart from his strong religious scruples, Walker was a good-hearted man. That he excelled his compeers in energy and resourcefulness is shown by his next appointment as contractor for the still more stupendous task of making the Manchester Ship Canal, the completion of which he did not live to see.

A man so much more lovable but certainly no less able in his own sphere, William Husband, only survived the opening of the Severn Tunnel by a few months. He died in April, 1887 at the age of sixty-four. The strain of the last few years had been excessive and no doubt proved fatal. Since he had returned to the Company forty-three years earlier they had benefited not only by his counsel but also his inventions, several of which had contributed to their fame as manufacturers as well as their profits. The most noteworthy was a pneumatic stamp for crushing ore.[1] It quickly superseded the time-honoured Cornish stamp, in which a battery of heavy bars of iron, each weighing several hundredweight, were lifted by cams and allowed to drop with the force of gravity on the material to be pulverised. Husband's machine had an oscillating cylinder worked from a crank-shaft which acted as a self-contained air-compressor that struck a blow on every rotation of the shaft, delivering many more blows to the minute than the gravity stamp. As the Cornish mines declined, these machines had a further advantage in lightness of weight for export, especially to those regions where mule-pack journeys had to be made. Other important improvements were devices to check the momentum of a Cornish engine if its load was suddenly removed by an accident (those great beasts could destroy themselves if allowed to "race"). One was the Safety Balance Valve for use at waterworks, where the danger lay in the release of load by a broken main. The other was the Safety Governor, for use at a mine,

[1] See Harvey & Co., Trade Catalogue, 1884, Trevithick Society Reprint 2009.

where the danger lay in a broken pump-rod. These ingenious contrivances would maintain any given load on the engine until it could be stopped.

Husband's death, which would have been felt as a severe loss at any time, occurred just when the firm was entering a new phase of revival stimulated by the Severn Tunnel contract, which had restored full employment to the works and drawn public attention to the nature and quality of its products. At the same time, hopeful prospects of a new market for exports in mining equipment were opening out in South Africa following the discovery of large new sources of gold in the Transvaal.

Harry Harvey took Husband's place on the Board and remained at Hayle as Manager of the Foundry while N. J. West went to London to take over the office. Visiting him early in 1888, W. J. Rawlings was much impressed by what he saw and heard. More staff was needed to deal with activities at the office and everything seemed to point to the need for a fresh programme of expansion and modernisation in the plant at Hayle. He wrote "It is simply impossible to carry out large orders and have producing plant only as before ... I think that what is now essential is the practical ability to turn out work to *time*, and that a short time".

These hints on the part of the Secretary and the assurance that he would back a vote for ample funds to be spent on reconstruction were enthusiastically received by Harry who lost no time in getting out plans and translating them into action, notably at the machine shop, in the boiler-making department, and at the shipyard, where a new slipway was put in hand.

William Harvey was now turned eighty-three and wished to retire. His life had been a well-rounded one. Sharing the fortunes of the Company and its direction, he had been preserved from the more harassing preoccupations of the ironfounding and engineering side. He had conducted his own department of merchanting with skill and good judgment and would leave it in a sound and flourishing condition. He had left his old home at Trelissick manor-house a score or more of years earlier and built himself a modest mansion at Hayle which he called Trelissick Lodge. It was carried out by the firm's masons and carpenters and remains an interesting specimen of their domestic architecture. Attached to it was a small court-house (now a garage) where he presided as Justice of the Peace.

William's nature was generous and retiring. When the limited Company was formed, he was pressed to take the chair, but he stepped down after only one month in favour of his son, Frank. Under the constitution, the directors retired each year and stood for re-election but, during his lifetime, Frank Harvey was always voted back into the chair. On William's resignation (June, 1888) his son-in-law, John Vivian, was appointed to the Board.

South Africa was now engaging the attention and aspirations of the Company and, among the new extensions at the works was a moulding shop devoted to the production of pipes for the Rand mines. John Harvey had started his foundry for the express purpose of making these things (then misnamed "pumps") to replace wooden ones for rising mains in the Cornish mines. The new product was the result of much experimenting on the part of Harry which ended in the discovery of an alloy of iron and steel which had a higher tensile strength than ordinary cast-iron which, up to that time had always been used. Consequently pipes could be made lighter and the freight costs of shipping reduced.

A quantity of winding gear and other likely essentials was made as well and sent, apparently in advance of firm orders, an agent at Johannesburg having been appointed to deal with sales. In 1889, a member of the Bickle family was sent out to South Africa to find out what was going on. This was Thomas, a foreman who, for many years, had been in charge of erecting and repair work in different parts of the country where Harveys' engines were installed. Jebus had now left their employment and was attached to a firm of consulting engineers at Liverpool but, at his own request, had been appointed Harvey's agent at that port.

Tom Bickle returned in the same year. He had an encouraging story to tell of the trade that could be won in the Rand if properly managed but said that the agent was unsatisfactory, giving preference in sales to the English firm where he had been employed. He also said that it was essential that an engineer should be sent out. These recommendations were adopted. The agency was transferred to three brothers, Cornishmen called Hosken, who were starting a business in Johannesburg styled "The Cornish Trading Company".

To give expert advice on the erection and maintenance of the machinery, G. N. Burden, an ex-apprentice, was dispatched to the Transvaal, accompanied by a further large consignment of goods "on appro".

In 1890 the Company lost the man who had been most forward in originating the plans for extension and re-organisation of the works, W. J. Rawlings. He was a man of temperate optimism and from his letters, written in a firm, strong hand, one gathers that he had full faith that, with the new improvements, and under the leadership of Harry Harvey, the foundry and ship-yard would be able to hold their own against the ever mounting competition from outside. As Secretary, Rawlings was followed by John Vivian but his place at the Board was not filled immediately.

In 1891, the cargo steamer *Ramleh*, of a nett tonnage just under the 4,000 mark, was launched. Since the two *Dordrechts* had been built for the Rhine Towing Company forty years earlier, the Company had specialised in building ships of that class — tugs and steam trawlers. They had also built small cargo and passenger vessels, including the *Cornubia* for the Hayle-Bristol service and two for the service between Penzance and the Scilly Islands, all less than 1,000 tons burthen. After the new slipway had been laid down they had made a bid for contracts of greater tonnage and, since the beginning of the previous year had launched four, of which the Ramleh was the largest. But competition had by now reduced the price per ton by nearly two-thirds of what it had been, and it was reluctantly decided to revert to their former more modest policy, "until more profitable prices can be had".

In South Africa, the three fellow-countrymen who had been awarded the agency and, furthermore, allowed to use the name "Harvey & Co" (less the style "Limited") had run heavily into debt with their suppliers. To tide over the difficulty it was arranged that the eldest Hosken should mortgage his premises to Frank Harvey — a private transaction. The situation was thought serious enough to call for investigation by a director, and the newly appointed Secretary, John Vivian, went out in January, 1891. On his return, it was decided to replace the agency by a fully-owned branch. When this was done, Burden was transferred to it with all the stock and, shortly afterwards, William Francis Trevithick Harvey was sent out as manager, Burden acting as his assistant. He was the son of the Chairman, Frank Harvey, and known in the family as Will. He had been taken into the office at Hayle straight from school in the Autumn of 1890 and he must have been a lad of great promise to have been entrusted so young and with so little commercial experience with such a commission.

It was not until December the 12th, 1892, that Rawlings's place on the Board was filled. It was taken by Francis Haniel Harvey who had won his spurs at the Severn Tunnel. Only two days later, the Company received one of the most severe blows in its history by the sudden death of Harry Harvey. Already the main structural improvements at the foundry had been carried out, though hampered by a scattered ground-plan, due to the piecemeal development at the works in former years. The modernisation

of equipment was also well under way, though a certain amount of out-
dated machinery remained, pending funds for replacement, drawbacks
from which many rivals in the Midlands and the North, having built all
anew, did not suffer. But what was done was but the framework of what
Harry had intended to do to keep his firm abreast of the times. His short
life of thirty-five years had been full of promise and no-one of comparable
skill and drive could replace him.

DEAD-WOOD AND SAP-WOOD

To have lost within five years three able directors who were either the
leaders or intimately connected with the engineering side of the business
was a staggering set-back to that department. There remained in it only two
qualified men, N. J. West, who, it was thought, could serve most usefully
by remaining in London, though now, nominally Manager of the factory,
while Haniel acted as Assistant Manager at Hayle. The latter was a sound
technician, though lacking in outside experience such as Harry had gained,
both in England and on the Continent. He was good-natured but without
the force of initiative which had characterised his brother and father.

The effect of those losses was soon felt, the more so as other factors
cropped up to depress trading and embarrass the management. By 1894,
a critical situation had developed which is revealed in a letter written by
Frank Harvey to his son, W. F. T. Harvey in South Africa, dated the 17th
of May, 1894. Will had now had his authority augmented by being given a
place on the Board and his father addresses him as a co-director as much
as a son.

We had our directors' meeting last Friday to consider the year's accounts. The
commercial part did very well and earned sufficient profit to have earned a
dividend of over 4½% upon the entire capital to be declared, but the factory
swallowed it all up by a loss, leaving only a nett profit of about £138, i.e. the
factory made a loss of £13500 after taking credit for the profit you made at
Johannesburg. It is terribly disheartening, and where the loss comes from it is
difficult to say exactly. Low prices, slack work, &ct, &ct, not up to date, other
people can cut us out. A loss, big or small, has now been the rule for several
years, except for two years when we had the Severn Tunnel contract. This
cannot go on or we shall be swallowed up, merchant part as well as factory.
We had a very full and anxious discussion at the directors' meeting, all being
present, and came to the conclusion that in the best interests of the Company,
the factory should be closed as early as practicable. This will be embodied in
the report about to be sent out previous to the meeting on the 12th June when
the shareholders will be asked to sanction the proposal. Mr Nicholas West
suggested as the only cure that he should come here as manager and Francis
[Haniel] Harvey go to London but, when pressed to say how he would effect

the cure, he could offer no practical suggestion beyond this, that he would get rid of Mitchell, one of the foremen of the fitting shop, and Littlejohn from the foundry!!

We are all of opinion that the mercantile part by itself will give satisfactory results to the shareholders. It has been the mainstay of the place in the past and has borne the brunt of very considerable losses made by the factory.

Of course it will be a terrible blow to the town and neighbourhood. We have about 580 men and boys working at present. But we feel we are not justified or required to carry on the factory for a sentiment only but for money. As time goes on there will doubtless be greater difficulties with labour. The eight hours question is surely and slowly going to rule. The employer's liability will throw greater onus on the employer and competition will not grow slacker. Until the general meeting of shareholders agree the matter cannot be settled, but I expect fully they will agree to close. Francis [Haniel] Harvey sees no other course, nor do I think does Nichs West.

Your Uncle Vivian went with me to see Mr T. Bedford Bolitho & tell him about it. He says he is not greatly surprised and sees no other course. The mercantile part will go on as before and, *unencumbered by the factory*, will do well I am sure. As to the Johannesburg branch, we do not see why Burden and you cannot carry it on quite as successfully after as before. We can doubtless buy for you everything you require, and probably as cheap, *if not cheaper*, than the factory can produce same. At present, not an inconsiderable portion is purchased which we send out, and such articles as stamp heads, shoes, dies, shafting, pitwork, and even engines can be purchased as well, if not with greater profit than if made by us. If well looked after here, and I am sure you must feel we are doing that at present for you, I fully believe that the change would be beneficial for the Johannesburg branch rather than otherwise, much as I regret to say so.

Personally, I feel all the dead weight of the factory with all the attendent worry *too great for me* & I am strongly for the closing.

The Chairman's guess as to the upshot of the mid-summer meeting was correct. In October, *The Engineer* and *The Colliery Guardian* carried advertisements offering Hayle Foundry for sale. The combined appeal produced only one reply — an application that was turned down. The works continued in operation, and were destined to do so for a further decade, during which the town was racked by uncertainty as to whether the Foundry would change hands, or be revitalised by the old firm, or close.

Meanwhile, at every meeting, one subject was brought up for "full discussion" with monotonous frequency under "Affairs in South Africa". At different times both Burden and W. F. T. Harvey were brought home to give information about the activities of the branch. They explained present difficulties and spoke hopefully of improved prospects, but the Board remained mystified and ill at ease and, in 1897, a newly-made director volunteered to go out and make a personal investigation. This was Major John Mead who had married Elizabeth Harvey West and was brother-in-law to the two remaining engineers of the Company. His offer to go was accepted and he sailed for Cape Town in July. During the visit, he kept a diary[1] which, apart from the subject of his mission, throws some incidental light on conditions in the Transvaal, little more than a year after the Jameson Raid, and the repressive taxation on the Uitlanders (non-Boers) by the Pretoria Government, "4d. on a 4 pound loaf, one shilling on 4 pounds of meat, 6d. for every half pound of butter eaten by a miner and his family", causing a general depression of trade.

He had long discussions with Will Harvey and Burden who, to his surprise, laid the blame for losses in money and custom on bad service from home. There was dilatoriness in the dispatch of orders and goods sent out were not up to standard. In the light of what eventually happened, one wonders how far these complaints were a smoke-screen of self defence. Mead took them seriously enough and his comments show that the Company was still in two minds as to whether to close or carry on the works. He makes suggestions for radical changes, "A first rate shop manager will have to be got — one up to date, who can push work out at a cheaper rate. The antiquated machinery at Hayle is incapable of competing with the machinery of today; Hayle Foundry cannot be made to pay without it. And so we have to face one of two things, either to stop the Foundry & throw away our 100 years old name & all its associations or to show ourselves worthy of the name & place in the position to which it is entitled. It is no doubt late in the day to do this, but though my connection with the firm is very recent, still I am not content to quietly sit down beaten".

Among the Major's discoveries was a most curious flaw in the interchange of information between the Branch and Head Office.

The thing must have been obvious to the former, though never revealed, as it seems, to the latter; "There is little or no water in the [gold] mines; H & Co's speciality of Pump is seldom required". His mission completed, he returned to England believing that he had got to the root of the matter. The following year the Johannesburg premises became untenable with the outbreak of the Boer War, and the management beat a timely retreat to their depot at East London, leaving a faithful Kaffir boy in charge of the office and the very considerable dump of stores.

The prospect of selling the foundry gradually faded. It must have been

[1] Diary now in the possession of Col. C. J. H. Mead of Mylor.

plain to everyone that it would have no future, even if revived by new plant, without those facilities on which it had always relied — free access to sea transport. But the commercial side of the business, now to be carried on and developed, depended on keeping the wharves, warehouses, and ships. So, at last, at a meeting on May the 19th, 1903, the doom of the foundry was sealed. A little later, a bidder for the machinery and tools (apart from the buildings) came forward — a Mr. T. W. Ward. In November, he was given the refusal of all the removable plant except a small selection of tools and light machinery intended for fitting up a repair-shop at the head of the quays. The whole of the remainder was valued at £10,000 — a fraction of what the foundry should have fetched as a going concern. Ward got his bargain for £50 less than the valuation price and issued a piecemeal catalogue of the effects in December. It must have been a sad mirthless Christmas at Hayle.

When the directors met in March, 1904, they were rid of the incubus that had been sapping their strength but faced with a deficit of some £60,000. This included a loss of assets in the factory, now being dismantled, leaving empty shells covering ground which could not profitably be re-occupied and, due to the closure, a general depreciation of the firm's Hayle property. This large sum was written off, adjustments were agreed, and the Company was reconstituted, shareholders receiving 20 £10 shares, fully paid up, and £12 in cash for every holding of £250 shares in the old Company.

In the new Company the same directors were appointed with Frank Harvey again in the chair. The old name, Harvey & Co. was retained and they described themselves simply as Merchants. But, by virtue of the repairshop which they had opened on that part of their domain which continued to be active, they announced that they were still Engineers, and F. H. Harvey was officially styled "Engineer", though his sphere had been so drastically reduced.

N. J. West was still a director though he did not return to Hayle when the London office was closed, but set up as a consulting engineer in London.

The South African branch survived the changes made at Hayle and was still in being.[1] On the return of the principals to Johannesburg after the war, it was found that the Boers had commandeered nearly all the stores, punctiliously giving receipts for what was taken to the faithful Kaffir boy, who was still there. The Branch was now supplied by goods bought from

---

[1] See Dawe, R. D., *Cornish Pioneers in South Africa*, St. Austell, 1998.

322

40. One of the Severn Tunnel Bull engines.
Photograph courtesy of Alison Hodge.

41. Three of the Severn Tunnel Harvey-built 70-inch Cornish engines.
Photograph courtesy of Alison Hodge.

other firms, some from their old-established neighbours, Messrs. Holman of Camborne, who had acquired the manufacturing rights for Husband's pneumatic stamps. But, at meetings, the recurrent phrase of "Affairs in South Africa were gone into and fully discussed" continues to be recorded, reflecting alternating hopes and fears. Burden resigned in 1905 and was replaced for a while. An attempt was made to amalgamate with a German connection, but this fell through. After much debate it was decided to close the Branch and W. F. T. Harvey was instructed to realise the stock and wind up. He was given power of attorney to act but seemed unable or unwilling to take the necessary steps.

In 1914, Will's power of attorney was cancelled and transferred to J. B. Read, the cashier, who was dispatched to Johannesburg to deal with the whole situation summarily. Shortly after he went out, Will resigned his post and his directorship. Read's probe had gone deeper and been more searching than that of John Mead. Whatever blame may be attributed to Will for mismanagement and subterfuge, the snare of an optimistic disposition, it must be remembered that he was sent out to a strange country, bitterly hostile to Englishmen and English interests, shortly after he had left school and with only a brief introduction to business and the way of the world. He lived on in retirement, settling in Durban till his death in 1940.

The successful measures which Read had taken for the winding-up, disposal of stock, and final closure of the Branch, were rewarded with a generous honorarium and, in 1915, he was given a seat on the Board in place of Major John Mead who had died earlier in the year. The total losses sustained in South Africa are put at nearly £300,000. The times were not propitious for any new adventures, for England was now at war with Germany and the fate of the whole country's future was in the balance, with the chances loaded against us. But the Company survived that difficult epoch and the still more trying years that followed, in which so many old-established firms disappeared.

Since early days, certain outlying depots had been established in west Cornwall, associated almost entirely with the merchanting side of the business — centres of distribution for coal, timber, and all building materials. Now that the foundry was closed, though Hayle remained the hub of the Harvey universe, those outposts grew in importance. The letters indicate that they had small establishments of some kind at Marazion and Penzance where the Norwegian ships, always fearful of the supposed hazards of entering Hayle harbour, could land their timber. In 1853, they established themselves at Camborne as "The Camborne Trading Co.". A few years later, they acquired and developed Porthleven (as already told) under the style of "The Porthleven Trading Co.". In 1868, they opened a branch at Helston and, in 1886, another at Truro.

These depots were semi-autonomous centres of distribution, each under a branch manager. They had ample storage accommodation for coal, timber, bricks, tiles, slates, lime, and cement. They had their own saw-mills and horse transport. Steam traction was not introduced until 1918 — one hundred and sixteen years after Trevithick had shown the way. The farm, which for so long had grown the provender for the great teams of draught horses, was let and eventually sold. The rope-walk had outlived the foundry twelve years and was only given up in 1916, the demand for that specialised article, the flat rope, had gone with the Cornish mines and, at sea, wire was rapidly replacing hemp.

The First War had given a rude shock to traditional landed interests and, the year after it ended, all the old "thirds" of Carnsew came into the market. Harveys, who still held these on the unpredictable "three lives" tenure, bought them, so that sole possession of those properties at Hayle for which John Harvey had fought so hard was added to those of the old enemy at Copperhouse.

The 'twenties-'thirties period was one of consolidation in times of slumps and political uncertainties. Any thought of fresh enterprise was extinguished by the outbreak of the Second War. It is quite inadequate to assess the nature of Harvey & Co's post-foundry operations under the simple heading of "builders' merchants". In addition to what this term usually covers, they were large importers of coal and timber and they were enriched (in the abstract) by a capital fund of tradition for they could claim a long unbroken term of trading dating back to 1787, when John Harvey had bought the sloop, *Providence*, to enable him to supply the mines with fuel and building materials as well as with the products of his foundry. In the course of that long time there had accumulated certain invisible assets in the form of inherited experience and skills in craftsmanship, descending from father to son. There were families who had a record of several generations of service to the firm, while all the principals were descended from the founder and retained the same high regard for quality in materials and workmanship on which their forebears had always insisted. They also

325

inherited the family bent for expansion which was again to assert itself after the long stand-still of the Second War.

In 1948, J. B. Read retired. Having triumphantly dissolved the South African mirage, he had had to sit out the enforced restraints of the two wars and the commercial doldrums of the intervening years. His place, as Secretary, was taken by J. T. W. Higgans who was a descendant of the founder, for his mother was a West but, unlike his predecessors in office, he was not yet given a seat on the Board. His appointment came at the beginning of a much more exciting period. The great post-war re-housing programme was already getting under way, a phase which, once more, favoured a forward policy of the Company. This prompted an entirely new departure in supplies for the builder. Hitherto, the trade had been in timber and the "heavy" class of building materials which, from the first, comprised slates, bricks, and lime, and, latterly flooring tiles, drain-pipes, plasters, and cement. In 1949 the scope was enlarged to include the "light" class as well — interior domestic fittings, kitchen equipment, decorating materials of all kinds, and heating appliances. The grim old boilermaker's shop with its lofty roof, supported by columns of twelve inch cast-iron "pumps", flange-jointed and bolted at the sections, was converted into a showroom for the new exhibits, whilst the branch depots were enlarged and adapted to stock these supplementals. At the same time, the accounting system was revised, brought up to date, centralised on Hayle. Mechanical accounting closed a time-honoured series, begun by Henry Harvey early in the last century and, for the first time, the massive leather-bound ledgers were not re-ordered.[1]

In 1957, Harveys acquired the business of Fox, Stanton & Co., timber merchants, an incident of particular interest, in that it rounded off a great part of our long story. It will be remembered that the Foxes of Perran and Falmouth were old competitors yet, at the same time, always friendly allies, often joining forces, as in the Haarlem engines contract. Their large iron-foundry at Perran, which was started only twelve years after that of John Harvey, had closed in 1857. It was exactly a hundred years later that the old alliance was consolidated by amalgamation with Harveys. Two of the surviving partners, G. R. Fox, well known for his wide experience in the timber trade, and A. F. Laity were given seats on the Board. Fox & Stanton had depots at Penryn and a saw-mill at Grampound Road which

---

[1] See footnote on page 330.

now became branches of Harveys though they continued to trade under their old name. In the same year the authorised capital was raised from £240,000 (at which it had long stood) to £300,000, and again in 1959 to £500,000.

An important new development in the merchanting of fuel was taking place, a trade for which John Harvey had bought his sloop, *Providence*, a hundred and seventy years earlier. First, intended to appease the voracious appetites of pumping engines at the mines, a growing domestic and municipal demand had enabled it to survive their extinction. Now coal, the old solid combustible, was being augmented and even out-rivalled by liquid fuels based on petroleum. Accordingly, in 1957, Harveys began the distribution of Esso heating and burning oils and could tell their shareholders shortly after that they were supplying them "to more than half the population of Cornwall". This work was relegated to a subsidiary company under the name Harvey & Co (Oils) Ltd.

In 1960, the old office-building with its typical Victorian clock-tower, which had been the nerve-centre of the establishment when foundry and ship-yard were in full and clamorous swing, was abandoned for a more up-to-date premises. There was still plenty of space in that capacious old boilermakers' shop to fit in a range of offices in two floors without impairing the amenities of the new show-room. The whole had now the appearance of a great pavilion with its flag-staff. A house-sign had been designed to figure on the flag that would fly there and to appear on the fleet of powered vehicles numbering over a hundred, from vans to 5 ton diesel cranes, as well as on office stationery. This conventional symbol, more in keeping with the realities of trade than armorial fictions, showed in a plain open rectangle, a small sailing-ship above the cross-bar of a massive "H" girder; below It a house, "which signifies our interest in building in the widest sense" (seen on the letterhead of the frontispiece).

In the same year the business of the Cornish Mines Supplies Co. Ltd. was acquired. Their headquarters are at St. Austell and they have branches at Penzance and Plymouth. Hayle's sphere of influence was thus extended to the far bank of the Tamar. In 1961 a close affiliation was arranged with the Devon Trading Company of Exeter and, thereafter, a director of either company sat on the other's Board.

Since the acquisition of Grampound Road, this branch with its saw-mill had become the centre of an entirely fresh enterprise which was thus explained by the Chairman, Mr. P. C. Buchanan, in his annual statement for 1959; "During the past year we have made a considerable effort to break into the market for the supply of farm buildings, chiefly of the Dutch barn and silo-cover type . . . Our service to the farmer has, we think, been much appreciated by him and has built up a connection with this important Cornish industry that will be of great value in the future". I have before me an illustrated catalogue dealing with the subject which has just been issued. It is titled *Timber Engineering Division*. The middle word has a pleasantly familiar ring — once again Harveys are constructors as well as suppliers! The pictures show a great variety of structures, for it is a feature of the service that designs are not standardised but made to suit the customer's local requirement; some have roof-spans of more than a hundred feet. All timbers used in these buildings and their accessory mangers and other feeding devices are impregnated on the spot by a pest-proof liquid (the Tanalith "C" process) under alternate stresses of vacuum and pressure.

Hayle harbour continued to flourish profitably with a yearly average of not less than 400 vessels using the port. Dues were now charged per ton of shipping instead of per ship, as formerly. The quays and the great marine reservoir which Henry Harvey had made in the face of such determined opposition had proved a lasting investment. In recent years, it had become necessary for the floodgates, first at Copperhouse, then at Hayle, to be removed for repairs. In view of the arguments as to their respective effectiveness, which had been urged by partisans in the bitter days of strife, it may be of interest to learn what happened when, for a period of several months, only one at a time could be worked. When the Copperhouse gates were removed, the channel was still kept clear by Henry's sluices at Hayle. The reverse happened when the Copperhouse gates were restored but those of Hayle were removed.

It was in 1961, when I had begun to learn the outlines of the Harvey saga, that I heard by chance how the Severn Tunnel steam engines were still at work, though under sentence of extinction in favour of the more fashionable diesel-electrical power. I lost no time in arranging to visit Sudbrook to see for myself those seventy-five year old survivals of the peak period of the Cornish engine and likewise of the world-wide reputation of Hayle Foundry.

At Sudbrook, I found myself in a little detached world, still mercifully undiscovered by the promoters of tourism. The buildings of the "Prince of

Contractors", T. A. Walker, somewhat diminished but scarcely added to, were in full use — cottages, mission-room, engine-houses. His doings and character were a living tradition still spoken about — "What you might call a bit of a dictator". The Manager, Mr. T. C. Stephens, who kindly welcomed me, had been born in the village and worked at the pumping station since he entered the fitting-shop at the age of fifteen. His father had been employed at the station and also his grandfather, who had come there when the tunnel was being excavated. He had the calm, assured, but unassuming manner of the man bred to steam. His strong devotion to his engines and his sorrow at the prospect of their imminent replacement recalled the emotional sufferings of that stolid Dutchman when the Cruquius engine made her last stroke.

It was easy to understand that sentiment when watching the action of the six Cornish giants, standing at either end of the large engine-house, their twenty ton beams pivotted on massive cross-walls so that their extremities, with pump-rods attached, faced each other across the twenty-nine foot gap of the shaft. The appeal of the steam engine is its similarity to a living thing — warm, breathing, palpitating. In the Cornish engine, the image is even more striking than in the commoner sort whose valve-gear works secretly by eccentric and slide-valve. All its actions are apparent to the eye in the up-and-down movement of the plug-rods whose cams and tappets touch off the timely action of inlet, equilibrium, and exhaust valves. And there is a semblance to human consciousness in that pause at the end of the up-stroke, when the engine bides its time for the valves in the pumps to close. I found the engine-men on duty all like-minded with their chief.

Having been clothed, cap-à-pie, in heavy oilskins, I was taken down the shaft in a lift and landed on an iron grating a foot or two above the water level of the sump into which the Great Spring poured, only to be flung up and out by the huge pumps with a fiendishly derisive squelching at the glands. Thence, I was taken into the header through which the Great Spring was led to its slaughter. It surged copiously by in a broad culvert with the speed and vigour of a mountain torrent. Retracing the few paces we had taken in that low passage and passing through a doorway, we stepped into a black abyss in which, our electric torch failed to pick out any object until turned downwards, when it caught the glint of a steel rail — we were in the Severn Tunnel.

It struck me forcibly that we had only just left the wide stream which rushed by us little more than a foot below the parapet we walked on, at the same level as at present. Any slight hitch or impediment occurring, and it would have been over its bank and flooding into the railway tunnel. Yet this contingency had existed, day and night, for seventy-five years! Mr. Stephens had said that the engines were in as good a shape as ever; they gave no trouble, they showed no sign of wear; so there had been no hitch. That was a supreme tribute to the principles which had always guided the Harveys of Hayle—employment of the best materials and workmanship. With 1964, I come to the end of my story though, as I said at the beginning, it is one without a denouement, because the Company continues and, in its latest phase, goes from strength to strength.

42. Harvey-made road sign in Hayle.

Photograph: Brian Sullivan

From page 326. Mr Brian Sullivan of Hayle recalls working as an office boy at Harveys in 1944/45. 'It was a Victorian counting-house where clerks stood all day at chest-high desks, entering transactions in copperplate handwriting into huge calf-bound ledgers and journals. The office was gas-lit [Harvey & Co. owned the Hayle Gas Company] and heated in winter by a massive coal fire. I copied letters into a letter book using a large screw-press.' See also Russell Webber, In Old Cornwall, Vol XII, No.5, 1999.

XXI

HARVEY & CO. IN HAYLE: THE LAST YEARS

BY 1966 WHEN EDMUND VALE'S HISTORY WAS PUBLISHED, Harvey & Co. was effectively a general builders' merchant, operating in part of its original site. The company also remained the owners of Hayle Harbour and much of the surrounding land.

In 1969 Harvey became part of the large United Builders Merchants Ltd. [UBM], trading as UBM Harvey, and from this point the long connection with Hayle began to weaken. Sluicing of the harbour ceased in 1972, the power station closed three years later and in 1977 all commercial traffic ceased. UBM Harvey now had branches throughout Cornwall and West Devon and by the time of the company's bicentenary in 1979, it was run from Truro.

In 1983 the company put the entire port of Hayle up for sale, amounting to 550 acres in 10 Lots. They were –

1. Harbour, South and East Quays
2. Porth Kidney Sands
3. Hayle Towans
4. North Quay
5. The Custom House
6. Copperhouse Pool
7. Viaduct Yard and Foundry Yard
8. Carnsew Pool
9. Lelant Water
10. Lelant Quay

A property company bought much of the land and then unveiled redevelopment proposals, a mixture of retail, leisure and housing. These were to be the first of a series of plans from an ever changing cast of owners in a roller coaster ride of unfulfilled aspirations, which continues to the present day. Fortunately these have no place in the story of Harvey & Co.

APPENDICES

CONTENTS

APPENDIX 1

RICHARD TREVITHICK'S ACCOUNT BOOK

From an account book of Richard Trevithick, the elder, dated 1775 (rectified spelling)

Dolcoath New Engine Account	414	12	3
Carloose Adventurers for materials	93	8	9
John Commins for boiler top &c	118	6	10
John Jones & Co (Bristol), for iron pumps[1]	131	9	4
Dale Coy.[2] for iron Pumps	63	0	0
Mr. Budge for erecting the Engine	50	0	0
Carriage of the Boiler, Cylinder &c from Carloose including attendence &c &c	1	14	4
Arthur Woolf per month[3]	33	1	9
John Harvey & Partners for putting in the Boiler and building the shed walls &c			
To new iron work as per account	187	10	4
To timber boards &c as per account	255	10	10

[1] For pumps, understand pipes (as explained in text).
[2] The Coalbrookdale Company, Shropshire, founded by Abraham Darby in 1709.
[3] Arthur Woolf, carpenter, father of Arthur Woolf, engineer.

APPENDIX II

From Letter Book No. I.

There are no records at this period showing how many men were employed at Hayle Foundry, but labour, skilled or otherwise, cannot have been easy to recruit locally. The following shows that importation was resorted to early. (Addressee unspecified. Probably the captain of a Bristol ship)

Dr Sir,   H.F. Decr. 27
                                                                 1791.
    Your favour of the 20th Inst duly came to hand and in answer Father desires me to write you to let the young man have a passage on board your Vessell & he will pay for the same, & 21s pr week to him. And if he do not like the plase he will pay his passage back, but he believes he will like Cornwall so well he'll not return as Cornish Girls makes good wives. You'll be pleased to show this Lettar to the young man who need not fear of Father's performance of the above & will satisfy you for your trouble.
                                        & am &ct
                                        Henry Harvey.

    There are letters to Jonathan Hornblower, inventor of the first compound engine and the first double-beat steam valve. At the time, he was employed as engineer at Wheal Unity, Tincroft, and Poldice mines, for which John Harvey had supplied him with his cast-iron pipes ("pumps"). That John's knowledge of metallurgy was not confined to the treatment of iron has been seen in his successful bell-founding and the following letter shows that he was regarded as an expert in non-ferrous alloys. The enquirer's "in" letter not having been preserved the prescription is not quite clear, but Hornblower is known to have used a kind called "lantern" brass.

Mr Hornblower   Haylè Foundcry
Penryn   Decemr 11 1792
Sir
We recd your letter of the 8th Instant. Father would advise you to make your Brass with the Inferior sort which is 7¾d per —? & Clean Copper, lid at the Copper House. His reason is you cannot mix the metal so well in pots as we can in the Air furnace. You may put a little pan Bras with the Inferior sort as it is very poor. You cannot mix Tin and Copper together, as it is so very dear, without loosing money by it.

    Is the "Inferior sort" zinc blende? The copper-tin mixture was still called brass and not then distinguished by the separate name of bronze. Hornblower, one of the most gifted pioneers of the steam engine, was ruined by a Boulton & Watt

333

APPENDIX

prosecution for infringement which, in 1799, gained the decision of a court, totally ignorant of mechanical matters, that the second cylinder of his compound was, in effect, a condenser.

THREE FAMILY LETTERS

H.H. to J.H. 1

Mr. John Harvey   Hayle Foundery
to the Care of Mr W*m* Reynolds   July 21 1793
Ketley Works, Shropshire
Hon*d* Father

Yours dated the 16th duly came to hand & am glad to Hear you enjoy a good state of Health. We all enjoy the same at present, Nancy have been poorly by reason of a cold but come much better. The reason we did not answer your letter of the 4th Inst because we writ you a letter of the 5th and a Bill (of exchange) Inclosed to your request thinking to hear from you immediately on the receipt thereof. Business with us goes on very well, Orders falling in as usual land all the men in very good economy at present, the greatest thing that oppresses us is slackness of water to execute the work. The Rev*d* Mr. Robinson have just dropt us an order for Castings for his refining furnace which he is now prosecuting with all expedition, & desired us to get a Bellows which we have ordered for to Mr. Rutter by this Post, and must Rely on you to get 50 Bushels of Bone Ashes for him if you conveniently can as we do not know who to send to for such an Article. Would advise you to buy some Pots, Kettles, Pudding Pans as we think they will answer, and chuse the Kettles not so deep as there are new patterns and, as you will be among them, think it a good time as we can have, mother desires you will buy a chest of soap, ½ yellow & ½ white. Copper is likely to get forward again, the Birmingham new Company stepped in last ticketing and bought all the ores in our neighbouring mines at upward of £85 Standard.

 People in both houses joins in duty & love

      & am your dutiful son
      Heny Harvey

 The iron works at Ketley, started by the Reynolds family, had become merged with the Coalbrookdale Company. William Reynolds was the first to devise an inclined plane whereon loaded barges were transferred by rail from a canal seventy-three feet above the Severn down to the river. Telford admired and wrote a detailed description of it. Sizeable remains of the work are still visible. Iron "pots and kettles" were a speciality of the Dale; the category included three-legged cauldrons, which had been exported in huge quantities to the American colonies before the War of Independence.

H.H. to J.H. 2

Mr John Harvey   Hayle Foundery
to be left at the Post office till   26 July 1793
called for. Liverpool.
Hon*d* Father

We received yours of the 21st Ins*t* and are glad to hear that you can be supplied with Ketley Iron. Our vessel is now load[ing] at Cardief but as soon as she arrives here will send her to Chipstow immediately. We favoured you with a few lines the same date as yours from Ketley and directed the same to the Care

334

of Mr. Reynolds in order it might meet you in good time in which we stated the principal objects of our little affairs & hope you have received it safe. There is one article in particular, that is, 50 Bushels of Bone Ashes for the Rev. W*m*. Robinson, which we rely on you to get or give we directions who we shall send for it to. In respect to the men, you know who are needful as well as we, can only mention James Otey he seems tolerable steddy at present, W*m*. West and self think he'll sute our purposes if he would Bargain for time better than take the chance of another man & your approbation of the same in your next concerning that matter, and as well what wages and time you'll think it best to agree with him for. And if we cannot come to agreement will wrote you immediately for to get one in his place. We have nothing at present to mention more than we have sent in our last and this. Mother gives her love to you and desires you'll take more care of yourself in future. We all joins in duty to you

& remain your dutiful Son
Heny Harvey

H.H. to J.H. 3
John Harvey   Hayle Foundery
to the Care of James Harvey Esq   Aug 9th '93
Bristol
Hon*d* Father

Yours of the 2 Inst*t* duly come to hand in which you say you mean to come homeward. Cap*n* Sampson sailed for Chipstow the same day your Letter was dated and hope ere this he'd load [ed]. You mention the price of Mr Reynolds's Iron to be £6 but think you made a mistake, if not it is good news. You said nothing about the men. I suppose you cannot get any now. Will West desires you'll try to get one in the Black or white smith line for finishing goods, turning &c. Shall send Messrs Wats George acc*t* per first vessel for Bristol as you desired. The famous Mr Brown is Kidnapp'd at last for making money, he and Commedore Halse. They where taken up at Penryn, the later turned King's evidence. Brown is in Bodmin Prison Have nothing perticular to mention. As to the mines, the prices of copper and tin, have not heard since I writ you last. Mother gives her love to you and desires you'll buy some glass and some large mouth*d* Bottles for Goose Berrys & what you can see convenient for the House. Cousins Jno & Nich Harvey are at Hayle & desires to be remembered to you. The works goes on as usual & all your children joins in duty

& am your dutiful Son
Hny Harvey

First Foreign Contact

Mr Peter Van Capelon   Hayle
Foundery
Dram   28th June
1794
Norway
Sir

Thro the recommendation of our Friends we request you'll send us as soon as possible to this place for our acct. the undermentioned Cargo & your Bill for the same, at the usual time will meet due Honour payable in London. We trust You'll send the Cargo of good Quality and also the Freight on as good terms as you send to others, that I may be able to sell on the same terms as my Neighbours. As we are quite unacquainted with you, nor have us done any thing in this Business before, it may be necessary that you be referred to for our Character, for which please to enquire of Mr Oxnam, Penzance, Mr Millet, Marazion, or any other in this Neighbourhood. Your sending an answer as soon as possible will greatly oblige my father Jno Harvey The Cargo as under, viz

200 pieces good redwood. Balk from 14 to 20 feet long. The remainder of the Cargo to be made out of 10 feet 1½ inches last or Common Deals, including ⅛ Wracks for a ship that is Calculated from 7 to 9 thousand Deals. Send no end or half deals than is absolutely necessary to Stow the Ship, and let the Captain's Privilege be last Deals.

Mr Peder Van Cappelen   Hayle Foundery
Dram   Dec 1794
Norway Sir

Your favour of the 26 July last we have recieved in which you said that one Capn Rugtod of the Adjictor should call and speak to us Concerning a Cargo of timber. There was such a man at Mr Gluyas at Marazion but never Calld to see us. If the Capn had not been turned by Mr Gluyas we think he would have Calld as he was within a mile of this place. However must desire to know if you can send us the Cargo as ordered early in the Spring. We would also wish to know the prices of wrt Iron Assortments as under viz

Flat Iron about 4½ feet long, 12 to 14 in wide, ⅜ in thick
Wgt Bars 4 inches wide, ½ in thick
　　Ditto 3 in wide, 1 in thick
　　Ditto 3 in
　　Ditto, ½ in Ditto
　　Ditto from ¾ in to 2½ inches square
Your answer per return will oblige my father for whom I am Your &c
　　　　　　　　　Heny Harvey

There are some interesting points in these letters. It was a bold departure, anyway, to make a bid for Norwegian timber and to request its delivery at "this place" when it is recalled how difficult it was for deep-laden ships to approach even the remote point of Hayle Sands and the further hazards to be met in carting the loads home. Mr Millet of Marazion was obviously a friend and must not be confused with his namesake of Penpol House. Mr Gluyas would seem to have been the same as he whose ropewalk and stock was acquired by Hannibal Curnow Blewett and translated to Hayle without Harvey's knowledge, precipitating the final split in the Blewett partnership. Henry would not have forgotten his advice to Captain Rugtod which must have been to sell his cargo to Copperhouse "within a mile of us" and not Harveys.

Swedish bar iron was in great demand at the time and the query about prices of iron in Norway must have been due to John's wish to make comparison of Swedish iron with those imported into the home market. The correspondence turned out to be the beginning of a long connection with Van Capelon and other Norwegian shippers.

APPENDIX

A striking contrast with the public preoccupations of the present day is the almost total lack of any reference, throughout the Harvey records, to the long and bitter war with France, which started in 1793 and lasted for twenty-two years. But three letters seemed to have a bearing on it. At the same time, they posed a conundrum. They spoke of an embargo on all shipping except such as carried coal. What could that mean? One had heard of the famous embargo imposed by Napoleon on all ships of France and her allies entering British ports or having any commercial relations with us. But why on earth should we lay an embargo on our own ships in our own home waters? Here is one of the letters.

Mr John Ayles   Hayle Foundery
Bideford   20 March 1795
Sir

As there is an embargo laid on all shipping except colliers we shall be obliged to send our Vessel (now at Appledore) to Swansea for Coals, therefore Cannot at this time take the Cargo of timber we were speaking of when at Bideford but hope ere long the Embargo will be taken off, when we will send her as soon as possible.

I am for my father J. Harvey
Sir, your most ob*t* Serv*t*
Henry Harvey

Two eminent historians whom I consulted could only make guesses wich did not seem to fit. But Mr Peter Heaton of the Bristol Public Libraries came to my aid with extracts from the local press which gave what must be the right answer in terms of an emergency measure of recruitment for the navy by the dreadful means of impressment. He cited several notices, among them, the following, from *Bonner & Middleton's Bristol Journal* of 1795

An order in council was passed yesterday [Feb. 18] for laying an embargo upon all vessels in the different ports of this kingdom. This measure is taken previous to the intended mode to be adopted for levying men for the navy . . . Mr. Pitt has settled with the Committee of Ship-Owners — That the expense of the requisition shall be defrayed by the nation. That £20 bounty shall be paid to them for each man. That the Ship-Owners shall be bound to find the men [20,000] seamen, and that the embargo shall continue until they do find them.

Although there is no mention of exemption for colliers, this must have been understood as the mines were of military importance dependent on coal for their engines. The ban was lifted on March the 28th for coastwise shipping which carried manufactured goods. This would not enable Harvey to collect the said timber but it covered wrought iron plates, bars, and nail-rods which were wanted from Crawshay's of Merthyr (delivered at Cardiff) and sent for. So John was little the worse off for the stoppage.

EARLY INSISTANCE ON VERY BEST QUALITY AT LOWEST OBTAINABLE PRICE
Capn Jasper Williams   Hayle Foundery
to the care W*m* Jenkins   9 June 1795
att the Ship Aground
Swansea
Sir

We have rece*d* a Letter from Mr James Haviland [the Brick Stores]. He can

APPENDIX

procure you a Cargo of Brick at Bridgwater for 24/- per Thousand & Crest at 2/- per Doz*n* and from the whole amount what they Comes to he'll deduct 7½ per Cent for ready Money (which is 1/6 in every 20/-). We think the price rather High, but when you arive there You'll inquire the price of other Merchts & if they will ship you a Cargo of as good Bricks as his on more reasonable terms, take them, but if Mr Havilons Bricks are as Cheap & as Good as theirs give him the preference, onely be sure to have the *best hand burnt* Building Brick.

> I am Sir
> Yours & c
> H. Harvey

Excerpt from the agreement between Harvey & Co. and the Cornish Copper Company drawn up at Millwood's House, Hayle, on November the 16th, 1818.

That the Cornish Copper Company shall be at liberty to build a Quay along the Eastern bank of the river *commonly* called the Penpol river from the road which leads across it from Hayle to Penzance to the point of the triangular piece of ground which is bounded on the west by the said river, and to the North by the river which runs under the greater floodgates and from that point to these Gates, without molestation from Messrs Harvey & Co. but without prejudice to their claim in respect of the undivided part of the Tenement of Carnsew to so much of the said piece of ground as they consider to be of that Tenement.

Messrs Harvey & Co. to be at liberty to build a Quay on the Western side of the first mentioned river downwards as far as the northernmost point of that bank without molestation from the Cornish Copper Company but without prejudice to their claim to the land on which the last mentioned Quay is proposed to be built, as tenants of Carnsew aforesaid or otherwise

And the agreement contains a further clause to the following effect:

That nothing contained shall be considered as affecting the right of the said Companies to do any Act which may be advised to be necessary or proper for the purpose of trying the title of the other to the Lands whereon the Quays are respectively to be built.

Signed by Joseph Carne and Henry Harvey.

Taken from the Brief. Neither the original or a copy of the full text appears to exist.

THE MEMORANDUM
Notes by Henry Harvey in 1828. They were evidently written when the trial at Bodmin was in progress but the result not yet known.

Forty Nine years ago John Harvey came to Carnsew & erected a small Foundry. Having very little Capital he began on a small scale. Three of his sons (two of them young men about 18 or 20 years of age) enabled him by hard labour & his perseverance to get on to enlarge the Foundry which was found very useful & which was the only one in the County until Messrs Foxes & Co of Perran wharf erected theirs. His two eldest sons both dyed young about 40 years since. Another Son was killed about 38 years since by means of one of the legs of a triangle breaking in weighing a heavy piece of Iron. This was a great loss, having only one left which was 15 years of age.

As his business increased he found it necessary to purchase a small Sloop to bring Iron & Coals for the use of his Foundry which cost him about £250, about 45 Tons Burthen. This was done in the year 1787 (41 years ago). Mr John Edwards being then a managing partner of the C.C.Co & Father to Mr J. S. Edwards, who is now a Partner & then a Solicitor, & naturally of an Arbitrary disposition & determined to monopolize the place, began to suspect that his namesake, when he purchased this vessel wo*d* not be confined to his Foundry but wo*d* be very likely (as he was concerned in several mines) to endeavour to supply them & the Country with Coals, Iron &c, & from this time the C.C.Co did every thing in their power to crush him. About 35 years ago he put some men to deepen penpoll river in order to bring up his Sloop near to his Foundry to save expense in discharging. Mr E. sent the C.C.Co*s* men & filled it. About 2 Years afterwards they filled up his Boreing Mill Leat, by which means he was obliged to raise his wheels nearly 3 feet, which nearly rendered them useless. About the same they also sent upwards of forty men & took down a lighter he had in building on Carnsew & obliged him to remove it to another spot to be finished. This was attended with great loss on account of injury done to the Lighter as well as time, having about this time (in the year 1795) built another Vessel about 80 Tons burthen which could not be discharged without the Lighter. The second or third voyage this vessel made she brought a Cargo of Limestone from Plymouth which was thrown out on the sand just below the Foundry. The C.C.Co sent Carts & carried away a great part of them & burnt them for their own use for Lime. They also removed a quantity of oak and other timber from a Plot which they claimed as Carnsew to a place where the tide flowed and which carried away a great many pieces before they could be secured, rolled Pumps and other Castings in Penpoll river &c &c. This was done with a view to prevent him from carrying on merchantise & wanted him to be bound not to do so but confine himself to his Foundry.

About 25 years since John Harvey died & his Son H.H. carried it on for

340

APPENDIX

himself for about 6 years, constantly annoyed by the C.C.Co, in which time he built another Vessel called the Elizabeth & two more lighters (the Vessel they attempted to prevent his launching as described in evidence). H.H. not being endued with so much patience as his father could not well bear such treatment & in order the better to be a match for them took in partners in 1809 which increased the Capital nearly £15000. By doing this the Trade was greatly increased, consequently a greater number of men was employed & some very sharp battles was the consequence. In a few years, however (say seven) his partners having embarked in speculations (independant of the Co) which proved unfortunate wanted their money & the greater part of them took out their Capital. The principal one, Mr Blewitt, who put in from £12 to £13000 took out upwards of £19000 & the others in proportion, after paying £5000 Cost in a Chancery Suit between ourselves. H.H. on the other hand had shares in mines (Whl Alfred £1000) independant of the Co which were productive, which enabled him with the profits of the trade to pay off Mr B & others.

After my Partners retired the C.C.Co made proposals with a view, as H.H. then understood, to a better understanding between the Companies & Articles of Agreement was drawn by Mr J. S. Carne & signed by himself on behalf of the C.C.Co & H.H. on behalf of H & Co. (It is necessary to remark that up to this time H & Co had no wharf for landing Coals or shipping Copper ores but were obliged to discharge their vessels in Lighters & discharge those Lighters again in Carts & carry it a considerable distance in Plots, & consequently the Vessels were deprived of copper ores as back freight to Wales). In one of those Articles it was stipulated that as long as H & Co were confined to their own 3 vessels (which they had at this time for carrying or purchasing of Coals that they were to be allowed to load from the C.C.Cos wharfs Copper ores in regular turns as other vessels. Afterwards, the C.C.Co violated this agreement & H & Co were obliged in their own defence to begin in earnest to bring up a Channel & build wharfs, which they began in the year 1818 & finished the same, notwithstanding every opposition from the C.C.Co in 1819, which cost in that time from £10000 to £15000. It was in this year that the C.C.Co built the Quay which is now claimed for Carnsew, & it was then that the argument was made without prejudice to the rights of each Company to build without further molestation.

Before H & Cos Quay was built the C.C.Co charged all the Copper Companys in Wales who lodged their ores on their wharfs at Hayle 8d per Ton, which would amount to £1000 a year on the whole quantity shipped from Hayle, which they immediately took off so soon as H & Cos wharfs was finished, so that the Copper Compys has paid no wharfage this 9 years, & before these wharfs were built H & Co paid for want of ores as back freight 5 or 6 / per wey [3 tons] more for their Coals than the C.C.Co besides the difference in expense of discharging the Coals, at least 2/ per wey more. From this great advantage the C.C.Co were enabled to make dividends regularly every year amongst themselves. But not so H & Co, for they have not been able to make a Dividend for 19 years, which was the cause of disatisfaction with Mr Blewitt & the other Partners who went out & took out their Capital which however paid them good interest as before stated, notwithstanding the Cost paid in the Chancery Suit. There are no other partners at present but H Harvey and E Harvey who are saddled with a property consisting chiefly of Buildings &

341

machinery & mines that is worth very little if the C.C.Co overpowers them.

About the time that H & Co began to build the wharf the C.C.Co began to build a Foundry on a very large scale & to make sure of crushing H & Co and, to make use of an expression used by one of C.C.Cos agents at the time, lets bleed him, meaning H & Co, in every vein they, by degrees, took away every one of their most useful men, even H Hs own nephews at very advanced wages, which greatly annoyed them at the time, until a new set of workmen could be learned the business, which of course took some years; and they still continue the same practice. This, however, must in the end fall on themselves as their expense is more than their trade will support. The Capital employed in their Foundry alone cannot be less than £30,000 including Buildings, Machinery, Stock of Iron, Brass, Tools, &c. & Book debts, which cannot pay them a shilling Interest, & I may venture to say that the work they turn out will not meet their great expense by more than £1000 a year, independant of the loss of Interest on the £30,000 Capital. Surely they are determined to crush H & Co or make him join them to form a monopoly.

When Mr Robt Michell came to Hayle as manager for the C.C.Co in Mr J. S. Carnes place H. H. was asked if some better understanding could not take place between the Companies. H. readily proposed that if they wod not continue to annoy him so in his Foundry & wod stay their hand in paying out money in making erections & building a Hammer Mill which they were then about to do, and wich they had been in the habit of getting from J S Vivian, & Battery Mill, & wd allow me to do that kind of work, which I was prepared to do and which in fact was the business I was brought up to, that they should supply a greater proportion of Coals, Timber, &c in lieu of it to all the mines. Mr Michells answer to which was nothing less than Consolidating the two concerns will satisfy the C.C.Co. I told him I had several nephews which I meant to bring up in the trade & wd not like that they should be servants to the C.C.Co, nor did I think that the mines in the neighbourhood could support the both concerns, reared up as it was by so much unnecessary Capital laid out by the C.C.Co, to little or no purpose, & that I should be saddled with their heavy saleries to a parcel of useless agents & a heavy Capital for Land that did not pay 1 percent, & positively refused their kind offer.

APPENDIX V

CUSTOMS

Discrepancy in extra charges.

Hayle Foundery within the Port of St. Ives, 31st July, 1830
To the Honourable Commissioners of His Majesty's Customs
May it please your Honours,

We beg to represent to you that we are frequent Importers of Norway Fir Timbers, principally for the use of the Cornish Mines; and of Slate brought Coastwise; that our point of discharging is from three to four miles from St. Ives where your Honours' Landing Surveyor and Landing Waiter for the Port reside; that the Vessels usually taken up by us for the timber trade bring from 200 to 240 loads respectively and are from five days to a week in being discharged, and that we pay to the Landing Surveyor 10/6 per day for every day during the discharge of each respective Vessel, and to the Landing Waiter attending the delivery 7/6 per day: and to the Tide Waiter attending the delivery of Slate 5/- per day.

We have long considered these charges as grievously burdensome, and are led to believe that your Honours will on our representation relieve us therefrom, & which we most humbly beg you to do.

We hope this more especially as at the Neighbouring Port of Penzance the Landing Waiter & Landing Surveyor of that Port attend on the same duty at Marazion, or St Michael's Mount, within the said Port, & three miles distant from Penzance where they reside, without any charge to the Importers, among whom we, the Subscribers hereto, are also to be numbered.

We have the Honour to remain
Very respectfully
Your Honours' very Obedient
humble Servants
Harvey & Co

CRITICISM

Liverpool 6: Octob: 1832

Messrs Harvey & Co
Gent*n*

We have to acknowledge the receipt of your Letter of the 2nd Inst. — You do not state that Messrs Bolithos would take Fine Stov'd Salt to Hayle per the "L'pool Packet" at 7/- per ton. Common Fishing Salt is often taken for 2/-per ton less than the former because it can be stowed in a much smaller compass. This, however, has no connexion with the subject on which we are at issue. If Messrs Bolithos chooses to take you 50 tons of Salt for nothing, does it necessarily follow that everybody else is to do the same thing?

343

APPENDIX

Freights, as you are aware, fluctuate daily, and it is the duty of the Captain to obtain the best going freight. Your remarks concerning Vessels taking parts of their cargoes & being well paid under such a system may apply to yourselves only — we never heard of owners being so easily satisfied but are convinced that in ninety nine cases out of every hundred the reverse is the fact. No man wo*d* be satisfied with part of cargo where the same expense of equipment was incurred, whether the Vesel took 40 or 50 tons.

When we agreed with Capt. Jones we had no idea the Vesel would have been so long detained. The detention was caused by circumstances over which we had no control. Is this therefore any reasonable ground against us?

After having instructed all the Ship Brokers in Town to do all in their power to obtain a Vessel (and own our personal exertions were not wanting) we chartered the *Dispatch* on the lowest possible terms and thought by so doing we were promoting your views and wishes, yet we are told in your letter now lying before us that we did not procure the Vessel for the purpose of serving you! This, we confess, is language to which we have been unaccustomed, nor can we divine a reason why you should thus plainly accuse us of deception! That we did charter the Vessel in order to serve you and not to benefit ourselves we aver; and if you disapproved of the charter why did you delay to inform us? We can guess the reason for the delay — Messrs Bolithos we fancy had not made their offer when you received advice of our having engaged the *Dispatch* and had you never heard from them would this unpleasantness have taken place?

In conclusion we beg to say that it is our fixed determination not to allow one shilling of the amount you claim. — On what principle either of justice or equity you call on us to pay such a demand we know not. We are to exercise the thankless task of procuring a Vessel for you, and then we are to be responsible for a portion of the freights! Truly, such notions of business are as novel in theory as they are unprecedented in practice. —

We remain respectfully
Gent*n* Your mo: obd Se*rts*
For John Blackburne & Co
T. Redish Jnr

AUSTEN'S ENGINE

Test of coal consumption by Fowey Consols engine, Mar. 22 & 23 1835
This celebrated engine, from its extraordinary and unprecedented power and astonishing rate of duty, having caused several engineers and others to express doubts respecting the truth of the reports as published by Mr Lean in his monthly lists, — the engineers, Mr William Petherick and Mr William West, at the suggestion of some scientific gentlemen of the county, and with the sanction and authority of the adventurers of those mines, have subjected her to a public trial.

A public meeting for that purpose took place at the above mines at noon on Thursday the 22nd instant, when J. S. Enys, Esq., of Enys, was requested by the meeting to nominate competent persons, totally unconnected with the mines, as a committee, for the purpose of conducting the examination, in conformity with the general usage on such occasions.

344

APPENDIX

The following persons were then appointed for that purpose:—

Mr Samuel Lyle

Mr Thomas Petherick

Mr John Budge

Mr John Bray

Mr William Renfry

Mr James Thomas

Mr Joseph Morcom Jr

Who undertook the duty and made the following report.

Statement of proceedings.

1st — The coal-sheds carefully examined and found to be quite empty.

2nd — Twenty-eight bushels of coal measured in the presence of the committee and others.

3rd — A bushel of coal weighed and found to be 94 lbs.

4th — The coal-shed door locked, the key kept by the committee and the door sealed.

5th — The committee's counter[1] at starting registered 00,000,660, and Mr Lean, the reporter's counter, 02,187,480. The counters locked and sealed as soon as their state was ascertained, and the keys delivered to the chairman of the committee.

6th — Quantity of grease delivered for the consumption of the engine 12 lbs., and oil 1 quart.

7th — State of the fires strictly examined.

8th — Water in the boilers, found to be at the regular working gauge.

9th — Steam gauge at starting 36½.

10th — Stroke in the shaft 9 feet 3 inches.

The trial commenced on Thursday, at 28 minutes after 1 o'clock, P.M.

During the trial, which lasted 24 hours and 27 minutes, the steam gauge fluctuated between 36½ and 45, shewing a pressure of from 36½ to 45 lbs. on every square inch of the boilers; and the length of the stroke in the Shaft ranged from 9 feet 3 inches to 9 feet 5 inches, but the duty has been calculated at the minimum of 9 feet 3 inches.

The exact quantity of coal consumed was 24 bushels.

On unlocking and unsealing the counters in the presence of every member of the committee, their respective states were found to be as follows, viz; —

Committee's counter registered   6947

Mr Lean, the reporter's counter, registered   2193767

shewing that the engine made 6287 strokes, which is found to be 4.29 strokes per minute.

The working of the Lilly lift was suspended, in consequence of the prang of the bucket breaking, and this lift remained idle from 40 minutes past seven o'clock in the evening, to 23 minutes past 10 o'clock at night, being 2 hours and 43 minutes, for which stoppage, three hours has been allowed in the calculation of the duty.

The steam gauge at the termination of the trial stood at 44, being 7½ more than at the beginning.

[1] A tachometer for counting the number of strokes of the piston.

345

	fms.	ins	ins	lbs.	
Tye, Rose, & Crown lifts,	97	3 and 15	box	44870.96
Lilly lift	20	3 and 10¼	box	4405.34
Puppy lift	13	3 and 10¼	box	2901.06

52177.36

Deduct for Lilly lift being idle J of the whole
time of working   551.00

51626.36

Duty, 125,095.713 lbs. lifted one foot high by a bushel of coal.

Four bushels of coal remained unconsumed at the conclusion of the experiment, making the whole consumption 24 bushels.

At the time the engine stopped, the fires were in equally as good, if not better condition, than at the commencement of the investigation.

The water in the boilers was higher at the conclusion than at the commencement of the experiment.

[Signatures of members of the Committee follow and those of six pitmen appointed to examine and report on the pump-work].

A circumstance of this nature was eminently calculated to excite the engineers throughout the county; and it appears that many exerted themselves to the utmost to raise their engines to a level with that of Fowey Consols: for a rapid advance in the duty of several engines became apparent.

43. Types of small sailing ship used by Harvey & Co.

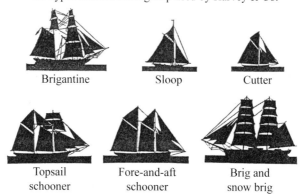

| Brigantine | Sloop | Cutter |
| Topsail schooner | Fore-and-aft schooner | Brig and snow brig |

Smack: a generic term for a single-masted fore-and-aft rigged coasting or fishing vessel, usually a cutter.

THE HARVEY FLEET DOWN TO 1844

The list is based on the registers of the Custom House at St. Ives as well as the records of Harvey & Co. The classification of rigs of the vessels varies in the two sources, but it must be supposed that the former, by the Surveyor of H.M. Customs, is more technically correct than the other. Harveys did not distinguish between brigs, snows, and brigantines but called all of them brigs—an older and more firmly established name. The brig was a two masted vessel square-rigged on both masts but having a gaff sail (spanker or driver) as the lowest course on the main mast. The snow was rigged almost the same except that she had a separate lower main mast stepped close abaft the other, on which a trysail was hoisted (as spanker, but having no boom). The brigantine was square rigged on the foremast and fore-and-aft rigged on the main. This doubtless made her more handy for coastwise work and tacking in confined waters than the brig. In the main text I have followed Harvey's names in agreement with mentions in letters and office books. In the following list I have given both — the Customs classification in italic, Harvey's, when differing, in brackets.

"Tons register" of a ship is a measurement of space and not weight based originally on the number of tuns (large barrels) which a vessel could stow in her holds. The figure representing tons register is always a much lower one than that representing the number of tons (weight) the vessel was able to carry. Tonnage, therefore, when mentioned in connection with merchant ships always means space and not weight (in warships it means displacement). The method of arriving at this space-measurement, which had obtained from times immemorial, was altered by Act of Parliament in 1836. After that year, tonnage is given by the new formula which makes the figure look a little less. Thus the tonnage of the *Elizabeth* [II] was reckoned 115 by the old measurement and 107 by the new.

LIST OF SHIPS 1787-1842

Tonnages and dimensions (length by breadth) from St. Ives Custom House Registers, also ownership.

1787 PROVIDENCE (I) *sloop*, tons, 36, dimens. 41' 3" by 14' 6". Built at Barmouth in 1777. Acquired 1787. Owner, John Harvey.

1795 HENRY (I) *brigantine* (brig), tons, 60, dimens. 55' by 17.2'. Built at Hubberstone (Appledore) in 1795. Owner, John Harvey. Sold 1819.

1805 ELIZABETH (I) *sloop*, tons, 50, dimens. 45' by 16.6'. Built at Hayle Foundry in 1805. Wrecked at, or near, Morwenstow 1820. Details in Cash Book for Feb. 1820 "Sloop Elizabeth. Paid expenses on saving sundry articles from the wreck of sd vessel & selling the same as per C. A. Harvey's account £35 11s. 5d. Ditto. Paid C. A. Harvey's expenses at Hartland Quay & c. on account of the loss of sd vessel £7 5s. 6d. Ditto. Pd. Capt. King's [the skipper] Disbursments as per acc. £42 7s. 3d. Reed, for sundry articles sold from the wreck of the sd vessel as per acc. £36 6s. 0d." She was not covered

APPENDIX

by insurance.

1810 ALFRED *brigantine*, tons, 71, dimens. 56' by 17.7'. Built at Barnstaple in 1807. Owner, Henry Harvey. This acquisition was at the beginning of the Blewett partnership The Register says "Vessel lost." This must have happened very soon after she came into service but I have found no particulars.

1814 FAME *brigantine* (brig), tons, 106, dimens. 63' by 19' 11¼". Built at Bideford in 1814 for Henry Harvey.

1820 JOHN ADAMS *schooner*, tons, 59, dimens. 57' by 16' 9½". Built at Neath for Harvey & Co. who are not, however, so named but as four shareholders — Henry Harvey, Merchant, Thomas Ellis, Merchant, William West, Watchmaker, Elizabeth Harvey, Spinster. The vessel was lost with all hands in December, 1823.

1827 ROSEWARNE *brigantine* (brig), tons, 111, dimens. 19.11' by 12.2'. Built at Bideford in 1814. Registered at St. Ives in 1815, when she is shown as being owned by a great number of shareholders, among whom were Henry Harvey, Thomas Ellis, Hannibal Ellis, and Captain Frank Cundy of Bristol. Captain Cundy appears to have bought all the others out and to have been sole owner in 1827 when the ship was acquired by Henry Harvey as sole owner.

1829 PARK *snow* (brig), tons, 117, dimens. 66.3' by 23'. Built at "Kilpine Pike" (?), Yorks, in 1800. Acquired in 1829, Henry Harvey holding 48 of the sixty-four shares and Captain James Banfield (then her master) holding 16. She was re-registered at St. Ives in 1836. when Henry Harvey held 52 shares and Captain James Gudge (now her master) held 12.

1830 PROVIDENCE (II) *brig*, tons, 90 (78, new measurement), dimens. 62' 2" by 18' 9". Built at Barnstaple in 1805. Acquired by Henry Harvey in 1830, ownership transferred by him to John Harvey Trevithick in 1843. Wrecked in the Towy estuary, 1833 and believed total loss, but salvaged (p. 353). Lost, Oct. 14th, 1853.

1832 PHOEBE *brig*, tons, 200, dimens. 86.4' by 23.3'. Built at St. George, New Brunswick in 1823, Bought by Henry Harvey in 1832. When she was offered (unsuccessfully) for sale in 1839. Henry quoted her tonnage by new measurement as 181 and said she would carry 220 tons (weight) drawing 12 feet of water. "Seven years ago she had between £1000 and £1100 spent on her. All the defective floors were taken out and replaced with new birch. Her beams are all served with iron staple standards & fore and aft iron knees." She was eventually sold in 1841.

1834 JOHN HARVEY *schooner*, tons, 77, dimens. 55' by 18'. Built at Hayle Foundry. Owner, Henry Harvey. Figurehead, man's bust.

1834 NAUTILUS *smack*, tons, 52, dimens. 47' 10" by 16' 3". Built at Hayle. Owner, Henry Harvey.

1835 HAYLE *brig*, tons, 129, dimens. 71.8' by 20.3'. Built at Hayle Foundry. Owner, Henry Harvey. She was specially built for deep sea trading to the Mediterranean and across the Western Ocean and was given stern galleries with a view to carrying cabin passengers. Figurehead, a man's bust.

1836 CARNSEW *sloop*, rigged "with a running bowsprit" (an exception in the sloop which normally had a fixed or "standing" bowsprit, but regular in the cutter), tons, 61, dimens. 51' 3" by 17' 2". In 1838, to give her greater hold capacity for transporting boilers, she was lengthened and re-rigged as a

348

ketch. Her tonnage was then given as 82 and her dimensions 61' 2½" by 17' 3". Built at Hayle Foundry. Owner, Henry Harvey.

1836 ELIZABETH (II) *schooner*, tons, 107 (115 by old measurement), dimens. 65' by 18'. Built at Hayle Foundry. Henry Harvey owned 56 of the sixty-four shares, Giles Gudge (now her master) was allowed 8. She was launched in November, only seven months after the *Carnsew*.

1837 HENRY (II) *schooner*, tons, 104, dimens. 67' by 17'. Built at Hayle Foundry. Owner, Henry Harvey.

1838 NANCY *schooner*, tons 104, dimens. 67' by 17'. Built at Hayle Foundry. Owner Henry Harvey.

1839 TRELISSICK *smack*, tons, 66, dimens. 53' by 16'. Built at Hayle Foundry. Owner, John Harvey Trevithick.

1839 MELLANEAR *smack*, tons, 37, dimens. 47' by 13'. Built at Hayle Foundry and launched in May, four months after the Trelissick. Owner, John Harvey Trevithick.

1840 JANE *schooner*, tons, 134, dimens. 74' by 19'. Built at Hayle Foundry. Owner, John Harvey Trevithick.

1841 JOANNA *schooner*, tons, 112, dimens. 68' by 18'. Built at Hayle Foundry. Owner John Harvey Trevithick, who transferred his shares to the Harvey Trustees on July the 12th, 1852.

1842 WILLIAM *schooner*, tons, 115, dimens. 70' by 18'. Built at Hayle Foundry. Owner, John Harvey Trevithick.

1844 FRANK *schooner*, tons, 95, dimens. 63' by 18', but altered in 1845 to 75' by 18'; with tonnage increased to 115. Built at Hayle Foundry. Owner, John Harvey Trevithick. The Stock Book for 1832 also names ten small craft — six lighters, three rowing boats and an "anti-dry-rot tank."

LETTERS FROM HARVEY'S SEAMEN

It will have been noted in the main text that Henry Harvey had only two ships making deep sea voyages, the brigs, *Hayle* and *Phoebe*. Both were used only occasionally for carrying goods for the Company; more often they were hired on charter. The other vessels were coasters of Great Britain and Ireland, making a few trips to the Continent. They were used mainly for the Company's business but, to keep loaded at intermediate stages of a voyage, they were frequently hired by word-of-mouth agreement between master and merchant (not full charter party in the legal sense). Captains of all ships wrote to the office every time they reached port and letters from the coasters are correspondingly the most numerous.

No logs from any of the vessels have been preserved and, it would seem that none were kept, though the keeping of logs, both scrap and fair-copy, had been the rule in other companies from a much earlier time. As to navigational instruments, we know that the *Hayle* had a sextant and a chronometer, and probably the *Phoebe* also. But there is nothing in the books or letters to show that the other ships had anything more advanced than compass and lead-line. Besides admiralty charts (which must have been a general issue), they appear to have relied on local knowledge gained by experience and that sixth sense which, in that day, the masters of small sailing ships developed to quite an uncanny degree. The rarity of serious disaster in the fleet, though going to sea at all seasons and in all weathers, is a striking tribute to the skill of their skippers. A small selection of their letters is appended, tending to show the nature of their dual tasks as daring seafarers and acute commercial pedlars.

APPENDIX

DEEP SEA

Two letters relating to the first voyage of the *Phoebe* after she had been acquired second-hand a year earlier and a good deal spent on refitting her. Part of the cargo she took out was cordage from the Hayle rope-walk, doubtless intended for sale to the lumberjacks.

Quebec 29th May 1833

Dear Sir

I avail myself of the Cherub's sailing from hence for England to inform you of our arrival here on 20th in*st*. after a passage of 47 days & a very unfortunate one. The Phoebe has proved very laboursome and has worked & strained considerably, which I can only account for by having the heavy round-house on her deck. We have had ever since we sailed a succession of gales of wind & on the 29th April when on the banks of Newfoundland we carried away our main yard in the slings & John Must the mate who was assisting in clearing away the wreck fell overboard from the main rigging and was drowned. I have much to regret in his loss as he was a good and able seaman.

On the 8th instant we got into the Ice to the Westward of the banks and were in it 36 hours, during which time the Starboard bow was stove in & the sides of the vessel a good deal rubbed. We succeeded in stopping the leak in the bows so that she did not much increase her water. On the 19th in*st*. the day before our arrival here having a pilot on board and thick weather we struck on the Red Island Shoals in the river St Lawrence but did not increase her water. I have had her on shore in the Cul de Sac & find that her bottom is not injured but keel is much splintered but will not require anything done to it til we get home. The bows also has been repaired & we now are about commencing loading. We have not suffered so much as some others. The Crown of London was totally lost in the Ice & the Edward of same port which we had spoken twice in the passage & were in the Ice together has been obliged to go into a dry dock to repair the damage she sustained in the Ice & sticking on the Shoals of this river. In short every ship has had a bad passage & many of them some damage.

During the last few days the new Timber has been arriving from the Country & when we arrived there was not a stick down, & there has also been a fall in the price since our arrival. Cordage I fear will not sell well but will do the best I can with it & I am glad I did not bring more with me. Indeed Quebec is a bad market for most articles & the people are ready to take any advantage. What I do will be through Mr Thos Curry. Mr Campbell has no timber & was obliged to purchase for the Adelaide, Vivian, at a higher rate than I can now do. Birch I find is very scarce but I shall be able to get a few loads. Red Pine Oak & Elm there is plenty of all sizes. I will write again before we leave.
I am Dear Sir
Yours very truly
George Swan

From Captain Swan's next letter dated the 8th of June—

I am sorry to say that I met with accident last evening in slipping of a plank & falling into the after hold. I have not broken any bones but am much bruised in my left side & ribs. I was immediately bled & now write in great pain but

350

APPENDIX

hope it will pass off in a day or two & not interfere with my employment. The cordage I have not been able to dispose of as yet & fear I shall be obliged to leave here for sale. There has been a very considerable quantity been sent out this Spring & auctions have been held but in every instance it has been bought in. Quebec appears to me to be a bad market to send goods & is a very expensive place.

The accounts of the losses by the Ice are really dreadful. Up to this time there are 13 announced & in one the Lady of the Lake upwards of 200 passengers lost & I fear we shall hear of more before we leave. Mr Vivian who takes this letter will no doubt call on you & report our progress as the Phoebe has been loading near to the Adelaide.

Henry Harvey Esqr

VOYAGES OF THE BRIG *Hayle*

One of the most interesting collection of letters relating to the early Harvey fleet is a budget of eighty-one from Captain Martin Bosustow of the brig *Hayle* covering eight years, from 1835 to 1842. For the first three years she was engaged in the Mediterranean trade, carrying outward cargoes of coal and (once) Ordnance stores for Malta, bringing back to London, Liverpool, or Glasgow (never to Hayle) currants and fustic (for yielding yellow dye) from the Greek islands, brimstone from Sicily, madder roots from Marseilles. There were always gaps between destinations, when skill and local knowledge was required to keep the vessel as well filled as possible, picking up short distance freights from port to port.

Bosustow was a first rate seaman, honest in all his dealings, strict but humane with his crews. He was well able to cope with those complexities of clerical work entailed in securing cargoes at a remunerative rate, in provisioning the ship, paying wages, and making the correct approach to officials at foreign ports. His letters are well expressed in clear handwriting. His only discoverable weakness was in the possession of a particularly sanguine temperament which caused him almost invariably to overestimate the likely profits of a projected voyage. He never became innured to the "untoward circumstance," in spite of its regular repetition which spoilt his forecast. While the keen Henry was perfectly satisfied with the achievements of the *Hayle*, the captain's letter announcing the end of a voyage nearly always contains an apologetic note expressing disappointment at results. The sort of untoward circumstance which could happen in those days besides foul weather and dead calms can be seen in such an incident as the following.

The *Hayle* left Penarth in September, 1835, with a cargo of coal for Ancona in the Adriatic. Before sailing, Bosustow wrote to a merchant at Zante to bespeak a full cargo of currants for the homeward voyage. But he was short-handed as he had had to discharge a seaman for insubordination. They had a rough passage, not reaching Ancona for 38 days. The carpenter, going aloft to close-reef the main topsail fell and was temporarily disabled, though "no bones broken," Before leaving Ancona, he had to lose another man because "he has been kissing the girls at Newport too closely and is under a course of mercury." When he reached Zante, the merchant denied having received his letter, maintaining that it must have miscarried. All the season's stock of currants had been disposed of.

The captain made the best of it by taking on 131 tons of fustic for Nice. "It is a small freight but hope to get a better charter from there. They export a great quantity of [olive] oil for St Petersburgh and other Baltic ports, hope to get a charter for that

351

APPENDIX

part, but if not, can always load for Liverpool at Marsailles which is close by."
But now comes the most untoward circumstance of all. It is related in a letter
from Nice dated February 17th, 1836. "At last I have the pleasure of informing
you of my safe arrival at this place from Zante on Tuesday 26th Janry in 14 days
from Zante, and after being brot in the port by the Harbour Master was ordered by
the Board of Health out again and to go to Villa Francha, a Bay about 3 miles from
Nice to perform 25 days quarantine with two quarantine Officers which they put
on board and a third in a Boat a small distance from the Vessel who watch'd us day
and night the whole time. I was allowed no communication with the shore even the
letters I had for the Merchant to whom the cargo was consign'd."

Failing to get a charter from Nice, Bosustow went on to Marseilles, where he met
with better success and secured a cargo for Glasgow of 108 tons of madder and 40
tons of brimstone "to make £305 freight in full." But through various causes was
detained 40 days in the port. He reached Glasgow on June the 5th, "after a very
long tedious passage of 7 weeks, having had a contrary wind all the time".

In 1838 the *Hayle* began making trans-Atlantic passages. The skipper's account
of one of these voyages and its coastwise successor is a fair sample of the small
ship ventures which were steadily multiplying in numbers all round the English
coast — daring uncoordinated private enterprises which gained us the carrying
trade of the whole world.

On April the 23rd, 1839, the *Hayle* arrived in London from Rio de Janeiro.
She had gone out on a one-way charter— "seeking," that is, free to make a
fresh bargain for the return voyage. But, contrary to Bosustow's expectations,
homeward freights were not only low but hard to get. The port was overcrowded
with expectant shipping diverted from Montevideo and Buenos Aires which were
cut off, due to the French fleet blockading the mouth of the River Plate. After
wasting a lot of time, he only succeeded in getting his holds little more than half
filled, and that with a nauseating cargo of wet and dry hides and, to make up, he
had ventured on a private speculation, buying thirty tons of rosewood (then all
the fashion in English cabinet-making) for £420, offering to share the profits with
Henry. The ship returned considerably lighter than her capacity, but although the
customs charged him £6 a ton duty on the rosewood it made a fair profit.

The optimistic captain, however, was somewhat disillusioned. He had written
from South America "I candidly confess I was never more tired of any place than
I am of the Capital of Brazil" and, on his return, "The Brazils is not so pleasant
for a Master as the Mediterranean." But, in London, there was nothing doing in
that direction. Henry suggested that the Baltic (for hemp and tallow) would make
a nice diversion. But, on the 9th of May, Bosustow wrote, "I beg to inform you of
my having again fixed the *Hayle* to load on the berth for Rio de Janeiro, expect to
leave about the last of the present month".

This change of heart seems to have been brought about by two inducements.
The captain had heard of a sure and safe means of dodging the British customs
by taking advantage of Colonial preference. "Several vessels has already arrived
from the Cape of Good Hope with coffee brought from Rio and other parts, by
which they save 6d. per lb. I hope to charter for that round before I leave London.
The coffee is taken to Table Bay, Capetown, landed, and taken on board again
immediately, by which it pays 6d. per lb. less duty than if taken direct from Rio
to London." Moreover "I feel confident freights will be good in the Brazils this
season, owing in a great measure to the disturbed state of the Negroes in the West

352

APPENDIX

Indies[1] and the high price of West Indian produce".

Here, too, was a golden opportunity to top up a meagre freight. "I expect also to get some passengers out, as there has been some applying and the vessel now on the berth is to clear on the 13th and has as many passengers as he can accomodate and might have more if he had room. I have to meet a party this day who wants to go, himself Wife, and two children. I asked him yesterday, £35 for himself, the same for his Wife, and £12 each for the children. He is coming this morning to look at the accomodation. If I can get £90 for them I suppose shall not refuse it. Of course I shall have to find them in everything except their beds, but think I shall be able to do it pretty well for that sum, their stock I think will not cost the ship more than £30." He writes again a few days later to say that the passage money has been agreed at eighty-five pounds, the last word is left to the wife, "and I have but little doubt that we shall then close." But they never appeared again and one suspects that the lady had sensed a redolence in the little cabin of the late cargo of wet hides. On the way out, the Hayle was hove to off Penzance and Bosustow got a letter put ashore. "We make out this time £270 19s. 10d. and had we the passengers as I expected, should have done well as far as the outward freight goes, but must now hope to do something fair home, as surely the River Plate will be open by the time we get out, and should freights be still low at Rio, will leave immediately the Cargo is out for that destination" — and proceed in ballast to the Plate ports.

The ship reached Rio on the evening of the 12th of August after a fair passage of 56 days from Penzance. On the following day the skipper wrote to his owners, "The Plate I'm sorry to say is not yet open which is the cause of the depression of freights here. There is they say 400 cargoes of Hides, allowing the cargoes to be of vessels of 200 tons, laying at Buenos Ayres ready for shipping, and at the commencement of the opening no doubt the freights will be enormous . . . However unless I can get something fair for Europe I will endeavour if possible to make an intermediate voyage," which meant, of course, going home via South Africa to test the cut-duty plan. He at once set about bargaining for a cargo appropriate to this middle passage. The additional distance on a direct course, as the steamer plies, is 4220 sea miles. In sail it would be so much more. If not fully up to the highest expectation, the enterprise didn't turn out too badly, as witness the captain's letters.

Messrs Harvey & Co

Rio Janeiro
Sept. 27th 1839

Gentln

I advise you by packet[2] of the 13th and also on 26th Ult by the Imogene, frigate, of the Hayle's being loading for Cape Town, Cape of Good Hope, and beg to refer you to those letters with respect to insurance &c.

I have drawn this day on you for forty three pounds seventeen shillings and three pence, at fourteen days sight, which please accept and place to account of Brig Hayle. My expenses here including commissions, port charges, lighterage, &c amounts to about £140 which, if I had been bound to England might have been obtained on account of my home freight but, being bound to the Cape, I could not obtain it in that way. I mentioned in my letter from

[1] Doubtless an allusion to the Bill of 1838, freeing all slaves throughout the British dominions.
[2] One of the Post Office fleet of fast armed brigs. There was a weekly mail service between Rio and Falmouth.

APPENDIX

London of my having £26 9s. 3d. to receive here from my outward freight which, with the bill now drawn, amounts to £70 6s. 6d. and the remainder I have laid out my own money for the full disbursement. We make freight in full £408 3s. 3d. which is to be paid at the Cape in Stirling on the right delivery of the Cargoe, and from thence hope to make you a good remittance. We are quite full, both Cabin and half deck and have on board 1477 bags of coffee and five hundred barrels of flour. At the first I thought we should have stowed more, but the flour has taken up more room than I calculated it would. We are all clear at the Customs and ready for sea and shall leave tomorrow morning wind & weather permitting.

I remain

Gent/ Your

Obeyt Serf M. Bosustow

The next is from Table Bay, dated November the 3rd.

I have the pleasure of again announcing to you the safe arrival of the Hayle in 35 days from Rio all well yesterday morning and also of my having again fixed her to load a full cargoe of Coffee at this place for London direct at 55/- per Ton and 5 pr Cent primage[1] — Java Coffee in bags of different sizes and Teirces[2], the Teirces to pay freight by measurement of 40 cubic feet pr Ton3, consequently hope to take more than we should do of Brazil Coffee in bags as they are all of the same size containing 160 lbs. in each bag. This cargoe is quite ready and shall commence loading immediately we have finished discharging the one we have now in, and expect to commence discharging tomorrow and shall have nothing to delay us but the weather as the consignees are anxious to get it on shore as soon as possible. The passage across has been as rough as one might have expected in the English channel in the depth of winter and we have had more reefing than we have had for the last twelve months put together. Our third or old Topsail has blown to ribbons . . .

Early in the new year, a series of severe gales struck the English coast. On January the 28th, 1840, the Secretary of St Katharine Docks wrote to Harveys to say that the Hayle was daily expected though not yet arrived at Gravesend, that the consignees of her cargo, Messrs Berles & Co. Ltd had arranged for a tug to stand by at Gravesend to bring the vessel up to St Katharine's Docks (and not the London Docks) free of charge. He solicited "the favour of your enclosing me a note to the Commander, confirming the wishes of the Consignees".

The Hayle did not get to London until a fortnight later. As soon as she reached home waters she had had to run for shelter into Penzance where, with the storm striking right into the mouth of the small harbour, she got little protection and some damage. Bosustow reported on February the 12th —

I have the pleasure of announcing to you our safe arrival here this morning. Our having been obliged to run in the Pier at Penzance, and the difficulty we had to hold her there &c, you are no doubt aware of, the expense of which I will no doubt be paid immediately by the Underwriters, and as Messrs Bolitho & Sons are the Insurance Agents shall address the Hayle to them inwards on

[1] Captain's perquisite for looking after cargo.
[2] Teirce for tierce, a medium-sized barrel, one third of a pipe, wine-measure. Ton capacity, not weight (see p. 343).

that account, not being bound by Charter as is usually the case.

We left Penzance on Friday evening at 6 o'clock with the wind about west, strong breezes, but before we got clear of the Bay had to close reef the main topsail and furl the fore one, had nothing set but the close Reef'd M*n* topsail & Foresail. For about 4 hours it blew a hurricane almost, when it moderated something. For the greatest part of the way had a strong wind. Brought up at 8 o'clock on Sunday evening in Margate Roads where we lay until Tuesday morning with a whole chain upon an end with a gale from S.W. by S.

Tuesday morning with the wind southward & westward, and in the evening brought up about 4 miles below Gravesend and this morning was towed all the way into St Katharine's Docks, as their Agent produced a letter from Messrs Berles & Co ordering the vessel to their Dock. I should have preferred the London Docks but of course must comply with the wishes of the consignees of the Cargoe, and was I to load for the Mediterranean next trip it will not make much difference but, if to the Brazil, should have to go to the London Docks to Load and, by so doing, would incur two Dock Dues.

He writes again on the 29th of February to say that a severe cold has prevented him writing earlier. His purpose of chartering for another deep sea passage has been altered by a tempting offer to carry 275 tons of wheat to Liverpool at a freight charge of £131 7s. 0d., less £2 5s. 0d. towards the expense of lighterage, as he must load the grain in the river and not in the dock. "My reason for getting to Liverpool is on account of another voyage as much, or more so, as for the profit we shall make in going there, Liverpool being a much better place for procuring outward charter than this is." — and only a matter of a few days sail.

On March the 10th he writes —

I beg to inform you I have this day setled my inward freight [Rio, Cape, London] do not make as much as I anticipated. We make in full £438.1 hoped we should have made near £500. As the coffee was not weighed at the Cape we could not tell exactly what we had in, and the deficiency I attribute partly to what we pumped out and perhaps the Coffee has also shrunk something in weight & we are paid freight on what we deliver at the Queen's Beam[1] . .. We leave the Docks tomorrow morning, expected to have left this morning, but the vessel not being full for'ard was compel'd to put a bulkhead across to prevent the Cargoe from shifting and which has delayed us a day. She is now again in good order and trust shall meet with immediate employment on our arrival at Liverpool.

The detailed statement of his transactions during the late voyage which the captain submitted has not been preserved and what he has given in his letters is not very clear. But it would seem that the Java coffee which the Dutch had imported to the Cape from their own colony in the East Indies was taken on board to replace the cargo of flour. Presumably the Brazilian coffee was dumped on the quay (according to plan) and then re-shipped but, naturally, without being weighed. Meanwhile some of the bags had got damaged by salt water during the rough passage across the South Atlantic and the wasted berries got into the bilges and was "what we pumped out". But both consignments, American and Dutch got away

---

[1] The weighing scale at the London Custom House. The modern office block of H.M. Customs and Excise perpetuates its memory being named King's Beam House.

with the rebate under Colonial Preference. The insignificant coastwise trip, largely undertaken, as explained, to pick up a profitable deep sea charter after a quick turn round, took the Hayle just one day less than three weeks. Bosustow gives particulars in two letters. The first is from Credan Head in Waterford Harbour, Ireland, dated March the 21st.

I beg to inform you of our arrival here today, having bore up from Carnsore point last night in a fresh gale from the E., being heartily tired of beating to windward and gaining little or no ground. We hauled out of Dock on last Wednesday week the 11th Ult, and being anxious to save the Easterly wind, took steam between us and another vessel to Gravesend, and by so doing it costs about one half the expense it would be to take a steam boat alone, say £3 for our share. But unfortunately we took the ground in towing down. The other vessel, though drawing 6 inches more water than ourselves, being astern of us, with the way we had at the time, came that much through the soft mud and came right into our stern, started our taffrail, and carried away our quarter boards and Main Gaff, and which detained us a day at Gravesend. However I got it put to rights for about £4, and what was almost as vexatious as any thing, disarranged all our nice paint work, having had her nicely painted at London. The other vessel, the Princess Victoria of Scilly, carried away her cathead, one stancheon, and all her head and, as we both got damage, had no other alternative than each to repair his own damage, and I believe his was the worst of the two. We left Gravesend again on the Friday and have brought up nowhere since until this afternoon. The wind at present is about E.N.E. and more moderate, hope to be off again tomorrow as I think the wind will draw from the S.E., hope in a few days to have the pleasure of announcing our safe arrival at Liverpool. The second letter is from Liverpool, dated March the 31st.

I have at last the pleasure of announcing to you the safe arrival of the Hayle, having been twice in Waterford and left that place the last time on Thursday last and got here this morning tide, all well. I wrote you the 25th Ult from Credan Head, Waterford Hart and mention'd then that I thought we should leave again shortly, and accordingly left the next morning with a light breeze from the N.N.W. which continued until the following morning, when it again came on to the N.E. and blew a heavy gale as much as we could carry [under] close reef'd Topsails, and having a grain cargoe and the wind right ahead, thought it best to bear up again, which we did with several other vessels bound here also, and left again last Thursday as I before mentioned. I believe, had I anticipated so much trouble in getting round I should not have taken the freight but must now be content and hope shall meet with something fair from this. Will let you know when I again find something that will suit. We have twelve laying days[1] here with the wheat but hope they will not detain us that time.

But the captain was once more disappointed in his anticipations. He wrote on April the 7th, "Things are very flat here at present... I wish the Hayle had been 100 Tons larger. A vessel of that size would pay much better in the Southern trade, but 130 Tons is too small for long voyages." This hint seems to have been taken as, thenceforward, the *Hayle* returned to the Mediterranean run.

[1] The number of days allowed in a charter party for loading and discharging which, if exceeded, the owners must pay dock dues (demurrage).

APPENDIX

Coastwise

In spite of the enormous development in the industries of coalmining, iron-founding, and copper-smelting which had been taking place along the Welsh coast since the latter part of the 18th century, port facilities everywhere remained as primitive as ever. In some places, complete boilers, cylinders, and engine beams had to be landed on the open beach at low tide with the vessel heeled over, and discharged by tackle rigged to the mast. Today, Newport has large docks with sixty hydraulic and electric cranes, lifting from 12 to 30 tons, and twenty hoists for elevating a loaded coal wagon and tipping it into the hold. In 1839 it had only a single wharf and one feeble and inadequate crane (described in a following letter). But, in that year, improvements at last began to be made. At Cardiff the first dock was opened and works in the treacherous estuary at Aberavon started (now magnified into Port Talbot) which had formerly given endless trouble to Harvey's ships. The first improvement is noted on page 356 when Captain Edwards was able to use a channel cut through the sandhills.

PROVIDENCE (II)

Laugharne 11th Decr 1833

Mr. Harvey
Sir

I am sorry to inform you that we have had the misfortune of being on Shore on the sands in Carmarthen bay where we struck about 10 A.M. on Monday last during a very thick weather. We stopt in the vessel 2½ hours after she struck, we then succeeded at great risk to make the Shore stern before not being able to see the land until we had passed in the boat through the breakers. Thank God we are all safe but I have lost all except a few things since picked up. The hull of the vessel holds yet together though her decks blew up an hour after we abandoned the vessel. We have got the sails and loose rigging and most of the materials out of the vessel and Mr Bird and another agent from Swansea are getting out the cargo. I noted a protest yesterday in time, but I find the cargo is not insured. From my exertions and constant fatigue and some bruises at the helm before she struck, I am nearly knocked up, for I have had no rest since I left home. We are four miles from the town of Lanstephan where I must get the valuable materials conveyed as soon as possible. My trouble is so great that I should like to hear from you by return of post. You'll have the goodness to acquaint my wife with our sad misfortune.

I will write you more particulars in a post or two when I hope to handle the pen myself. With great respect I am
Sir,
Your Most Olbig*d* H*bl* Serv*t*
William Veal

Letter from Samuel Warren, Harvey's shipwright, directed from Carmarthen, December the 28th, 1833. He has been sent to report on the condition of the *Providence*. Having gone by coach, first to Launceston, then to Barnstaple, then by the Ilfracombe packet to Swansea, he reached Carmarthen late on the night of the sixth day. From Swansea —

i was obliged to follow on to the Eastward, the roads of which was all but impassable the Country being so inundated with water, but i reacd here Safe

357

But much washed. The following morning i went to the Quay, being the most Public Place, where i larned where the Providence was — i hired a Boat which landed me near the Spot — i could not then stop any time has i wished to meet Cap*n* Veal — i had then to proceed by land near five miles to Laugharne. But i stopped short at a village called Lanstephan near two miles from the vessel and sent to Cap Veal. He met me in the evening with Mr Wilson Junr, but the tide was in therefore i could not Board the Providence till today.

i went this morning to Laugharne seen all the materialls. The whole with a very little exception his in an entire state. The Greatest of Exertions must have been used to have preserved them as they are. The lower Mast, lower Rigging, tops, caps, Bowsprit his standing. There his now an Explanation how the Decks came to Blow up Cap*n* Gudge with myself was surprized at when the vessel went ashore. She remained stern to the sea. The sea Beat in the stern above the Stern Rails laying the Decks open. The Quarter Deck his gone with three of the beams part of the Main Deck, the two Main Hatch Beams, one Lower Beam that has been broke this some time. She then canted and laid head to the sea and Docked herself. She could not have beat on the Beach little or nothing — there is not one single treenail shattered in the Both sides that we could discover today. The Counter his entire but the Buts ends his a little moved up on the wing transom. But the transom his Defective which accounts for that the sheer is lifted a little on the Starboard side, the other his not. The Keelson his broke but from the Clamps upon it i suppose was hounded before. Cap*n* Gudge[1] may have some Recollection of it. The seam in the Bow his Quite Perfect but that of the Bottom his hollow on both sides, which was before but must be expected to have gone worse.

From what i have now seen of the vessel upon a calculation i should say 300 Pounds would put the Providence in better condition than when she left the Port of Hayle. A Carmarthen Builder has been there before i arrived. He Estimated at 200, but to repair here would be Quite out of the Question. She will cross the Channel has she now his with some thin Board on the deck rather than make a Great Sacrifice. I have endeavoured Sir to have been has Explicit as i could. Mr Wilson Jun*r* has been Inspecting very minutely the Vessel, Materials, and cetra—whether he intends to Purchase i don't know. He attends Monday at Laugharne to the Sale, after which I shall proceed to Pembroke. There Sir i shall act Cautiously. There his timber in this Neighbourhood which i mean to see and in my next you shall receive the Particulars — i have some intimation that Mr Wilson has some timbers but there is now a large falling of timbers near Lanstephan.

Your Obedient Servant
Samuel Warren

Compass Errors

Considering the various kinds of iron cargoes carried in Harvey's wooden ships and their disposal on board it is remarkable that only a few cases of compass error seem to have been thought worth reporting in letters. As already told, it nearly caused disaster in that most critical voyage in 1843, when the great twelve foot cylinder was shipped to Holland.

[1] Captain Giles Gudge, master of the *Rosewarne*.

358

APPENDIX

The following is from Captain Philip Andrew of the *Carnsew* who was bound (before she was enlarged and converted from sloop to ketch), from Hayle to Waterford with two large Cornish boilers (apparently carried on deck) and an iron engine-beam in the hold with a quantity of ballast. To make something more on the journey than freight on the goods to be delivered, a call was first to be made at Newport where the ballast would be exchanged for coal to be sold in Ireland. The letter is addressed from Ilfracombe, dated September the 24th, 1836.

Sirs,

we Sailed from St Ives the thursday and goat 35 Miles of[f] the Land when it Came on to blow from the SW and thick and Durty & as we could not Depend on our course, we found our Compasses out the way 6 & 8 points, at 8 Oclock that Night we put the vessel about expecting to fetch St Ives but we could not by 6 Miles. At 2 Oclock the Friday morning we bore away to run up the Channel it Bload Hard and a great Deal of Sea and it proved very thick all the passage up. We made Lunday Island at 1 Oclock the friday and at 6 we went in to Combe. Our vessel Behaved as well as we could expect with that weight on Deck but the Cargo in the Hold settled to port so that the vessel ad 3 Strakes List when we came Here, we Have Received no Damage and as we Have this thing on Deck we must weight until there is a Settlement in the weather So no [more] at present from you

　　　　　　Obet Sert
　　　　　　Philip Andrew.

This was not the only adventure the captain met with on that voyage. He reached Newport the following Thursday and wrote to report his arrival nine days later, having been delayed in reaching the appropriate berths for discharging the ballast and loading coal. Then "I am sorry to inform you that on Friday morning when on Ships duty I was molested & robed of nine sovereigns & two half crowns which my purse contained, the person being taken by the Police & put to prison. To day the eleventh I was necessitated to appear before the Magistrates & am bound to appear at Usk next Quarter Sessions or pay the fine of forty Pounds."
The *Carnsew* had to wait a further week at Newport before the case came on at Usk and the skipper was perhaps feeling nervous about the nature of rumours reaching Hayle. They might learn that the robbery took place "when on ship's duty" at a public house and that the "person" was a woman. At any rate a letter was addressed personally to Henry on the eve of the hearing from an eye-witness of the incident, one who would certainly be regarded as a man of impeccable character. This was John Denvir, the agent for Stonehouse & Co. He testified that the captain had come to his office to enquire where the man who unladed the ballast could be found. Denvir told him that the likeliest place was a nearby inn and thither he escorted him. There they naturally had a friendly drink together which in no way affected the sobriety of the sailor. Emerging from the inner sanctum into the tap-room, to locate the man they hoped to find, "Captain A. was assailed by a party, male and female, for something to drink." This was refused. A scuffle followed, during which, one of the women abstracted his purse. She was later taken into custody. Having justified the skipper's presence in a public house whilst strictly on ship's duty the writer demolished the other possible aspersion: "I am perfectly satisfied that Captain A. had no improper connexion with the woman in question, it being the middle of the day."

APPENDIX

Newport Dec. 12, 1839

Gentlemen

I have to inform you of my safe arrival here this morning all well after a very troublesome Passage. The Larbord Boiler gave a way and hove us down on our beam ends and was obliged to let fly every sail to right her, and split the jib and was like to be on the Stones. I never wish to be so neer a gain as I was very much frighten the Vessel was not fit for sea that morning as it is running a risk of lives & Property. The Vessel have three strakes list now in the River, it was a good thing that the wind cast to the N.W. for us. There is 8 or 9 days stem here now but hope to be load by this day week.

But nine days later he writes—

I am sorry to inform you that we are not discharge as yet. The crane chain broke three times and they will not risk it again, fering that they will break the Crane by the sudant jurks. There is a new chain making and we shall have to wait. I have purches [purchases] up to help and still they are a fraid to try until the new Chain is made. I have not lost any time as yet for loding but shall if not discharge by Monday. I shall demand my demurage from last Wednesday as we have been waiting every tide since. It was a good job that the first Boiler was half on the shore when the Chain Broke. If it had fell on the decks it would broke every thing before it. The greatest damage don is 1 stanchon & Brused the comings. I was about to prise it off at the time. Had I my prise it would have smashed me in atoms. No one was hurt as I never had such misfortune since in the employ. I hope to get the outher out safe.

[The mate, however, had gone sick and been sent ashore, a certificate for which the captain encloses. A further letter is sent on the 27th to say that the boilers are safely landed.]

Letter from Captain Richard Edwards, Schooner *Henry Harvey*

Aberavon 8 Dec 1839

Sir

Wee arived to aberavon on Tuesday Evening & Pased up the New Cut which was filling up at that time. Had we been 1 day later wee should bee obliged to wait to go over the New Bar which we should not be able until the Top of Next Spring. We discharged 2 barges & got in birth on Saturday morning & Discharged the Remainder the same Day.

The Nancy, Captn Andrew, arived on the same time but had no water to the works until Saturday but cant Discharge till Tuesday. The freights at aberavon is Reduced for Waterford is 9/- per Ton, but cant Load us sooner than a fortnight by Reason of Coal so scarce which we thought would not answer. We went to Neath, Swansea, & Llanelly but could not suite at either Place. After we came back wee heard of bar Iron & Tin Plates for Liverpool at Mr Smith's which wee both agreed & chartered last Evening at 12/- Per ton & to Load the first of next Spring Tide. Laying Days at Liverpool 6, after which 2 Pounds Per Day.

Mr Smith ships at Margam copper works & the first opportunity I shall Tow Round from the New to the old Harbour light. I have attended the Post office & Received no letter from you. Wee shall write you as soon as wee arive to Liverpool.

APPENDIX

Letter From Captain Giles Gudge, Schooner Elizabeth Bound
For Rouen. April 1839

I am sorry I have to inform you of the dreadful accident we have met with
from a Brig running before the wind between the hours of three and four
o'clock yesterday morning. She ran aboard of us & carried away covering
bord, Paint Strake, three Stansions, one of the [k]nightheads, Bowsprit, jib
boom, Topmast, & cutwater. I should think that we have got from forty to
fifty pounds damage and how our two mast did not go overboard I cannot tell
as the stays were all carried adrift. The Brig struck us on the starboard bow,
the bulwarks & rails from the forerigging to the [k]nightheads are all gon &it
was a good thing we fell in with a schooner belongin to Chester who had the
goodness to lend us a large spar to rigg for a bowsprit or otherwise if we had
been towed in it whould have added to the above som forty or fifty pound
without doup. The vessel makes but little water, we maneg with a littel help
to get her into Limmington Channel last Evening where I thought we should
have got our dammeg repard, but cannot without long detension, so I hope
to get to Cowes this day tide. It will take six or seven days to replace the
damage I expect. I should like to have your advice to know how to maneg.
Could Mr Warren come up, I should be glad if he could. I shall be In whant of
money here. I shall get the dameg repaired as soon as possible Otherwise the
Marchants whould bring the ship in for damaged for detension. I expected to
have lost the vessel & our lives all together as she was broak all open forward
& so much wind & seas under single Riff Mainsail at the time about five leags
S.S.W. from Donnose Point, the [Isle of] white, wind E.N.E. at the time we
was rund aboard of. I should have been in France this day without doup. The
Brig that ran on board us said to belong to Settin bound to America, a vessel
about four or five hundred tons I should think.

But he never mentions that the offender left her figurehead and cutwater on board
the *Elizabeth*.

361

APPENDIX VII

To the Commissioners of   Hayle Foundry, Oct 9th, 1845
the Haarlemmer Meer Drainage
Gentlemen,
On your request we enclose a statement as arranged on the 17th inst. by the Subcommissioner, particulars of which were left in their possession duly certified by your appointed engineer.
From our last payment was deducted the sum of £12,000.
The circumstances of this case being so well known to you that it will be unnecessary to enter on many particulars by way of defence. The interest we have taken, the great expense we have been at to ensure the success of this great undertaking, and the favourable result must plead for us. We beg to state briefly a few of the leading points. After the Contract was signed and the plans delivered we, with your engineer, commenced practical consultations relative to the construction of the said machine. You will have observed that the alterations and additions, & expense consequently, very much time was necessary to arrange and make more than would have been had we blindly followed the plan as proposed to us. Instead of this we linked ourselves with your engineer, took the more interest as though executing a scheme of our own, spared no exertion or money in purchasing and making Tools in order that the said machine should be as perfect as we could possibly make it. On that point we have satisfied ourselves.
Our men were sent to erect the said engine as soon as we well could after hearing that the buildings were ready to receive the engines. The time in erecting has exceeded by far the time we calculated on, but on enquiry we do not blame our men. The difficulty and care in moving such massive work and the last long severe winter are points brought forward by them, and we must say that altho it has taken more time than we expected it has been unavoidable. It is the first engine of such magnitude [ever to have been made]. Calculation of time could only be guessed at and the object too serious to be hurried forward to perhaps a failure. It has been a serious pecuniary loss to us but we feel this will be repaired by the success of the undertaking.
We feel confident that on reflection you will never sanction our punishment for doing so well our duty.
          We remain
             Your obt Servants
             Harvey & Co
             Nichs Harvey

To Nicholas Harvey, seeking advice and co-operation in the design and manufacture of chains and winches (crabs) to be used in critical hoisting operations at the construction of his railway bridge at Chepstow. He has come to Hayle and spent the morning at the Foundry discussing his problem and now (from the White Hart Hotel?) puts matters into writing with some second thoughts.

Hayle
Nov 5th 1850

Dear Sir,

This letter I meant should have been sent to you respecting chains, and which may yet reach you, was to the following effect.

I want six lengths of 130 fathom each of 1¼ chain. They are to be used with blocks (30 inch sheaves) and crabs for lifting some heavy and costly parts of a large bridge erecting at Chepstow. The chains will be subjected to a strain of 10 to 12 tons, never exceeding the latter, but with the jerks and irregularities of action unavoidable with the use of blocks and crabs — however carefully applyed. It is of the greatest importance to me to ensure the nearest possible approach to certainty as regards the perfection of the chains as any accident would inevitably cause the destruction of work of grand value and delay the opening of a line of 100 miles — which is to be finished by a certain day under a contract with another company. With the view to stimulate makers to emulation I have some idea of having half the chains made by one house and half by another and bringing them into direct comparison. But I wish first to hear what can be suggested by the makers to satisfy me of the quality of their chains particularly as to the care bestowed on their manufacture and with selection of all the materials used. I don't attach any value to the ordinary guarantees unless indeed a manufacturer would become really liable for all the consequences of a failure. I would much rather be satisfied that every possible care had been used, neither do I like proving a chain or anything else much beyond the load it will have to carry in practice.

Under these circumstances I wish to know 1st, whether you can suggest any good mode of ascertaining or satisfying me of the perfect state of a chain.

2nd, at what price and in what time you will make such chains of the best quality, either the whole or half the quantity named.

3rd, what assurances or guarantee you can suggest — and 4th, whether you would take them back and at what price — after very little wear.

As regards the crabs, as explained to you this morning, I intend making them double, passing the chain round two barrels — was to avoid any riding or ringing of the chains. But I had proposed to make them of two complete separate crabs as being more saleable afterwards. If you prepare your design

APPENDIX

for double barrels in one frame, which would of course make a better job I shall only want six sets — but the strain upon the chains will be 10 to 12 tons instead of 6 as stated and the number of men double what I stated — I shall think it a good plan to apply the power to each barrel and only one set of gear need be used when the weight lifted is less than 10 tons.

If your experience would lead you to groove the barrels to receive the chain instead of putting wood round them I shall be obliged by your advice on this or any other point.

I will send you the drawing of the blocks when ready but I should not wish to delay your reply as regards the chains and crabs.

I am my dear Sir
Yours very truly
I. K. Brunel

Nicholas Harvey Esq.

APPENDIX IX

1852 Partners under the first deed. N. O. Harvey, W. West (III), John West, W. Harvey.

1854 Second deed of partnership. W. J. Rawlings added. W. Husband returns to the Company and opens the London office as Manager.

1861 Death of N. O. Harvey: His place as partner and Engineer taken by W. Husband.

1863 Third deed of partnership. Partners unchanged.

1868 Death of John West: his place taken by N. J. West. Frank Harvey appointed partner. Acquisition of Copperhouse quays and dock.

1875 Acquisition of Copperhouse Foundry premises.

1883 Reconstruction as Limited Company with W. Harvey, Chairman, W. J. Rawlings, Secretary, Frank Harvey, Commercial Manager, W. West, N. J. West. W. Husband, Engineers and Henry Whitford, Solicitor.

1885 W. Husband goes again to London to take charge of the Company's office and premises.

1887 Death of W. Husband. N. J. West takes charge of the London office.

1888 W. Harvey retires: his place taken by John Vivian.

1890 Death of W. J. Rawlings.

1892 F. H. Harvey appointed director in place of W. J. Rawlings (Dec. 12). Death of H. N. Harvey (Dec. 14).

1893 Death of W. West (III).

1897 John Mead appointed director.

1904 Following the closure of Hayle Foundry the Company was reconstituted. The Board was then Frank Harvey, Chairman; John Vivian, Secretary; F. H. Harvey, Engineer; C. E. Whitford, John Mead and N. J. West.

1909 Death of N. J. West.

1914 C. V. Wills appointed director.

1915 Death of John Mead. J. B. Read appointed director.

1921 Richard Hughes appointed director.

1923 Resignation of Frank Harvey and John Vivian.

1928 C. P. Harvey appointed director.

1929 Resignation of Richard Hughes.

APPENDIX

1930 Death of F. H. Harvey. H. W. M. Simons appointed director.

1945 Death of H. W. M. Simons. V. B. Wills appointed director.

1947 P. C. Buchanan appointed director.

1948 Retirement of J. B. Read, when J. T. W. Higgans succeeded him as Secretary.

1949 D. P. Harvey appointed director.

1950 Retirement of C. V. Wills.

1951 Retirement of C. E. Whitford. His place taken by W. G. Harrison, his partner in the old established firm of Paynter and Whitford, the lawyers so often mentioned from earliest days (now Whitford & Sons).

1957 Merger with Fox Stanton & Co., two of whose partners, G. R. Fox and A. F. Laity then join Harveys' Board.

1958 Retirement of C. P. Harvey.

1960 J. T. W. Higgans appointed director, continuing to act as Secretary. Acquisition of Cornish Mines Supplies Company Ltd.

1961 Quotation for shares secured on the Bristol Stock Exchange. Affiliation with The Devon Trading Co. of Exeter. F. E. Baker appointed Director.

44. A Harvey-made cast-iron 'leading light' on the harbour wall at Porthleven.

Photograph: Pete Joseph

366

APPENDIX X

NOTES ON THE HARVEY-TONKING FAMILY

In one respect the historians have dealt rather shabbily with Henry. His personal life has either been ignored or dismissed as of little importance because he never married. We will see how his private life was as involved as his business affairs and appreciate his patience as a businessman, administrator and father figure.

Henry lived at Foundry House which was maintained by his spinster sister Elizabeth (Betsey) 1779-1848 sometimes assisted by their niece, Nanny, 1801-1840. His eldest sister Joanna, 1757-1836, was married to William West, 1751-1831, whose engineering skills were an asset to Harvey & Company. The next sister, Anne, 1770-1808, married John Harvey, 1769-1809, in 1794. He was a well-to-do cabinet-maker of Helston but not known to be a relative of the Harveys at Hayle; the couple were to have six children. Disaster struck when both parents died within a year leaving their children as orphans. Henry and Elizabeth took the children into their care at Foundry House, bringing them up and educating them. Some, notably Nicholas Oliver and William Harvey, together with John Harvey Trevithick were to take leading parts in the operation of the company in future years, creating the line of Harveys that took their surnames from elsewhere but were to form the later Harvey companies.

Henry's devotion to his family's needs also involved the six children of his sister Jane Trevithick, 1772-1868. He provided the means by which his sister brought up all her children to make good their lives in spite of the inattention of their errant father.

Although Edmund Vale produced a very full account of the Harvey company in Hayle, he omitted any reference to the Tonkings who must have been a significant, well-known part of the community. It may be that even in the 1960s, the Harvey Directors felt this was better left unsaid. There now seems no reason to omit it. This is how they came about.

Henry Harvey was a much respected pillar of local society, one on whom much of the community relied. Although he did not marry he maintained two houses in Hayle. One was the formal family home at Foundry House where he and Elizabeth brought up Anne's six children. The other was Mellanear on Foundry Hill, Hayle. Everyone knew that this was the residence of Henry's lady friend, Grace Tonkin, 1793-1865. Between 1818 and 1837 Grace bore Henry no less than eleven children, nine of which survived. She was the daughter of Thomas Tonkin a miner from St Just. A tithe map of the period shows that Henry's Mellanear House was leased to Grace.

At the time their first child was born, Henry was forty-three and Grace eighteen-years-of-age. One can conclude that Grace gave the ever-busy, responsible Henry a new interest in life. The children were all christened at St Erth church with Harvey

367

APPENDIX

as their second name and their father shown as 'Henry Harvey, Merchant'. Henry insisted that the name Tonkin should bear an additional 'g' to make it distinctive from the many other Tonkins; Henry was not one to hide the love of his life under a bushel. It is frequently and erroneously said that Henry's father, John, had forbidden him to marry the housemaid but John had died in 1803 when Grace was just four-years-of-age and about fifteen years before the liaison. Henry, a prominent figure and the major employer in Hayle, was affectionately known locally as 'The little Cap'n'. In the absence of any evidence to the contrary, we suppose that he was also a model of social responsibility and as such his activities with Grace must have been the subject of much discussion. Although Henry was to live until he was seventy-five and Grace died at the age of sixty-six, the average age at which their children departed was only twenty-five, six of them sadly dying before Henry.

In all, Henry was father to Grace's nine surviving children and uncle to six for each of his two sisters' children, a total of no less than twenty-one boys and girls who looked to him for financial and fatherly support. He treated his extended family with love and responsibility. Prior to his death in 1850, Henry made a deed of settlement in favour of his many nephews and nieces. In 1838 he made over property he owned in Stithians and St Gluvias to set up a trust fund for his illegitimate children and their mother. The children were all suitably educated and many of them set up in business in Hayle where they prospered. Henry would have been justly proud of his brood and their descendants.

Philip M. Hosken

THE CHILDREN OF HENRY HARVEY AND GRACE TONKIN

JOHN HARVEY TONKING (1818 – 1838)

EDWARD HARVEY TONKING (1821 – 1824)

WILLIAM HARVEY TONKING (1822 - 1843)

FRANCIS HARVEY TONKING (1823 – 1853)

HENRY HARVEY TONKING (1824 – 1844)

RICHARD HARVEY TONKING (1825 – 1856)

JULIANA HARVEY TONKING (1828 – 1849)

EDWARD HARVEY TONKING (1830 – 1831)

EDWIN HARVEY TONKING (1832 – 1869)

JAMES HARVEY TONKING (1833 - ?)

CHARLES HARVEY TONKING (1837 – 1908)

APPENDIX XI

WHAT REMAINS OF HARVEY'S IN HAYLE TODAY

Space precludes more than a brief overview here as to what remains of the great Harvey enterprise in Hayle today. The interpretation of what survives is complex and those who would wish to know and see more, are advised to arm themselves with the guides listed in the supplementary bibliography at Page 372. In addition the website at www.hayletowncouncil.net/walks.htm has excellent information and walks, which can be downloaded for personal and non-commercial use.

In his 1979 bicentenary booklet, "Harveys, 200 Years of Trading", Cyril Noall could write that, "the Cyclopean ruins of Harvey's Foundry still dominate the western end of the town but all is now peace and stillness where once the furnaces roared." Much has changed in the last thirty years; there have been grievous losses but more recently welcome conservation, restoration and adaptive re-use of the surviving structures has begun.

In 1969 a disastrous fire virtually destroyed the former Boilermakers' Shop and Sawmills, which had been converted into a showroom. 1980 saw the loss of the Carnsew limekilns and in 1984 came the wanton destruction of the Coppersmiths' Shop and the Erecting Shop known as the Coliseum, undoubtedly one of Cornwall's finest industrial buildings.

In the area of Foundry Square, White's Warehouse on the north side, is the former Hosken, Trevithick and Polkinhorn bakehouse. This operated as Hayle Steam Bakery, and though remodelled in the late nineteenth century, still includes part of the 1828 Stores. At the rear are remains of furnaces from the 1840s. It passed out of Harvey's hands to J. H. Trevithick Holdings in 1852 and then to the great Cornish trinity, Hosken, Trevithick & Polkinhorn. John Harvey House, with its distinctive clock tower, dates back in part to the 1780s and housed head office, the nerve centre of the entire Harvey operation. It has cast iron structural columns and two fireproof strong rooms made of ship building plate. On its west side are more traces of the original 1780 foundry. Barclay's Bank was part of the Harvey empire as their Emporium, while Foundry House, mainly of 1895, is on the site of the foundry offices and shop. The current building is in the same style as White's Warehouse and like that building passed to Trevithick in 1852 and was rebuilt as the Cornubia Biscuit Factory of Hosken, Trevithick & Polkinhorn.

The White Hart Hotel was built in 1838 by Henry Harvey to accommodate customers visiting Hayle. Beside it the Masonic Hall of 1824 was built as the original White Hart, also by Henry in order to provide a living for his sister Jane, the wife of Richard Trevithick, who spent much of his time away from home including many years in South America.

In Foundry Yard, off Foundry Square, is the huge Granary or Foundry Barn. Dating from 1835 this building has been stabilised pending repair by the Harvey's

Foundry Trust. At its north end are remains of the Boring Mill and Erecting Shop; these contained a boiler house and large steam engine. There is an aspiration to re-erect an 1863 50-inch Harvey beam engine here. Further north near the railway viaduct are the walls of the Pattern Shop, while across the yard is the timber framed and clad Drawing Office, supported at first floor level on former iron mine drainage pipes. To the south are remains of a Grist Mill, Ropewalk and Millpond, now a public open space. Elsewhere in Hayle can be seen a Wagon Shed and Timber Store as well as housing for workers, managers and the Harvey family. To the north of the Carnsew hillfort, much embellished by Henry Harvey is the restored Crimean War mortar. This was manufactured and improved by Harvey & Co. under sub-contract to the Royal Ordnance Factory

There is a vast range of industrial and transport remains to be seen in Hayle and it is thanks to pioneering works such as Edmund Vale's book that these now receive due value and appreciation.

45. Foundry House, the former Harvey offices and Emporium and, later, the Cornubia Biscuit Factory.

Photograph: Pete Joseph

HAYLE from the Air.

46. Aerial photograph of Hayle in the early 1900s after the closure of Harvey's Foundry.
Photograph courtesy of the Morrab Library.

47. The Harvey's Foundry farm.

Photograph: Harvey's Foundry Trust

48. John Harvey House, Foundry Square.

Photograph: Harvey's Foundry Trust

372

APPENDIX

APPENDIX XII

1. Steam Engines

Engines with Public Access
- East Pool Mine, 90″ Beam Pumping Engine, 1892 for Carn Brea Mines, to East Pool 1923. Stopped 1954. Static. National Trust
- Levant Mine, 27″ Beam Winding Engine, 1840. Stopped 1930. Working. National Trust
- Crofton Pumping Station No. 2 Engine, 42″ Beam Pumping Engine, built as Sims Compound 1845, rebuilt 1905. Working
- Kew Bridge Pumping Station, 70″ Bull Pumping Engine, 1855. Working
- Kew Bridge Pumping Station, 100″ Beam Pumping Engine, 1869.
- Cruquius, Haarlem, 84″/144″ Annular Compound Pumping Engine, 1845. Movable but not in steam.
- Fresnillo, Mexico, 2 x 40″ Rotary Beam Engines for ore crushing, 1852. Static
- O'okiep, Cape Province, South Africa, 50″ Beam Pumping Engine, 1882. Static

Dismantled or Inaccessible
- Goonvean China Clay Pit, 50″ Beam Pumping Engine, 1863 for Penhalls Mine, St. Agnes, to Goonvean 1910. Stopped 1956. Dismantled and stored for proposed re-erection in Hayle.
- Carpalla China Clay Pit, 40″ Beam pumping Engine, 1863 for West Polbreen Mine, St. Agnes, to Carpalla 1915. Stopped 1944, dismantled 1952 for Science Museum Reserve Collection. Stored dismantled.
- Tresavean Mine, worm geared, double cylinder, steam capstan, 1881. Later at Cook's shaft, South Crofty, stored dismantled at King Edward Mine.
- South Crofty Mine, Robinson's Shaft, Horizontal Duplex Capstan, 1882, latterly working on air. Preserved but currently inaccessible.
- East Pool Mine, Taylor's Shaft, fragments of two Harvey beams preserved, one dated 1852.
- Grenville Mines, 90″ Beam Pumping Engine [Fortescue's] 1870s. At Cook's Shaft, South Crofty 1922-50. Soleplate and bob stools only, restored to original Grenville Mines engine house.
- Hammersmith Pumping Station, 72″ Beam Pumping Engine, 1854. Engine scrapped 1945. Hollow-work beam only preserved at Kew Bridge Museum.
- Sudbrook, Severn Tunnel, 2 x 50″ Bull Pumping Engines, 1876/7. Ceased work 1962, one to Science Museum Reserve Collection, one to National Museum of Wales. Neither accessible.

- Sudbrook, Severn Tunnel, 75″ Beam Pumping Engine, 1886. Beam and parallel motion only preserved at Swansea Museum.

Engines of other manufacturers rebuilt by Harveys
- Crofton Pumping Station No. 1 Engine, 42″ Beam Pumping Engine by Boulton & Watt 1812. Rebuilt by Harvey 1844. Working
- Kew Bridge Pumping Station, 65″ Beam Pumping Engine by Maudslay 1837. New cylinder by Harvey 1860. Working
- Prestongrange Mining Museum, 70″ Beam Pumping Engine by Mare of Plymouth, 1853. Rebuilt, including new beam, by Harvey 1874

2. Other Products

- Penrhiwceiber Colliery, Mountain Ash, Harvey Balance Bob of 1855 seen and buried during shaft capping 1986
- Crown Mines Museum, Johannesburg, Cast mortar box, 1886
- Crimean War 13.5 ton, Dolphin Handle Siege Mortar on display in Hayle

This is very much a work in 'progress'. The Trevithick Society will be delighted to receive corrections, amedments and news of hitherto unknown Harvey artefacts.

A VERY DIFFERENT HARVEY PRODUCT

48. Mr Joff Bullen with the Harvey crucifix.
Photograph © Cornwall & IOS Press 2008

When the Trevithick Society was first considering a reprint of this book, an appeal was made for material of interest to include in the new edition.

Camborne mining and engineering historian Joff Bullen made contact, having recalled the story of an Anglicised German who had adopted the name, John Whitbread. This man was working for Harvey and Co. at Hayle in the early nineteenth century and in 1840 he produced a bronze casting of the figure of Christ. As Mr. Bullen says, "It is a remarkable piece of foundry work."

The figure came into Mr. Bullen's possession from the late Mr. T. R. Harris, whose manuscript history of the Harvey Company was a great help to Edmund Vale in writing the first edition of the Harvey story. The Christ figure is now complemented by a mahogany cross, itself the product of Mr. G. B. Bailey, a retired pattern maker at Holman Brothers, Camborne.

John Whitbread's presence at Hayle is still further evidence that Harvey & Co had a reputation well beyond Cornwall and the United Kingdom at this time.

375

APPENDIX

APPENDIX XIV

SELECT BIBLIOGRAPHY

Books

Buck, Colin & Smith, John R, *Hayle Town Survey*, Cornwall Archaeological Unit, Truro, 1995

Burton, Anthony, *Richard Trevithick: Giant of Steam*, Aurum Press, London, 2000 and 2002

Dawe, Richard D., *Cornish Pioneers in South Africa*, Cornish Hillside Publications, St. Austell, 1998

Earl, Bryan, *Cornish Mining: The Techniques of Metal Mining in the West of England, Past and Present*, Bradford Barton, Truro 1968. Revised Edition, Cornish Hillside Publications, St. Austell, 1994

Ferguson, John, *Forged and Founded in Cornwall*, Cornish Hillside Publications, St. Austell, 2000

Harris J R, *The Copper King: A Biography of Thomas Williams of Llanidan*, Liverpool University Press, 1964

Harris, T. R., *Arthur Woolf, 1766-1837: The Cornish Engineer*, Bradford Barton, Truro, 1966

Harvey & Co, 1884 Trade Catalogue, reprinted by Bradford Barton, Truro, 1973 and Trevithick Society, 2002, 2005 & 2009

Hayle Townscape Initiative: Heritage Trails, No date

Noall, Cyril, *Harveys: 200 Years of Trading*, UBM Harvey, Truro, 1979

Noall, Cyril, *The Book of Hayle*, Barracuda Books, Buckingham, 1984

Pascoe, Harry, *The Book of Hayle*, Halsgrove, Tiverton, 2005

Pascoe, W H, *CCC The History of the Cornish Copper Company*, Dyllansow Truran, Redruth, 1981

Sullivan Brian, *Hayle Town Trail*, 1983

Todd A C, *Beyond the Blaze: A Biography of Davies Gilbert,* Bradford Barton, Truro, 1967

Wigley, Edward, *Hayle – A New Industrial Town of the West*, Chapter 5 in Todd A C & Laws P, *Industrial Archaeology of Cornwall*, David & Charles, Newton Abbot, 1970

Articles

Carter, Clive, *Steel Ships and Iron Men*, Archive, Number 8, December 1995

Carter, Clive, *The Cornubia and the Hayle Packet Service: A Cornish Confederate*, Journal of the Trevithick Society, Number 30, 2003

Coombe, Megan G, *The Industrial History of Hayle*, Industrial Archaeology, Volume 10, Number 1, February 1973

Fairhurst, Arthur, *Mining the Sea: The Extraction of Bromine from Sea Water at Hayle*, Journal of the Trevithick Society, Number 26, 1999

Fairhurst, Arthur, *Mining the Sea: A Race against Time*, Journal of the Trevithick Society, Number 29, 2002

Fairhurst, Arthur, *A Natural Solution: Abstraction of Water from Loggans Stream, Hayle*, Journal of the Trevithick Society, Number 31, 2004

Fairhurst, Arthur, *Torrey Canyon, Memories and Reflections*, Journal of the Trevithick Society, Number 34, 2007

Ferguson John, *The Copper Slag Blocks of Hayle Cornwall: Remains of a late 18th Century Industry,* in Historical Metallurgy Society Special Publication: *The Archaeology of Mining and Metallurgy in South-West Britain.* Peak District Mines Historical Society, 1996

Ferguson John, *Foundry History Underfoot; More light on Cornish Iron Foundries and Allied Works*, Journal of the Trevithick Society, Number 34, 2007

Hodge, James, *The Severn Tunnel Pumping Engines*, Journal of the Trevithick Society, Number 27, 2000

Webber, Russ, *An Insight into the Chipping Department at Harvey's Foundry* 1851-56, Journal of the Trevithick Society, Number 27, 2000

Webber, Russ, *Harvey's Infamous 144 Inch Cylinder Casting*, Journal of the Trevithick Society, Number 31, 2004

Webber, Russ, T*he Source of Moulding Sands used by Cornish Foundries in the Eighteenth and Nineteenth Centuries*, Journal of the Trevithick Society, Number 34, 2007

HARVEY'S FOUNDRY TRUST
CONSERVATION: REGENERATION: EDUCATION

The history of Harvey's Foundry in the 20th Century was one of decline. The closing of the Foundry in 1904, the changes to the kinds of industry associated with the Harbour, the transition of the company to become a builders' merchant and the eventual sale of the harbour and associated land all contributed to the desolate appearance of the area today. In the late 1980s a group of local campaigners, in tandem with the Hayle Town Trust, fought to list the few remaining structures and eventually the Granary Barn, Engine House, Harvey's offices, Plantation Stores, the Pattern Shop and Foundry farm were protected and renovation began.

The Harvey's Foundry Trust was formed in 2003 to promote the appreciation of the history of Hayle and undertake the regeneration of the Foundry site. The Trust worked in partnership with Penwith District Council, supported by the Prince's Regeneration Trust to focus improvement and change on the Foundry area, start to address the physical dereliction and create new work spaces to act as a catalyst for change in the town. This work has seen the transformation of the site into a vibrant commercial centre. We intend to add to our existing offices and craft workshops in Foundry Lane and develop an interpretation and research centre charting the important role played by the Harvey's and Copperhouse Foundries from the late 18th Century onwards and to highlight Hayle as a very significant part of Britain's Industrial Heritage. We will make the Foundry site a place for people to visit, work, relax and learn.

Contact details:

Harvey's Foundry Trust
John Harvey House
24 Foundry Square
Hayle
TR27 4HH

www.harveysfoundrytrust.co.uk

THE TREVITHICK SOCIETY

For Industrial Archaeology in Cornwall
Registered Charity No. 246586

The Trevithick Society can trace its history back via the Cornish Engines
Preservation Society to 1935 and is therefore one of the oldest organisations in
its field.
   The Society's objectives are to educate the public in Cornish industry and
technology, including its history around the world, by

•   Encouraging and assisting in the preservation of buildings, machinery and
    sites connected with mining, engineering, china clay working and any other
    industry in Cornwall

•   Collecting plant, machinery, records or other property connected with the
    above, encouraging their display and publishing any relevant matter

•   Discussing with local government and other parties involved in the
    development and regeneration of existing and former industrial sites to ensure
    that heritage and preservation issues are given due consideration

   Membership of the Society is open to all who support its objectives and share an
interest in Cornwall's industrial and engineering history and heritage.
   Members receive the award-winning Journal of the Trevithick Society, an annual
series which has been running since 1973, and a quarterly Newsletter.
   More information about the Society, its activities, collections and publications,
can be found at www.trevithick-society.org.uk; for membership details contact
membership@trevithick-society.org.uk or write to PO Box 62, Camborne,
Cornwall TR14 7ZN

INDEX

INDEX

INDEX

383

INDEX

HAYLE HARBOUR

ENTIRE CORNISH PORT
FOR SALE

On the instructions of **UBM** **Group Limited**

WEST

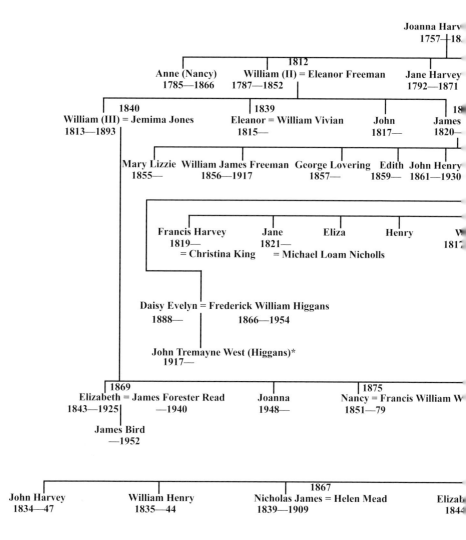

Joanna Harv
1757—18.

	1812	
Anne (Nancy)	William (II) = Eleanor Freeman	Jane Harvey
1785—1866	1787—1852	1792—1871

1840	1839		18
William (III) = Jemima Jones	Eleanor = William Vivian	John	James
1813—1893	1815—	1817—	1820—

Mary Lizzie William James Freeman George Lovering Edith John Henry
1855—   1856—1917   1857—   1859— 1861—1930

Francis Harvey   Jane   Eliza   Henry   V
1819—   1821—   181
= Christina King   = Michael Loam Nicholls

Daisy Evelyn = Frederick William Higgans
1888—   1866—1954

John Tremayne West (Higgans)*
1917—

1869			1875
Elizabeth = James Forester Read	Joanna	Nancy = Francis William W
1843—1925	—1940	1948—	1851—79

James Bird
—1952

		1867	
John Harvey	William Henry	Nicholas James = Helen Mead	Elizab
1834—47	1835—44	1839—1909	1844

The tables were compiled by the author from various so
Directors. The name of Mary Anna Pool, marked † was

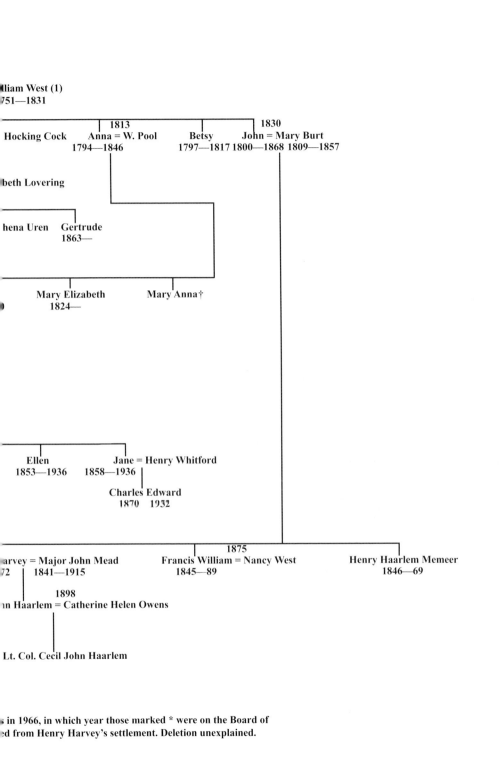

lliam West (1)
751—1831

1813
Hocking Cock   Anna = W. Pool   Betsy   John = Mary Burt
             1794—1846   1797—1817 1800—1868 1809—1857

beth Lovering

hena Uren   Gertrude
            1863—

Mary Elizabeth   Mary Anna†
    1824—

Ellen   Jane = Henry Whitford
1853—1936   1858—1936

         Charles Edward
          1870 1932

1875
arvey = Major John Mead   Francis William = Nancy West   Henry Haarlem Memeer
72   1841—1915   1845—89   1846—69

      1898
n Haarlem = Catherine Helen Owens

Lt. Col. Cecil John Haarlem

in 1966, in which year those marked * were on the Board of
d from Henry Harvey's settlement. Deletion unexplained.